THE
PROFESSIONALS

George Seymour, prime mover for the establishment of the IMM and its first President, 1892–94

The Professionals

The Institution of Mining and Metallurgy 1892–1992

A.J. Wilson

By the same author

Sky Sweepers (RAF at war), 1942
The Pick and the Pen, 1979
Jubilee of the Copper Development Association, 1983
The Life and Times of Sir Alfred Chester Beatty, 1985
The Amax Centenary, 1987

with Sir Ronald Prain
Copper, the Anatomy of an Industry, 1975
Reflections on an Era, 1981

with Edward Wharton-Tigar
Burning Bright, 1987

Published by
The Institution of Mining and Metallurgy, 44 Portland Place, London

ISBN 1 870706 26 9

Printed in England by Stephen Austin, Hertford

Contents

v

Acknowledgements

This book is not intended to be a history in the accepted sense of the word. The reader will find too many omissions in terms of records of meetings, resolutions, elections, declarations of intent, statistics and technical matters for it to be regarded other than what it sets out to be—a story of those who have contributed to the development of the Institution of Mining and Metallurgy over the past hundred years.

As a former newspaperman, I learned the wisdom of the saying, 'People matter more than things'. Any institution or corporate body of whatever nature is basically a collection of individuals and its success, or failure, is the sum total of their endeavours, skills and loyalties. In *The Professionals* I have tried to bring to life some of the names appearing most frequently in the archives of the IMM stretching back to the closing years of the last century, and to focus on others only occasionally mentioned, if at all, but whose contributions have been of no less value.

Researches involved discussions with more than a hundred people within the Institution and throughout the international minerals industry generally. Some of them I have known personally for more than 35 years; others are new friends. Without exception they cooperated in every way possible. I am most grateful to them all, and it would obviously be invidious to mention any by name.

For much basic material relating to members of the IMM who served in the Tunnelling Companies of the Royal Engineers in two

World Wars I have to thank Lt-Colonel Phillip Robinson, of the ADP Branch at RSME Headquarters, Brompton Barracks, Chatham, and Dennis Gillard, a keen student of mine warfare on the Western Front between 1915 and 1918. My thanks are also due to Forrest S. Anderson for his reminiscences of tunneller Donald Gurrey, recorded in Chapter Six, and to Dick Hobson for assistance with information on Sir John Norton-Griffiths.

The Institution's staff at Portland Place were unfailingly helpful throughout two years of research and preparation of the script, and I should like to express special thanks to the Secretary, Michael Jones, and the head of the Library Services, Mike McGarr, and their assistants for their help, and for delving so deeply into the records to provide answers to questions which must at times have appeared to be endless.

A.J.Wilson
November 1991

I hold every man a debtor to his profession.—Francis Bacon, 1561–1626

CHAPTER ONE

The Beginning

From his seat on the platform at Winchester House in the City of London, George Seymour, partner in the firm of Bainbridge, Seymour and Company, consulting mining engineers, looked down at the gathering of formally dressed gentlemen in the rows of chairs in front of him.

For nearly two hours there had been lively debate. Now the time had come to vote on the matter that had brought such a distinguished audience together.

Seymour, the chairman, was quietly confident. He was gratified to see that there were between 50 and 60 people in the hall, leaders of Britain's metal-mining engineers and metallurgists. Good, solid people, reflected Seymour, men who had attained eminence at home and abroad and were anxious to improve the status of their profession and to safeguard its future.

There, for example, was Arthur Charleton, a graduate of the famous Freiberg Mining Academy in Germany, whose career had spanned the world from Bohemia to India, from the mountains and mineral-rich basins of Canada to the deserts of Australia, from the Pyrenees to the inhospitable interior of Brazil and other South American countries.

With him was an old Freiberg colleague, William Frecheville, who had mined cobalt and manganese in South Africa before going on to manage gold mines in the United States and India. Seymour remembered that it was only three years since Frecheville had come to London to 'settle and start a consultancy'

1

Founder members and early Presidents. Top left, Walter McDermott, metallurgist of international repute. Top right, Arthur Claudet, member of a London family firm of assayers and metallurgists whose clients included the Bank of England and the Royal Mint; he was Hon. Treasurer of the IMM for its first 21 years. Right, Arthur Charleton. Already by 1892 his work as a mining engineer had spanned four continents but the urge to travel and explore was as strong as ever and he was abroad as much as he was at home.

Prominent among the metallurgists was Arthur Claudet, whose father had founded the family firm in Coleman Street, for years assayers to the Bank of England and the Royal Mint. Not far from him sat Walter McDermott, whose knowledge of the metallurgy of Yorkshire iron and Cornish copper and tin was second to none and whose expertise had been exported across the Atlantic to build crushing plants and concentrators in many mining states of America, in Mexico and Newfoundland.

There, too, was S.H. Cox, a Royal School of Mines graduate, who had worked in New Zealand and Australia before returning to London to join its ever-growing corps of mining consultants.

Seymour was encouraged to see that several members of a younger generation of engineers had found time to come along: men such as Savannah Speak, only three years out of mining school, but already with practical experience in the Orange Free State and South-West Africa. Seymour had heard that he was now toying with the idea of going to Australia to try his luck in a land that promised so much for the young professionals.

Then there were the academics, headed by the ample but dignified figure of Professor Alfred Huntington, chief of the Metallurgical Department at King's College, London. A man of many parts, Huntington had contributed much to the understanding of metallography, the science of the internal structure of metals, and had carried out important laboratory investigations into the metallurgy of gold and silver. He was one of the first to experiment with electric furnaces, along with Sir William Siemens, and was a pioneer of aviation.

Seymour was sad to see, however, that the chair next to Huntington was vacant. At previous meetings it had been occupied by one of the giants of mining education. Sir Warington Smyth had been the first professor at the Royal School of Mines when it opened its doors 40 years earlier, and his teaching had done much to balance the sturdy merit of the old mine captains with theoretical and applied science. Since their last meeting the old man had died in ripe retirement, leaving a legacy of wisdom that would last for generations.

So far, the meeting had gone very much the way that Seymour had hoped. He realized that there were one or two in the hall who had reservations about the venture that he was about to propose.

THE MINING JOURNAL.

January 16, 1892.

PROPOSED INSTITUTION OF MINING AND METALLURGICAL ENGINEERS.

◆

The Institution formed and a commencement made. Harmonious Meeting.

A MEETING for the purpose of promoting the formation of the Institution of Mining and Metallurgical Engineers, concerning which a good deal has appeared in our columns of late, was held at Winchester House, Old Broad-street, on Wednesday last. There was a goodly and representative attendance, amongst those present being Messrs. George Seymour, A.R.S.M., M.Inst.C.E. (Chairman of Committee) ; Arthur C. Claudet; S. Herbert Cox, A.R.S.M., F.G.S., F.C.S., Member of New South Wales Government Commission to the late International Exhibition of Mining and Metallurgy ; Professor Huntington, of King's College ; R. J. Frecheville, M.Inst.C.E., late her Majesty's Inspector of Mines; Frank Brain ; William Thomas ; A. Wood ; Matthew Gray ; H. M. Becher ; W. F. Wilkinson; Joseph Garland; Ernest Smith; William Warren; George Attwood; J. B. Daring ; J. H. Collins ; A. H. Collins ; A. G. Charleton; William Gray; Edgar Jackson; W. H. Herdsman; Walter McDermott; R. de H. St. Stephens ; R. St. Stephens ; Charles H. Powell ; T. East Lone; F. E. Harman; S. J. Speak; Eugene Hoefer; J. W. T. Bousfield; J. O'Donoghue ; F. H. Mason ; J. Stevens ; Benedict Kitto, F.C.S. ; Professor E. J. Ball ; Ernest R. Woakes ; C. Warnford Locke ; C. J. Fauvel ; G. H. Horne ; C. Heinrich Trinks; Alfred Woodhouse ; H. G. Groves ; A. Mervyn Smith; G. S. Ullathorne ; Charles K. Western ; Percy T. Ogle ; C. F. Roseby ; John H. Cordner James ; W. M. Trewortha James ; D. A. Louis ; Edward Stables ; F. Coulson Bunn; R. E. Commans ; P. Bosworth Smith ; F. Mould ; F. B. Scott ; Charles F. Smith ; James J. Shedlock ; Claude Vautin ; and Geo. A. Ferguson, Editor of *The Mining Journal*, Hon. Secretary.

The following was the text of the circular-letter calling the meeting :—

PROPOSED)

INSTITUTION OF MINING AND METALLURGICAL ENGINEERS.

Editorial Offices of *The Mining Journal*,
18, Finch Lane, London, E.C., *7th January*, 1892.

SIR,—It has long been the opinion of a number of prominent mining and metallurgical engineers that it is desirable to establish in London an institution, corresponding in some respects to the Institution of Civil Engineers, whose object would be the general advancement of mining and metallurgical science, and more particularly the promotion and acquisition of that species of knowledge which constitutes the profession of a mining engineer. Accordingly I have done myself the honour of inviting, on more occasions than one during the past year a number of representative gentlemen in the mining and metallurgical professions to meet at this office, in order to consider the expediency of forming an Institution of Mining and Metallurgical Engineers. Mr. George Seymour, M.Inst. C.E., Assoc. R.S.M. (of Messrs. Bainbridge, Seymour and Co,) presided at each of these meetings, and at one of them a committee was appointed to consider and draft the basis of a constitution and code of bye laws and regulations. This committee—consisting of Mr. George Seymour, East, M.Inst. C.E., Assoc. R.S.M. ; Mr. S. H. Cox, F.G.S., F.C.S., Assoc. R.S.M. ; Mr. C. J. Alford, F.G.S. ; Professor Huntington and myself—has met several times, and now submit the following (provisional) basis, upon which it is believed, the proposed Institution might be founded :—

᠊ BJECTS.

The Institution of Mining and Metallurgical Engineers is established for the general advancement of Mining and Metallurgical Science, and more particularly for promoting the acquisition of that species of knowledge which constitutes the profession of a mining engineer.

CONSTITUTION.

The Institution of Mining and Metallurgical Engineers shall consist of four classes—viz., honorary members, members, associates and students.

HONORARY MEMBERS shall be either distinguished individuals, who, from their positions, are enabled to render assistance in the prosecution of mining and metallurgical engineering, or persons eminent for scientific attainments and experience in pursuits connected with the profession of a mining and metallurgical engineer, but who may not be actively engaged in the practice of the profession.

MEMBERS.—Every candidate for admission into the class of members, or for transfer into that class, shall come within one of the following conditions : He shall be more than 30 years of age, and shall have been for at least five years in a responsible position with regard to mining and metallurgical work and shall be at the time of his candidature occupied in pracical mining and metallurgical work and no other ; or, he shall prove to the satisfaction of the Council that he is a fit and proper person, by reason of his scientific attainments, to become a member,

Part of *Mining Journal*'s inaugural meeting report. George Ferguson, the editor, made an office available for the IMM at the paper's headquarters and acted as Hon. Secretary for the first few years

On the other hand, he was encouraged by the pile of letters of support on the table in front of him—good wishes from such eminent authorities as Thomas Bewick and Charles Algernon Moreing, whose jointly owned consultancy had won international repute; Edgar Taylor, grandson of John Taylor, the acknowledged 'father' of British mining, whose traditions his heirs were vigorously pursuing in India and other parts of the globe; and distinguished scientists such as Professor Rupert Jones and Dr Henry Woodward.

Seymour's own record was by no means insignificant, though with his plastered hair and chubby face, adorned by a heavy curling moustache, he did not fit the popular concept of a mining adventurer. A Lincolnshire lad, orphaned when young, he had been brought up by an uncle, an eminent shipowner who had him trained, in England and in France, as an engineer. He worked first for a phosphate producer in Spain and later made expeditions to Iceland, on one of which he was wrecked on the island's rocky coast. His partnership with Emerson Bainbridge had broadened his experience and he had gained recognition for his shrewd and thorough assessment of mines in many different parts of the world.

Seymour had worked hard for several years to bring his audience together and to convince them of the merits of the resolution that he was about to propose. There were several on whom he knew he could count for support. Chief among them was George Ferguson, editor of the profession's leading technical magazine in Britain, the *Mining Journal*, who now sat with him on the platform. The two exchanged glances that confirmed that it was time to act: so often before they had been close to success only to be set back at the last moment.

Outside, on this cold damp thirteenth day of January 1892, darkness was gathering and the sounds of a city preparing to return its workers to their homes were beginning to drift through the windows. Only a few hours earlier, some 20 000 vehicles, drawn by sweating horses, had lumbered in over London Bridge, fanning out in the awakening metropolis to mingle with hundreds of streetcars, buses and cabs. Now the huge operation was being put into reverse.

For the affluent gentlemen sitting in Winchester House it was not too great a problem to get back to their terraced houses, huddled around the little green parks and squares of the capital, or to modern homes in the already sprawling suburbs. Most of them would fit comfortably into the seat of a growler, or a two-wheeled hansom cab—'the gondolas of London', as Disraeli called them—which provided the smartest and fastest way to travel for anyone who could afford the fare: a shilling for two miles, and sixpence a mile thereafter.

But no one liked to be abroad in the City after dark when thieves and ruffians were on the prowl, though thankfully the crime rate had eased since the main streets had been lit by gaslamps following the invention of the incandescent mantle a year or two earlier.

The audience had begun to fidget in anticipation of the move home, but were still as Seymour rose from his chair.

'Gentlemen, with your permission, I now propose a resolution. It is that an Institution of Mining and Metallurgical Engineers be, and is hereby, formed, and that a Council be elected with the object of organizing the same, and of balloting for the first members.'

All hands pointed to the ceiling; as far as could be seen there was no one in disagreement; the motion was unanimously adopted. The election of a council was little more than a formality as a 'shadow' committee had been operating for some time. The 'hunters' in fifty waistcoat pockets now showed that it was four o'clock. George Ferguson was hurriedly thanked for volunteering his services as honorary secretary, and for an offer to provide the new institution with temporary headquarters at the offices of the *Mining Journal* in Finch Lane.

The members filed out into the darkness—and to a new dawn in the history of the British mining profession.

CHAPTER TWO

Before the Beginning

For more than six years the establishment in London of a professional qualifying body for engineers in the metal-mining industry had been very much a personal crusade for George Seymour. He had persistently canvassed his friends in the consultancies, among the managements of international mining companies headquartered in the City, and the technical staffs of schools and universities throughout the country. He had missed no opportunity to extol the benefits that would follow the formation of such an institution.

He did not, however, make much headway until George Ferguson joined his cause and brought a new impetus, backed by the contacts and influence of the paper that he edited. The *Mining Journal* had a reputation for getting things done—sometimes by rather unorthodox methods. The paper had been launched in 1835 at a time when British mining had begun to demand not merely a chronicle but a critical analysis of its conduct and development. That was precisely what was provided by its first editor, Henry English, a name that is inextricably bound with the early history of technical and trade journalism.

One of the great missions of English's life was the reduction of the appalling rate of accidents in British mines, especially in the collieries: this he sought to achieve by the introduction of stringent safety measures, enforceable by law, and the setting up of a proper relief organization for the families of victims of the disasters. The climax came in September 1844, when at Haswell

Colliery, in the heart of the Durham coalfield, 95 miners were killed in an underground explosion. English redoubled his efforts. When bureaucracy tried to brush him aside he made a personal appeal to Queen Victoria, 'as a wife and mother', to use her royal prerogative to order an inquiry into the miserable conditions.

It worked. The Queen talked to her consort, Prince Albert, keenly interested in the promotion of industry and science. Within a few days English received a letter from the Prime Minister, Sir Robert Peel, promising immediate remedial action.

George Ferguson, third to occupy the *Mining Journal*'s editorial chair, was in the same mould as his paper's founder. Among his contributions to the industry's development was the promotion of the first-ever International Mining Exhibition, held in 1890 under the shimmering glass of the Crystal Palace, originally designed by Joseph Paxton for the Great Exhibition of 1851 in Hyde Park, and later dismantled and rebuilt at Sydenham in south London. The timing had been perfect. The previous 20 years or so had seen great advances in technology, particularly in the metalliferous field. Mining had suddenly assumed much greater importance in the world than ever before—as an industry, a profession, and as a vehicle for investment. Mining countries of all five continents contributed to the Crystal Palace show with stands and demonstrations; the exhibition went on for eight weeks and the aisles were crowded every day.

The quickening pace of scientific and technological progress, not only in mining but in many other disciplines, had already produced in the second half of the nineteenth century an increasing number of highly skilled men and women. A new 'professional class' was emerging from a society that, in Britain at any rate, had hitherto been broadly distinguished by landowners and capitalists at one end of the scale and 'workers' at the other. Predominant among the new professionals were engineers, chemists, physicists, architects, medical men and teachers who, in the course of time, tended to organize themselves into institutions and associations for the promotion of their interests.

As organizing secretary of the International Mining Exhibition, Ferguson made sure that some part of its profits was channelled into helping to turn George Seymour's dream of an institution for metal-mining engineers into reality.

In formulating their plans the two men found it more than a little irksome to have to acknowledge that in the United States some such organization had been operating successfully for nearly 20 years. As Seymour stated at the 'first preliminary meeting' on 13 January 1892: 'The admirable American Institute of Mining Engineers [AIME] is, in itself, at once a reproach and an example to us. Vast as are the United States, their aggregate area is relatively small when compared with the area controlled by the Ruler of the British Empire'.

For Ferguson, the pioneering AIME was a personal embarrassment in that it had been the brainchild of a contemporary, and to some extent rival, publication, *The Engineering and Mining Journal*, and, more particularly, of two distinguished journalists, Richard Rothwell and Rossiter Raymond, who in turn edited the paper for many years.

On both sides of the Atlantic the most serious constraint to the acceptance of mining engineering as the business of a professional man was the lack of technical education. To promote a professional class in mining it was necessary that its members could demonstrate that they had been properly trained in the complex theories of the discipline as well as in its practicalities. And, except for a few isolated centres in continental Europe, the facilities for such education were very rare indeed.

In the United States the problem had been brought sharply into focus by a sudden realization that successful mining required more than a keen pair of eyes, a shovel and a washing pan. Three great rushes for gold had taken place within a few years in the middle of the nineteenth century. First, the 'Forty-niners' had streamed into California across dusty plains and mountains by wagon train, or by ship round Cape Horn. Fortunately for them, geological evolution had exposed California's veins of gold to swift-flowing streams that washed away the surrounding rock and concentrated the mineral in sand-bars and along the bottom of the river-beds. Gold was there for the picking; in many cases it was simply 'first come, first served'.

Ten years later the scene moved from California to the sage-covered Washoe Mountains of Nevada. There the Comstock lode was to yield more than $30 million in gold and silver for the lucky ones. Meanwhile, another rush built up when 150 000 adventurers headed for Colorado, their 'prairie schooners' proclaiming their destination: 'Pike's Peak or bust'.

For most of them it was 'bust'; the landscape was soon well

scoured for placer-gold, and it became obvious that new skills would be required to mine the veins of minerals that plunged deep into the earth. It was in the period of consolidation and reappraisal that followed the early rushes that America's first mining school came into being at Columbia University in 1864. Before then the country's professional mining men were those lucky to be born of parents wealthy enough to send them abroad for their education—to the world's first technical university in Freiberg in Germany, or to one of the other old-established mining schools in continental Europe. Such men formed the core of the AIME when it began in 1871 and, with graduates from Columbia University and other technical institutions that sprang up in the next 25 years, headed a new generation of engineers who were to take American mining into the next century.

In mid-Victorian Britain the state of technical education was described by Matthew Arnold, poet-son of the great reformer of Rugby School, and himself a leading educationalist, as 'a ruinous system of blunder and plunder'. Despite the fact that by then the United Kingdom had already begun to export practical mining expertise to many far-off lands (including the United States), it was at least 100 years behind other major European powers in providing engineers, metallurgists and geologists with the sort of training that would enable them to attain professional status in a world that, as Georgius Agricola, a Saxon medical practitioner, had noted three centuries earlier, tended to regard the occupation of mining as 'one of sordid toil, and altogether a kind of business requiring not so much skill as labour'.

As a qualified professional in his own field, Agricola was probably the first to recognize that, without some formalized education and training, mining had little chance of moving away from the popular concept in which it was held. When Agricola was born, at the turn of the fifteenth century, a slumbering world was awakening to the first lights of the Renaissance. In Italy Leonardo da Vinci and Michelangelo were at work; Columbus was on his second voyage to America; Vasco da Gama had rounded the Cape of Good Hope to open India to shipping and trade; everywhere there was the excitement of new discoveries, new sciences and new art forms.

At Leipzig University Agricola found himself caught up in the turbulence of new learning. After graduating he taught Latin and Greek for a while before joining the ever-swelling stream of young

G. AGRICOLA

Quid Medici poſſent manibus? quas iungere plagas
Vlceribus ſordes, ſigna movere loco?
Extitit hic ſolus qui pondera, viſcera Terræ
Rimatus, nobis bella metalla fodit.

scholars to Italy, where he studied at the universities of Bologna, Venice and Padua, and took his degree in medicine. Returning home in 1526, he was appointed physician to the little Bohemian town of Joachimsthal on the slopes of the Erzgebirge ('ore mountains'), in the midst of the then biggest metal-mining district of Central Europe. It was there that a natural interest in the work of his patients blossomed into what was later to become an infatuation: he spent all his time outside his medical duties visiting mines and smelters, and chatting to the most learned of the workforce.

Out of his researches, which he continued long after he left Joachimsthal to take up more senior posts at Chemnitz, came *De Re Metallica*, which brought together in print for the first time virtually everything that was known of mining practices and techniques, metallurgy, geology and industrial chemistry. Written in Latin to ensure its widest circulation, it was first published in 1556. Agricola did not live to see his work in print, but for two centuries it remained the leading textbook for the world's miners. Italian and German editions quickly followed, but English-speaking miners had to wait another 350 years before they were able to read what had become one of the greatest and most highly treasured scientific classics of all time.

Georgius Agricola did much more than produce a mining textbook. Equally important was his vigorous campaign against some of the prejudices that mining had suffered for close on 1500 years, ever since the days of Ovid, who censured those 'wicked men' who, not content with the earth's bounty of herbs, grain, fruit and vegetables, 'even descended into the entrails of the earth, and . . . dug up riches, those incentives to vice, which the earth had hidden and removed to the Stygian shades'. Ancient philosophers had contended that gold and silver encouraged vanity, envy and crime; the great Pliny looked upon iron as 'the most deadly fruit of human ingenuity'. Even copper and tin were regarded as sources of the newer forms of evil, and lead, too, was 'an agent of death', being used in molten form to 'wring confessions from the innocent' and 'made into balls for muskets to bring death to many a brave man'.

Agricola was at pains to debunk such denunciations, and strove to prove that metals were essential to the uses of mankind. Taking them from the earth was no more wicked than catching fish from the sea, he argued; even agriculture had come to depend on tools of metal. Classical scholars of the sixteenth century rallied to Agricola's support but, although some of the stigma was progressively removed, mining never enjoyed much social acceptance. Saxon miners did not help the cause by cloaking certain of their activities in a secrecy known only to families and guilds, or to other closely knit societies. There was an aura of mystery surrounding some of the mines, and medieval Europe was not gentle with those suspected of witchcraft.

Copper smelting in Saxony in medieval times. This woodcut from *De Re Metallica* shows a smelter being tapped with a hooked bar to let the melt flow into the forehearth. The figure in the foreground carries a basket full of charcoal on his head

Deeply conscious of the need for a broader education among mining men, Agricola admonished his friends in the industry to study the arts and sciences: philosophy, for an understanding of the origin and nature of underground rock structures; surveying and arithmetic to help in sinking shafts; architecture, for construction work both above and below the surface; drawing for machine design; and law to protect the rights of those who discovered and developed mineral resources.

It was in this manner, together with the profound effect that the publication of *De Re Metallica* had on the local community, that the foundations were laid for the establishment at nearby Freiberg of a central source of mining and metallurgical information that was later refined into a formal curriculum to provide a nucleus for the world's first mining academy. Freiberg opened in 1765 and continued to be the most important centre of mining knowledge and teaching long after the establishment of similar institutions elsewhere.

Twenty years after Freiberg's inauguration the École des Mines was founded in France by decree of Louis XVI. For several years it provided an exclusive academy for aristocrats before the Revolution sent its royal patron to the guillotine and the Comité de Salut Public decentralized it into the provinces to provide practical instruction for a new generation of mineworkers. Life at the École was not always easy in a country in which public support for monarchy or republic swung with such frequency and violence, but in the scientific field the academy was able to exert a stabilizing influence. The names of some of its earliest professors indicate the level from which it developed: René-Just Haüy, one of the founders of the science of crystallography; Louis-Nicolas Vauquelin, discoverer of chromium; and Dieudonné Dolomieu, who, for want of paper, wrote his treatise on geology on the margins of a Bible while he languished in prison. Many students were no less distinguished: Auguste Laurent graduated as a mining engineer in 1830 and went on to become one of France's outstanding chemists; Benoît Fourneyron invented the hydraulic turbine; and Michel Chevalier was president of the society that promoted the first Channel tunnel scheme. Thousands of others who studied at the École made substantial contributions to French development, not only in mining but in every branch of engineering and science.

In Russia, mining instruction began early in the eighteenth

century as part of Peter the Great's plan to overtake the developed countries of western Europe and ensure victory in his wars for access to the sea. Among the first schools was one in the capital, St Petersburg; initially, it was something of a preparatory school for Freiberg, but years later it developed into the Leningrad Academy, which, at its peak, was to boast 10 000 students and a teaching staff of 600.

Even in Spain a formal mining education was available long before Victorian Britain could be shaken out of its lethargy. A school was started at Almadén in 1777; it later moved to Madrid and grew rapidly with the expansion of Spanish mining, which was given impetus by the redevelopment of the ancient mines of Rio Tin , a major source of the metal wealth in Roman times. By the beginning of the nineteenth century several cultural centres of continental Europe had facilities for the training of mining engineers—some of them independent colleges, such as those at Schemnitz in Hungary and Clausthal in Germany, others as departments of established universities.

In Britain, however, things were very different. In the early part of the nineteenth century there was little opportunity for the study of any of the sciences. Universities were still under the antiquated domination of classical teaching, and the limited scientific instruction that was given was confined to the lecture room; laboratory work for students was unknown. In the mining industry there was no compelling reason why a manager or supervisor should even be able to read or write. As in other trades, the tradition of apprenticeship was the common initiation for new recruits; at all levels the young learned from their elders.

Paradoxically, it was a man not even a native of the mining districts in which he was to make his reputation who was first to recognize Britain's backwardness in technical education and he determined to do something about it. John Taylor, from Norwich in the heart of agricultural East Anglia, was the eldest of seven children of a cloth and yarn merchant, but emerged as one of the most respected and influential men of science of his day.

Even Taylor's training was little more than the usual apprenticeship undergone by thousands of young men of his time. Moreover, his entry into the mining industry was the result of a blatant piece of nepotism. He was barely 19 when, in 1798, he visited mines in the Tavistock area with members of the Martineau family, with whom the Taylors had strong ties by marriage. The Martineaus derived much of their considerable prosperity from brewing, banking and sugar refining, and were also part-owners of Wheal Friendship, one of Devon's largest copper mines near Mary Tavy.

Impressed by John's comments on the mine, and anxious to help their friends' son to find a post, the Martineaus invited him to take over management of the property. In an industry in which managers were invariably appointed from the ranks of those with long practical experience, to bring in such a young and unqualified outsider seemed to be a recipe for disaster. But the Martineaus—and other shareholders of Wheal Friendship—were never to regret the invitation. Nor was John. He made a resounding success of the job and went on to manage other mines in Devon and Cornwall, in the Peak District, the Yorkshire Dales and the Pennines. Very soon he found himself in charge of metal mines in almost every mining district in Britain.

More important than John Taylor's personal successes was his determination to transform the traditional practices of British mining into a scientific discipline. As early as 1829 he published *A Prospectus of a School of Mines in Cornwall*, in which he drew attention to the increasing need to merge practical and theoretical skills to improve efficiency and safety. He proposed that the school be located at Redruth, centre of mining in the West-country, then the biggest copper- and tin-producing district of the world.

At first little was done to put his proposals into effect and the impetus switched to London, where Henry De La Beche, following the footsteps of William 'Strata' Smith, 'father' of English geology, was working industriously to prepare an updated geological survey of the British Isles. De La Beche, who had been drawn to his calling by a boyhood fascination for the shells and fossils embedded in the cliffs of his Devon home, persuaded the government to fund a small museum for his collection of rocks and records at Charing Cross, and this became a centre of a campaign for a school to teach the rudiments of mining and metallurgical processes.

As the middle of the century approached, a more favourable atmosphere for scientific work began to develop, stimulated in no small measure by the interest and encouragement of Prince Albert, who conceived the idea of the Great Exhibition of 1851. De La Beche—by this time Sir Henry—pushed his claim for a more fitting home for his collections, and in 1848 government approval was given for building to start on a Museum of Practical Geology.

From then it was but a short step to the ultimate goal. The pressure that Sir Henry was able to bring to bear was irresistible. Support came from everywhere: from the nation's leading scientists and educationalists; mineowners and mineworkers; the principal mining and manufacturing towns; even a House of Lords committee backed the proposals. In a year when the attention of the world was directed to London and its glittering palace-of-all-nations in Hyde Park, the Royal School of Mines came into being—initially under the cumbersome title of the 'Government School of Mines and of Sciences applied to the Arts'—housed, with the Geological Survey and the Mining Record Office, at the Museum of Practical Geology in Jermyn Street.

*　　*　　*

The opening of the Royal School of Mines (RSM) was a personal triumph for De La Beche, but its real significance lay in the fact that it was the first time that a British government had invested money in higher education—an important breakthrough in state recognition of the necessity for scientific and technical training in a country where industrial expansion was proceeding at a phenomenal pace.

In Cornwall progress had also been made, but its pattern reflected some fundamental differences in outlook between those who promoted the movement in London and those who supported its concept in the Westcountry—differences that are still discernible today when the RSM is compared with its Cornish counterpart.

De La Beche's aim was always for a national institution, graced by a royal charter and with all the prestigious trimmings that went with it. In Cornwall, the main purpose of John Taylor and his friends was to produce a better educated and more highly skilled miner to sustain and improve the local industry.

In Cornwall—and to some extent in Devon as well—mining was the very lifeblood of the people who formed as tight a community as Agricola had encountered on the slopes of the Erzgebirge in medieval times. For generations Cornishmen had learned their trade at the rock-face underground, passing down their skills from man to boy. No one was more aware of this than John Taylor. His project to set up a mining school at Redruth had foundered, partly through lack of funds and partly because of the attitude of some of the old mine captains, who did not relish their galleries being filled with 'know-all schoolboys'.

When Taylor returned to the attack in 1837 it appeared that the financial problem might be solved by Sir Charles Lemon, a wealthy Member of Parliament, who offered to launch a scheme for a mining college at Truro by donating a site, putting up money for the building costs, and endowing the project with £20 000 on his death. This seemed the answer to everyone's prayers. But prayer is a fragile commodity, and when Sir Charles insisted that the college should be 'strictly conducted on Church of England principles' the nonconformist Cornishmen would have none of it.

A year later it would appear that Sir Charles modified his sectarian attitude by agreeing to go shares with Lady Basset, member of a well-known Westcountry family of philanthropists, in establishing a 'class of young miners' at a school at Tuckingmill, near Camborne. This was the first of a number of schools set up in the various mining areas for periods of about three months each year, with a team of lecturers travelling between them.

These 'migratory schools' were quite successful, though the numbers of pupils were relatively small. The big breakthrough in the Westcountry did not come until 1859 when, at a public meeting at Camborne, the Miners' Association of Cornwall and Devon was founded. Although the objects of this association were diverse, one of them was 'to aid the young miner in the neighbourhood of the mines by elementary instruction in the facts and principles of mechanics, geology, mineralogy, chemistry, hydrostatics, pneumatics and other sciences connected with mining'.

Subsequently, the Miners' Association provided instruction for upwards of 150 pupils each year, spread over a dozen centres. In Camborne the success of the classes led the Basset family to give a site, and to build and furnish a chemical laboratory that formed the basis of the present Camborne School of Mines. By the early 1890s regular mining schools were also established in Redruth and Penzance, and in 1909 the three full-time Cornish schools were amalgamated to form the School of Metalliferous Mining at Camborne, leaving Redruth and Penzance to meet local demand for classes in specialized subjects.

*   *   *

With the nucleus of a formalized system of technical education at last established, Britain moved into a better position to meet the demands of an industry that had developed over the past two or three decades with such speed and complexity. The practical skills that had made the Cornish miner famous were no longer sufficient: mining was now a world of high technology, a world of rock drills and explosives; efficient ventilation and pumping systems; complicated machinery; improved underground haulage; and, on surface, sophisticated plant and techniques to concentrate and smelt the ore.

Mines—not only in Britain but throughout the world—were now being worked deeper and deeper; larger and lower-grade deposits were being exploited. Properties that retained the old methods slipped into decline; those which responded to the new opportunities needed men attuned to technological change. And it was not only their expertise that was in demand but their reputation as well, for it was only by having such men in the managements or on the boards of the mining companies and consultancies that confidence could be inspired among bankers and investors, and the necessary funds secured for further development.

It was natural, therefore, that the thoughts of the more senior of this new breed of engineers, and of some of the academics at the schools, should turn to the desirability of setting up an institution that would enable information to be collected from mining developments all over the world, to exchange ideas and to formulate a code of conduct and qualification for the profession. Already there was the precedent of the AIME across the Atlantic. Those who knew their history were also aware of an attempt to form an international body a century earlier. In 1786 a group of scientists from seven countries met in Schemnitz in Hungary to form the Societät der Bergbaukunde. Its object was 'to collect everything for the advancement of mining in the widest sense, and to pass this information on for the benefit of humanity and of the countries in which it can be applied'. In no time at all it had set up branches in 15 countries, most of them in Europe, but including also North and South America, and Russia. Among its members was the Scotsman James Watt, inventor of the steam engine; the Frenchman Lavoisier, founder of modern chemistry; and the German Goethe, whose great literary works overshadowed a substantial contribution to science and mineralogy.

The character of this society was very much a product of the Age of Enlightenment and reflected the cosmopolitan way of thinking at that time. It was probably too academic to become effective, its proceedings more like the musings of ancient philosophers than practical engineers. It lasted only five years, never meeting more than once in the same city, after which its distinguished members went their separate ways.

In 1818 the Institution of Civil Engineers was founded in Britain and incorporated by royal charter 10 years later. It did not, as had originally been intended, represent all branches of engineering. Particular specializations, such as the Mechanical Engineers (1847) and the Naval Architects (1860), formed their own professional bodies. In the mining industry the growth of such institutions, except in Cornwall, was at first associated almost entirely with coal. The earliest, founded in 1852, was in the North of England, centred on the Durham coalfield. Seven other similar regional organizations came into being in the next 30 years.

As time went on, the concept of a national London-based mining institution gained increasing support. One of its most vociferous advocates was Theodore Wood Bunning, secretary of the North of England Institute. Well aware that the regional bodies would not willingly part with valuable offices and libraries—or their local influence and prestige—Bunning changed course slightly and proposed a federation of all coal-mining institutions with headquarters in the capital. Sir Lothian Bell, a leading advocate of scientific education, chaired a meeting in London in 1888 and in the following year the Federated Institution of Mining Engineers was inaugurated under his leadership.

By this time George Seymour was well into his campaign for an institution for metal-mining engineers, but some of his colleagues were more cautious. Some pressed for an amalgamation with the coal miners. Surely, it was argued, they were all in the same basic business, and there was not all that much difference in the major practices and disciplines. No, said Seymour, the coal miners were too big and too strong; the metal-mining men would be swamped and their voice would not be heard; the same applied to the Civils and the Mechanical Engineers, who would, according to Seymour, care little for their papers and their views. They would have to go it alone or not at all.

There was another question that was difficult to answer. Did Britain really have sufficient numbers of metalliferous mining engineers and metallurgists to sustain an independent institution? Even some of the leading practitioners, among them the Australian-born Algernon Moreing, who later became one of its most ardent supporters, confessed to niggling misgivings. The American Institute, he argued, already had a membership of 2000; Britain would be hard pressed to muster more than a couple of hundred.

Moreover, everyone was conscious of the fact that metal mining in Britain was not what it had been a quarter of a century earlier. Prince Albert's Great Exhibition of 1851 had marked the pinnacle of the home-based industry. Not long afterwards a decline had set in—a decline that accelerated in the 1860s as lower-cost production, particularly in copper, began to come onstream overseas. Mineral-rich Cornwall suddenly became a disaster area. One after another the big mines closed down; underground workings were flooded; surface buildings crumbled, and smokeless chimneys were grizzly monuments to a once thriving industry. Hundreds and then thousands of miners were thrown out of work. Mass emigration was soon in full swing: the 'Cousin Jacks' flooded into North America, lured by the discoveries of gold, and fanned out to many other lands where their reputation as the best hard-rock miners had gone before them.

But if Britain no longer possessed a major metal-mining industry within her own shores, she had something that was far more valuable. She had an EMPIRE—an empire such as the world had never seen before and which offered enormous potential for mineral exploration and development.

Smaller than Sweden or Spain, Britain in the nineteenth century ruled a quarter of the landmass of the globe and more than a quarter of its inhabitants. Queen Victoria reigned over much of Africa, the Indian sub-continent, practically all that mattered in the Middle East, Malaysia, Burma, Australia, New Zealand and Canada, as well as hundreds of islands scattered in the Pacific and Atlantic oceans. It was said that 'the sun never sets on the Union Jack'. Schoolchildren sang hymns to the glory of the Empire, exhorting the Almighty to stretch its bounds wider still and wider:

> *God who made thee mighty,*
> *Make thee mightier yet.*

Its rate of growth was bewildering. Lord Palmerston, best loved if not the most able Foreign Secretary of his era, wryly observed that the colonies were multiplying so rapidly that he had to 'keep looking the damned places up on the map'. In some extraordinary way Englishmen—Scotsmen, too, but not many Welsh—had persuaded most of the dark-skinned peoples of the earth that the British Isles was the home of a race that was meant to be master of the world. After all, Britain had been the birthplace of the Industrial Revolution and had become the 'workshop of the world', leading all others in manufacturing, trade, shipping and banking.

Very largely, the imperialists ruled by consent, and wherever possible they acquired their new possessions by persuasion rather than brute force. If there were any 'troubles', however, the situation was swiftly and firmly dealt with by the despatch of a gunboat, or a minor massacre by the occupying military 'to teach the natives a lesson'.

At the head of this so-called family of nations, Queen Victoria, an ageing, dumpy lady seldom seen by the public after the death of her beloved Albert, was regarded as divine by millions of primitive people living in mud huts in distant lands; they gave her unstinting loyalty and sought her protection from tribal enemies and white-faced entrepreneurs, who made promises in her name, most of which were unfulfilled.

For succeeding British governments the driving motive in building up the overseas possessions was basically quite simple—to expand markets and extend political influence. Canada had been an acquisition of the Hudson's Bay Company; the conquest of India had begun with a small trading post on the west coast; Africa, the Dark Continent, had been awakened through the missionary zeal of David Livingstone, followed soon by the opportunism of Cecil Rhodes, who dreamed of a Cape to Cairo railway and planned to finance it from the minerals that he hoped to find on the way.

As George Seymour had reminded his supporters, vast though America might be, it was small compared with the empire of the Great White Queen. And already that empire was showing signs of becoming the richest source of minerals that the world had ever known.

*   *   *

First of Britain's major possessions to demonstrate its mining potential was Australia. As Joseph Paxton's engineers were putting the finishing touches to the Crystal Palace for the Great Exhibition in 1851, an English geologist was despatched to Melbourne to investigate a story of a shepherd boy named Chapman who had walked into a jeweller's shop with 38 ounces of gold that he was supposed to have collected on a sheep station 100 miles to the north. The news quickly got around: fortune hunters rushed to the area, but were turned back by police when farmers complained that their pastures were being trampled.

By the time the geologist arrived in Melbourne, Chapman—and the gold—had vanished, but in the Blue Mountains northwest of Sydney a former sheep farmer, Edward Hargreaves, newly returned from the Californian fields, found gold in a creek that he optimistically called 'Ophir'. It was this discovery that triggered a rush that not only changed the lives of thousands of Australians but began an emigration from Britain that did much to ease the home country's unemployment problem.

Back in the Melbourne settlement—which in the meantime had been proclaimed a separate colony and named Victoria after the Queen—people suddenly remembered Chapman and his 38 ounces of gold, and prospecting became a major preoccupation. Within a year there were a quarter of a million workers at the Victorian diggings; the population quadrupled in four years; and the yield of gold, valued at £13 million in 1852, rose to more than £100 million by the end of the decade.

In New South Wales the alluvial deposits found by Hargreaves in the neighbourhood of Bathurst were also rich, but never as alluring as the Victorian fields. For 20 years or so gold mining in the colony remained a small-working operation, but the industry put new life into the wastelands and Sydney blossomed into a city that promised to become mistress of the southern seas.

Sixteen years after the Bathurst finds John Nash, an out-of-work miner, stumbled upon gold-bearing quartz at a place called Gympie in Queensland and, in doing so, helped to lift the colony out of a period of acute depression. Discovery followed discovery: the alluvial fields at Cape River (1867), Ravenswood (1868), Gilbert (1869) and Etheridge (1870). Then, in 1872, the important mine at Charters Towers was found, an industry was established and a colourful community developed into the second city of the colony.

*   *   *

It has often been argued that if the introduction of vein mining in North America gave rise to the American Institute of Mining Engineers, then the development of gold mining in British India was largely responsible for the creation in London of the Institution of Mining and Metallurgy. Certainly, the Indian enterprise underlined the importance of a professional approach to overseas mining and brought into focus the growing need for an institution to serve the needs of British engineers, not only in India but in other parts of the globe.

For years gold had been found in small quantities in India, but it was not until 1880 that attention was directed to a vast plain, covered with grass and scrub, 40 miles east of Bangalore in Mysore. It was here that the famous Kolar mines—Mysore, Champion Reef, Ooregum and Nundydroog—were developed, largely through the expertise of three generations of the descendants of John Taylor, the man who did so much to raise Cornwall to industrial eminence in the early part of the century and who had headed the first drive for technical education in Britain.

At first, production from the new properties was trivial, but, with the development of deep mining under the direction of John Taylor and Sons, it rose dramatically. The Taylors tackled the problem of rockbursts and devised methods to minimize their occurrence; they went thoroughly into the causes of pneumoconiosis and the environmental effects of working in very high temperatures, and the air-conditioning plants that they produced were among the first in the world. For 70 years the

Taylors managed the Kolar mines, coping not only with their technical and development problems but with all the political difficulties that arose after Indian Independence. Even when the mines were nationalized in 1956, the firm was invited to continue as consulting engineers.

In India and Australia, Victorian Britain had things pretty well to herself, but in Africa competition was brewing. For more than 100 years there had been only three major European powers active in the continent: Portugal, France and Britain. The Portuguese had been sailing round African shores for centuries and had colonies in Angola and Mozambique; the French were well established in the north and in western equatorial regions; Britain was dominant in the south and in large pockets on the east and west coasts. It was quite a cosy arrangement, and the colonists did not interfere with each other very much.

But in the second half of the nineteenth century two 'pushy' nations joined the Africa club: Germany and Italy. There was also a mysterious new member: King Leopold II of the Belgians had somehow got his hands on what was potentially the most lucrative territory of all, the Congo 'Free' State. A constitutional monarch in his own country, Leopold became a despot in the Congo: the Belgian Parliament disclaimed responsibility for what he did (and for a long time, how he did it), leaving the King to rule an area half the size of Europe without the consent of its inhabitants, without even the knowledge of most of them.

The big scramble for Africa was now on. Bismarck, who had previously had little enthusiasm for German colonial expansion, snapped up Togo and Cameroon in the swamps of the west, and laid claim to Tanganyika in the east. But what worried the British most of all was the Iron Chancellor's takeover of South-West Africa, not for what it offered in those days—large quantities of sand—but because of its strategic importance and its juxtaposition with British interests in the Cape. In Whitehall it was regarded as a most unfriendly act, a rattling of the German sabre.

To everyone's surprise, what looked like becoming an explosive situation was settled without a shot being fired. So ready to quarrel about trifles in Europe, the great powers agreed on the share-out of Africa with little fuss—in fact, with a great deal of goodwill and diplomatic courtesy. Bismarck invited the interested parties to a conference in Berlin; maps were produced and lines drawn upon them with not the slightest regard for topography or anthropology. Curiously, most of the frontiers that were agreed in the vaulted music room on the Wilhelmstrasse in November 1884 remain basically unchanged despite the conflicts that have followed the decolonization of the territories. As the historian Thomas Pakenham has observed: ' . . . most African nations accept their frontiers with the mixed feelings with which people accept their parentage . . . they are their title deeds, the only part of the colonial legacy they dare not tinker with.'

Meanwhile, in South Africa the discovery of diamonds near the banks of the Orange River in 1870, and of gold in the Transvaal 14 years later, was opening up the country. By the time George Seymour was expounding the merits of a London-based institution for metal-mining men, Cecil Rhodes had secured a royal charter for his British South Africa Company and his emissaries had obtained mineral concessions from African chiefs from the Limpopo to the southern borders of Leopold's Kingdom of the Congo.

Opportunities for the adventurous prospector and professional mining engineer were enormous—and continued to be so for many years to come.

CHAPTER THREE

Action City

Those who founded the Institution of Mining and Metallurgy in the last decade of the nineteenth century were well aware that the hard core of its membership would inevitably come from engineers who either lived abroad or spent the greater part of their working time in foreign lands. The Institution would have to be international in its concept and in all its practices. The founders were also unanimous that it should be headquartered in London.

The choice was an obvious one, for London in the 1890s was the centre of the world. In less than 100 years its population had trebled to five million; the advent of trains and steamships had helped to make England the largest exporter of goods, and London the biggest port. The gold sovereign was the strongest currency on earth, and the City the hub of international banking and commerce. There were ten postal deliveries a day and a British overseas telecommunications service, which had begun with the laying of the Atlantic cable in 1866, was soon to gird the globe. Even the world's clocks were regulated from Greenwich: London was the centre of time itself.

Such technological and commercial advancement cloaked another picture of the capital that was not so attractive. Much of London stank—from the excrement of the thousands of horses that hauled its transport and from a sewage system that was at best inadequate, and in the poorer districts non-existent. Another hazard was the icy fog that blew in from the North Sea to mix

Heart of the Empire. In the 1890s England was the world's biggest
exporter and London the largest port and city.   Even the world's clocks
were regulated from Greenwich. London was the centre of time itself

with grimy smoke from homes and factories, resulting in impenetrable 'pea-soupers' that blacked out the city and hung like a shroud over the slums that sprawled eastwards from Whitechapel and gave cover for Jack the Ripper as he sought his victims among London's 80 000 prostitutes.

But the professional classes—engineers, doctors and lawyers—were not unduly concerned with what went on on the other side of the street. England was an 'upstairs, downstairs' nation, and this pattern had yet to be disturbed by social revolution, though there were rumblings in the North, where Keir Hardie was getting the Labour movement off the ground.

It was said in these times that one-third of all miners on earth were British—a statistic that was viewed not wholly with pride by the founders of the IMM. With the decline of Cornish copper and tin mining since the 1860s, to speak of mining in Britain conjured up visions of 'black-faced scallywags' talking a mixture of dialects that the more delicately nurtured inhabitants of the South could scarcely understand. To the general public, mining meant *coal mining*—as it does very largely today—and the horrors of some appalling pit disasters were still fresh in people's minds. So were the abuses perpetrated by some unscrupulous mineowners that required employees—among them women, and children, sometimes as young as five or six—to work underground for 12 to 14 hours a day in horrific conditions.

True, there had been considerable reform since Lord Shaftesbury had taken up the cause of the miners and their families nearly 50 years earlier, and *Mining Journal's* Henry English had petitioned the Queen for an inquiry into the safety of the collieries. But it was a long time before the dreadful picture began to fade, and this was undoubtedly a reason for the reluctance of many potential members of the IMM to throw in their lot with the Institution of Mining Engineers, catering almost exclusively for those engaged in coal mining.

In politics, the year of the formation of the IMM saw the resignation of the venerable Lord Salisbury, the very 'spirit' of the Victorian era, and the advent of a Liberal government under Mr Gladstone, then in his sixtieth year in the House of Commons and, at 80, beginning to feel the infirmities of age as he continued to crusade for Irish Home Rule.

In France the Panama Canal scandal was about to break; in Germany Rudolf Diesel patented his petrol engine and Carl Benz built his first four-wheeled motor car. In Norway the explorer Fridtjof Nansen, with the blessing of the Royal Geographical Society, began to build his revolutionary ship *Fram* to resist the ice of the Polar seas; and in New York the Czech Antonin Dvořák became director of the National Conservatory of Music and started to compose his 'New World' symphonies.

London, the imperial capital, was bursting through the fog to show the world that even if it were not the most beautiful of cities it was one of the most vibrant. Within the Square Mile frock coats and top hats were gradually being replaced by lounge suits and bowlers for the well-dressed businessman. Women had abandoned the bustle; the hems of their dresses were rising; knickers replaced the old thick petticoats—not so much as a reflection of sexual emancipation as a necessity imposed by the bicycle age. And if amorous young gentlemen misconstrued the purpose of the trend, a new hairstyle, which required long and deadly hairpins to keep it in place, added to a girl's armoury in the protection of her honour.

The theatres were crowded. Melba sang at Covent Garden. Oscar Wilde's 'Lady Windermere's Fan' could be seen at the Haymarket; Pinero's 'The Second Mrs. Tanqueray' was at the St James's. Bernard Shaw's star had begun to rise and he was working on 'Arms and the Man', later to make its debut at the Avenue. 'Charley's Aunt' was a favourite among those preferring their humour less subtle—and remained so for the next 100 years. In the music halls, always packed to the doors, the 'Naughty Nineties' were epitomized by Lottie Collins, who sang 'Ta-ra-ra-boom-de-ray' and tossed her skirts in a manner that would not have amused Queen Victoria—but which would doubtless have delighted the son who was to succeed her to the monarchy.

Compulsory schooling, introduced ten years earlier, followed by free libraries and the sudden outburst of popular journalism, sent thousands scurrying to the bookshops: Kipling, Thomas Hardy and Robert Louis Stevenson were household names, as was soon to become Arthur Conan Doyle, who began writing the 'Adventures of Sherlock Holmes' in *Strand Magazine* a few months before the IMM was born.

For fresh air diversions Londoners could have a weekend excursion for as little as five shillings—fifteen, first class—on the Southern Railway to resorts on the Kent and Sussex coasts, there to enjoy their new freedom by cavorting shamelessly on the seashore, while more elderly visitors could be propelled along the promenade in bath chairs. Cycling, which 20 years earlier had been nothing more than the amusement of a few whimsical enthusiasts, was now a national pastime, bringing the country-side into the orbit of thousands who had never seen a green meadow or field of cattle. Soccer sprang into the front line of spectator sports after the formation of the Football League in 1888, but cricket was still the game of the English traditionalists. In the winter of 1891–92, when deliberating the formation of the IMM, potential members found time to scan the pages of *The Times* for news of the Test Matches in Australia—and were gratified to learn that England was having a comfortable run, thanks to the veteran Doctor Grace and A. E. Stoddart, one of the few men ever to represent his country at both cricket and Rugby football.

At her home at Osborne on the Isle of Wight, which she seldom left, the old Queen, who had come to the throne as a young girl in 1837, was living out the last years of her reign, which, apart from the Crimea and the South African War, soon to break, represented the longest period of peace that the British people had ever experienced. For this, and much more, Victoria was loved more reverently than any other monarch. For sixty years her name and influence had held the race together and her empire had grown and prospered beyond all expectations.

She was, as Lytton Strachey wrote, powerful because she was wise. She had in her time appointed 15 prime ministers—from Melbourne, who rendered her so many personal services when monarchy was new and fresh to her, to Gladstone and Disraeli; she had been through the Industrial Revolution; had known the joy of marriage with Prince Albert and the desolation of life without him; the pleasures and trials of motherhood. Victoria was England—and England was Victoria. Her reign was not only fruitful to the happiness of mankind throughout the most brilliant of historic epochs but it paved the way for new opportunities in the century that was soon to dawn.

*   *   *

Though by no means commodious, the offices of the *Mining*

Journal occupied a prestigious position in Finch Lane, linking Threadneedle Street and Cornhill, close to the Bank of England, the Royal Exchange and the Stock Exchange. It was here in the early days of 1892, in the midst of the hurly burly of a busy publishing house, that George Seymour came with a few colleagues, at the invitation of editor George Ferguson, to put the finishing touches to the IMM constitution.

In defining the objects of the Institution, they spared few words, stating simply that its aim was 'the general advancement of Mining and Metallurgical Science, and more particularly for promoting the acquisition of that species of knowledge which constitutes the profession of a mining engineer'.

The Institution was to comprise four classes of membership: members (later to be referred to as 'corporate members'), honorary members, associates and students. Members were to be not less than 30 years old and have five years' practical experience in the profession, or a working record that would satisfy Council that they were 'fit and proper persons' for admission. They were to pay an entrance fee of three guineas and an annual subscription of two guineas. The minimum age for associates, paying two guineas on admission and one-and-a-half guineas a year, was 25, and three years' practical experience was needed to qualify. Entrance fees were waived for students who intended making a career in the profession, but they were to pay one guinea annually and be over 18. Honorary members were identified as 'distinguished individuals' or 'persons eminent for scientific attainments and experience in pursuits connected with, but not necessarily actively engaged in the profession'.

Sole direction and management of the Institution's affairs were vested in a Council of no fewer than 12 members—later, that figure rose to 20 and it has been increased further over the years. The Council was also responsible for electing a President to serve no longer than a two-year term, together with two vice-presidents and two honorary treasurers.

Not surprisingly, George Seymour was elected first President by a Council composed largely of those who had attended the inaugural meeting. At first there were rather more 'chiefs' than 'Indians': 16 members were elected to the Council, headed by Professor Huntington and J.H. Collins as vice-presidents and Arthur C. Claudet and C. G. Warnford Lock as honorary treasurers. Collins, a Cornishman, had been chief chemist at the

Spanish mines of Rio Tinto, whose history had already spanned nearly 4000 years, and had also worked in Scandinavia; Warnford Lock had gained early experience in Iceland before going to America to manage mines in the Black Hills of South Dakota.

George Ferguson was confirmed in his role as secretary—unpaid, of course; in fact, the *Mining Journal* editor was able to put £100 into the kitty, representing part-profits of the 1890 Mining Exhibition, which his paper had sponsored, and which he had tucked away for some such purpose.

The first general and 'ordinary' meetings were held on 18 May, 1892, at the Museum of Practical Geology in Jermyn Street, still then the home of the Royal School of Mines, which it shared with the Geological Society and the Mining Record Office.

Formal business having been concluded, George Seymour rose triumphantly, if a little nervously, to deliver his presidential address. Appropriately, he embarked on a dissertation on the state of metal mining in the world or, as he put it, to 'the dimensions of that illimitable commercial empire of ever abundant wealth, which absorbs not only the arbitrary limits of our own enormous possessions, but the surface and, indeed, far below the surface of almost every civilized and barbaric State'. He felt it no exaggeration to say, in the words of the hymnist Bishop Heber, that metalliferous mining, like Christianity, extended

> *From Greenland's icy mountains,*
> *To India's coral strand*

and he drew applause when, with an apologetic look towards the ceiling, he dared to suggest that it was difficult to determine which had made the bigger contribution to the prosperity, civilization and happiness of mankind.

Seymour went on to deal with the current position in Australia, which had already produced gold worth £300 million, and progress in India, Malaya and throughout the British colonies. He had some prophetic words about South Africa, forecasting a 'golden harvest' for the Transvaal. He also noted that further northwards in Africa 'the indomitable Anglo-Saxon race is pressing forward with irresistible energy and force' into Mashonaland, where 'an ancient, forgotten and now apparently unrecognizable race, attracted so far as we can judge by lust of gold again, pushed their way amongst hordes of savages . . . and founded fortresses and settlements for the protection of their miners of which, after the lapse of unknown centuries, substantial relics still remain'.

From the inception of the Institution it was accepted that the chief vehicle for gathering and disseminating knowledge about the industry would be papers submitted by members for presentation and debate at regularly held meetings. These were the 'ordinary' meetings as defined in the constitution to be held 'from time to time', but, in practice, usually once a month. Members were invited to submit their manuscripts to Council for scrutiny and, if accepted, a date would be fixed for presentation.

The reading and debate of papers was the sole purpose of the ordinary meetings, for which a quorum of 12 was necessary, and it was clearly laid down that there was to be no discussion on the running of the Institution's affairs, which was to continue to be strictly the prerogative of Council. Any such matters could, of course, be raised at the annual general meeting, scheduled for March each year, or at special general meetings, which could be called by the Council 'on a requisition in writing of not less than twenty Members and Associates, specifying the nature of the business to be transacted'.

At the second ordinary meeting in June, H.M. Becher read a paper on mining in the Malay Peninsula, which gave rise to long and learned discussion. Other early papers dealt with gold mining in India, mining in Peru, nickel mining in New Caledonia and such technical matters as the decomposition of auric chloride obtained in the chlorination of gold-bearing materials, the metallurgy of lead and the economic treatment of low-grade ores.

A paper entitled 'The practical operation of the cyanide process on the Witwatersrandt (sic) (Transvaal) gold fields' by M. Eissler was of special interest, not only for its content but also for the fact that the audience included John Stewart MacArthur, generally accepted as being the founder of modern hydrometallurgy. MacArthur made his discovery in 1887, assisted by the brothers Robert and William Forrest, who were practising medicine in Glasgow. The experiments were carried out in the basement of the brothers' clinic, and the process immediately received industrial success in New Zealand in 1889 and in South Africa in the following year. In the two decades that followed the cyanide process doubled the world's gold output.

Appropriately, at the reading of Eissler's paper Professor

Huntington, President-elect of the Institution, who had worked on the metallurgy of gold with the famous Dr Percy, was in the chair and MacArthur contributed to the discussion.

At the end of its first year the IMM had a membership of around 200 and a balance at the bank of £378. What was more important, it had a record of well-attended meetings at which a dozen papers had been read and thoroughly debated. Knowledge was being accumulated; it now had to be disseminated. The first volume of *Transactions*, recording the full texts of the papers and edited accounts of the discussions, together with other news of the Institution's progress, was prepared and made available to all members. By now the Institution felt itself sufficiently well founded to employ a salaried secretary, who took over the routine work from George Ferguson. At the same time, Arthur Claudet undertook the editorship of all published material, combining this task with his job as joint honorary treasurer. Claudet was, in fact, to prove an indefatigable worker for the IMM until his death 20 years later, and he occupied the presidential chair in 1906–07.

Early in 1894 office space was rented at Broad Street House in New Broad Street, and although this was never considered to constitute a permanent headquarters, it enabled the Institution to become independent of the *Mining Journal*'s hospitality. Eight years later the Institution was able to announce that it had secured 'a commodious suite of offices in Salisbury House, London Wall. . . The new offices include a library and waiting room, and these will serve as headquarters for members resident abroad, during their temporary stay in London.'

By this time membership had soared to more than 1000 and the list of locations in which members were at work, either temporarily or permanently, was beginning to read like a world gazetteer. Every country in Europe was represented; in Asia addresses ranged from Borneo to Burma, from China to India, from Japan to Siam; in South America there were members in Argentina, Brazil, Bolivia, Chile, Peru, Paraguay and Venezuela; more than 100 were in Australasia; about the same number were working in the United States and there were more in Canada and Mexico. In the continent of Africa members were to be found from Egypt and Tunisia in the north to Cape Colony in the south; from Mozambique in the east to the gold fields on the west coast; from the Sudan to Swaziland; and, of course, the biggest concentration of all in the rapidly developing mines of the Transvaal.

The prime benefit of this great spread of membership across the globe was, as Arthur Charleton reminded those who attended the first annual general meeting of the twentieth century, that the Institution, though British in its constitution, was eminently a cosmopolitan body. It had in a few short years become the focal point of a free interchange of ideas, the catalyst for learned papers on a variety of subjects of international scope and interest, presented and discussed in London, the very centre of the commercial world. Moreover, the honour and prestige of membership was becoming more and more highly prized. No one, whatever his nationality, who wished to make his mark in the world of metal mining could afford not to be a member of the Institution of Mining and Metallurgy.

*   *   *

Some even falsified their age to obtain membership.

One morning in June 1897, Charles Moreing, senior partner in Bewick, Moreing and Company, one of London's leading firms of consulting mining engineers and Council member of the IMM, called at the Institution's office in New Broad Street and introduced a stocky, round-faced man with a good growth of beard and a noticeable American accent. Moreing announced that he wished to propose his companion for associate membership. An application form was produced and the American filled in the details, declaring that he was 'over 25 years of age'. He then scribbled on the back of the form his reply to the somewhat naive demand for a 'full and accurate statement of experience and qualifications', and added his signature—'Herbert C. Hoover'.

If Hoover had been required to produce his birth certificate it would have shown that he had overstated his age by two years and two months. It was not the first time that he had claimed to be older than he was. In fact, the man who was to become the 31st President of the United States was getting quite used to doing so. Son of a village blacksmith in Iowa, Hoover lost both his parents before he was nine and was brought up by an uncle, who sent him to Stanford to study geology under John C. Branner, later to become the University's most controversial president. He graduated in 1895 and got a job helping to map the gold belt of California.

Finding the task monotonous, he left for Nevada, 'forty-niner' country—gold-mining country—in the foothills of the High Sierras, a logical place for a young geologist seeking experience.

But jobs in Nevada were hard to come by. Hoover eventually got one pushing an ore cart underground ten hours at a stretch, seven days a week, for two dollars a day. No man could start lower on the ladder—and few were destined to climb as high as he. After a month or two he was back in California, this time working for Louis Janin, Freiberg-trained and one of the most eminent mining engineers in the American West. Almost at once Hoover showed exceptional talent as a 'mine scout', evaluating properties and prospects over a wide area of California and New Mexico, which he found even tougher than Nevada with its roaring saloons and gunplay, gambling dens and brawling adventurers in search of gold.

In the winter of 1896–97 when Bewick Moreing sought an American engineer for mine examination and exploration in the Australian 'outback'—the firm was already established near the new towns of Coolgardie and Kalgoorlie—it approached Janin for a recommendation. While the Freiberg man did not want to part with his able assistant, he felt that he could not let him miss such an opportunity to further his career, or to collect the rewards of an appointment said to be in the region of $10 000 a year.

There was only one snag: the candidate was supposed to be at least 35 years of age. When Hoover expressed his doubts about his youth and inexperience, Janin promised to 'fix it'. Meanwhile, Hoover prudently grew a moustache and beard so as to look a little more mature before arriving in Australia. And when in March, 1897, he sailed to Europe to be briefed by his new employers, he entered his age on the ship's register as 36.

In London Hoover stayed at Moreing's home and was somewhat abashed by English formality in dress and manners: he was especially embarrassed by the manservant who attended him when he dressed and scarcely hid his contempt for the young American's meagre wardrobe.

Hoover did well for his firm in Australia—his beard took his colleagues by surprise as they had expected a younger man!—and, later, in China, where he and his wife were caught up in the Boxer Rebellion and lived through the siege of Tiensin. He wrote papers for the IMM on gold production in Western Australia and on the Chinese coal fields. By 1901 he had become a partner in the firm, and for the next seven years travelled extensively on its behalf, circling the globe five times. He left to start his own consultancy with an office in London Wall Buildings, not a stone's throw from IMM headquarters, where he continued to enhance his reputation and increase his already considerable wealth. By this time he no longer had need to disguise his youthfulness as he had reached the ripe old age of 34.

Culturally, Hoover's outstanding contribution to mining in the English-speaking world was his translation of Agricola's *De Re Metallica*, in which he was helped by his wife and Stanford sweetheart, Lou Henry—a much better Latinist than her husband. The Hoovers grappled with the ancient manuscript, sentence by sentence, in all their spare time. They lugged it across the world for the odd moments that might be available to work upon it in foreign capitals, in lonely mining camps, in ships and trains. At last, in 1912, it was finished and superbly published on sixteenth century linen paper, bound in vellum, and with all the old prints and illustrations.

Three thousand copies were produced, more than half of which were sent as gifts to friends, to institutions and libraries. And to ensure that everyone in the profession had a chance to obtain a copy, the remainder were put on sale at a price that hardly covered the binding. The Hoovers made Agricola famous in the twentieth century and in doing so added stature and understanding to the industry and the men and women who worked in it.

Hoover was a good friend of the IMM: he was always anxious to put the profession's functions and responsibilities into perspective and to promote the role of the Institution as the qualifying body for engineers in the industry. To those who thought him too zealous in this regard he would tell of an incident during one of his many voyages across the Atlantic. He had shared a table with an English lady 'of great cultivation and happy mind', who contributed much to the conversation during the days at sea. At the final breakfast, as the ship entered New York harbour, she turned to Hoover and said, 'I hope you will forgive me, but I should like to know, what is your profession?' Hoover told her.

'Why', she said, 'and I thought you were a gentleman.'

*   *   *

Above, Herbert Hoover as he
appeared when he joined the IMM
in London on his way to Australia
in 1897; top right, mining engineer,
editor and author, T.A. Rickard—'a
pepperpot of a man . . . a burr
under the saddle'; right, John Hays
Hammond, one of the outstanding
mining engineers of his day. He
joined the IMM in 1893

Unlike Hoover, John Hays Hammond was an American who always looked and felt at home in England. Short in build, with clear blue eyes, neatly dressed and cravated under a high wing-collar, he did not have the cut of an adventurer. His politeness and charm seemed more attuned to a Victorian drawing room than the rough and tumble of the mining camps, but those who underestimated his toughness and expertise were soon to regret it. Another Freiberg man, he was to become perhaps the most eminent mining engineer of his time, and certainly the highest paid.

Hammond joined the IMM a year after its inauguration—and he had much more to write on the back of his application form than Hoover. Like many others who had been academically trained in the latter part of the nineteenth century, he was at first at some disadvantage when he began to look for a job in the American West. George Hearst, the man who made a fortune from the Comstock Lode in Nevada, told him bluntly that he 'did not want any kid-glove engineer'. But Hearst hired him, and as time went on Hammond was able to persuade his boss that, like it or not, an era of scientific mining was dawning that would replace the hit-and-miss methods of the pioneers.

As a youth, Hammond had taken the Arizona stage coach to Tombstone to hear from Wyatt Earp's lips the story of the famous gun battle at O.K. Corral; he could also tell of a meeting with a drunken down-and-out named James Marshall, who in 1849 had spotted the little yellow specks of gold in the millrace at Sutter Creek that sparked the first rush. After leaving Hearst, Hammond worked at the Coeur d'Alene silver mines in Idaho and was involved in the classic legal battle that raged there for four years over a mining title and ended with the judge ruling that the mine in question had been discovered by the prospector's jackass. Hammond headed the management of the silver mines when labour disputes burst into violent conflict and it was he who hired the Pinkerton detective Charles Siringo to infiltrate the unions and discover their plans for disruption.

The year in which he joined the IMM Hammond was in London for talks with Barney Barnato, son of an East End Jewish shopkeeper and one of the most colourful characters in South African gold mining. Barnato offered him $50 000 dollars a year to develop his interests on the Rand. But the arrangement did not work out; Barney ignored his engineer's recommendations and

Cecil Rhodes takes a rest in Matabeleland. On his expedition there in 1894 he was accompanied by IMM members John Hays Hammond, Frederick Hatch and J.A. Chalmers. Also in the party was Dr Jameson, who less than two years later was to lead the ill-fated Raid against the Boers

Hammond resigned. Almost immediately a telegram from Cecil Rhodes sent him hurrying to Cape Town where, sitting together on the slopes of Table Mountain, the two men put their names to a scrap of paper that made Hammond chief engineer of Rhodes's Consolidated Gold Fields and, soon afterwards, of The British South Africa Company, which held the mining rights of Mashonaland and Matabeleland in the far north.

It was Hammond, perhaps more than anyone else, who pioneered deep mining on the Reef and brought untold wealth to the country. He was assisted by a strong Anglo–American team that included three other IMM members: geologist Frederick Hatch, who became President of the Institution during the first world war; S. J. Truscott, a future professor of mining at the Royal School of Mines; and an engineer named J.A. Chalmers, who, according to Hammond, was 'a conscientious and thrifty Scot'. Hammond took Hatch and Chalmers along with him when in 1894 he made an expedition with Rhodes and Dr Jameson into the remotest parts of Mashonaland, including the region of the mysterious Zimbabwe ruins, which George Seymour must have had in mind when composing his presidential address to the IMM a couple of years earlier. Hammond was fascinated by the ruins, which he figured must have been the focal point of a great mining industry of an age impossible to identify. In the surrounding forts he found the remains of iron smelting and crucibles with cakes of gold still in them.

Years later, when working for the Guggenheims in the United States, he was able to discuss his finds and his theories with the novelist Rider Haggard, who had made Zimbabwe the setting for *King Solomon's Mines* and was a guest in Hammond's private railcar, clattering over the tracks across the Western plains.

It was on his trip into the African bush, around the campfire with lions roaring close by, that Hammond found himself being talked into politics by Rhodes and his charming and persuasive henchman, Doctor 'Jim'. Here, he took the first step towards becoming a conspirator of the infamous Jameson Raid, which ended in his imprisonment and sentence to death—probably, but not certainly, the only member of the IMM to face a judge wearing a black cap.

Ironically, it was Barney Barnato and not Cecil Rhodes who bailed him out and enabled him to start on the second part of his career, which was to prove just as exciting and profitable as the first.

*   *   *

In the early years of the twentieth century, when it was consolidating its position as an institution of increasing influence and prestige, the IMM benefited as much from its critics as from its friends. Prominent among those who looked critically at its affairs was a man who, having reached the peak of his career as a mining engineer, decided that he could serve the industry even better with his pen. At the age of 40 and with a 20-year record that stretched across the globe, he rapidly became the foremost mining journalist of his time, setting a standard of technical writing never before attained and seldom equalled in the 50 years since his death.

Thomas Arthur Rickard was not a particularly attractive personality. Few honest critics are. He was brash and he was aggressive. Someone once described him as 'a pepper pot of a man . . . a burr under the saddle', and he did not altogether disagree with this picture of himself.

There were so many Rickards in the Cornish mining community from which he sprang—so many *Thomas* Rickards that he was always known simply by his initials, T.A. His grandfather, James, had gone to California for John Taylor and Sons soon after the rush of the 'forty-niners', and his father, whose four brothers were all to become mining engineers or metallurgists, managed ventures from the Ural Mountains to the Iberian Peninsula; in fact T.A., who was born in Italy—only because 'my mother was there at the time'—was fluent in German and Russian before he could speak much English.

Graduating from the Royal School of Mines in 1885, he sailed to the United States to work for an uncle who managed mines for a number of British companies in and around Central City, in the Rockies of Colorado. The boisterous life of the mining camps was not, however, to his taste; he disliked violence of any kind and refused to carry a gun for his own protection. He took an early opportunity to get away from it all, and before he was 25 he was on his way to Australia to assess projects for a promoter whom he had met at Leadville and who had been impressed with his work.

Rickard had loved writing from childhood, and Australia gave him the time and the chance to develop his talent. He wrote for newspapers and magazines in Melbourne, Sydney and London, and began to submit manuscripts on technical subjects to the American Institute of Mining Engineers at a time when Dr Rossiter Raymond had just become its secretary and editor. Raymond, who had at various times been soldier, mining engineer, orator, poet, theologian and international chess player, recognized the young man's flair and encouraged it: he would send Rickard letters a dozen pages long, explaining corrections to his articles and making suggestions for their improvement. From Raymond, Rickard learned the art of presenting technical material in an attractive and readable way without losing the dignity of the subject.

Returning to the States, Rickard opened an office as a consulting mining engineer at Denver, and for 10 years life was busy and rewarding. On a second trip to Australia in 1897—a year after he joined the IMM—he met Herbert Hoover and, although the two men were working for different principals, they agreed to exchange reports on 'wildcat' prospects, thereby saving themselves much time and trouble.

By now Rickard, who approached everything in a systematic manner, began to look around for a wife; he did not need to go outside the family circle, which certainly encompassed most of the mining world, and chose one of his numerous cousins, Marguerite, daughter of the uncle who had given him his start in mining 13 years earlier. Family ties were further strengthened a few months later when Marguerite's sister, Ninette, wed Rickard's young assistant, Alfred Chester Beatty, not long out of Columbia University and ultimately to become one of the great mining entrepreneurs of his time.

Denver in these days was a good place for business. Colorado was pitted with holes that their owners hoped would become mines, and not far to the south lay Cripple Creek, rapidly developing into the world's biggest gold field. In 1899 Rickard wrote his first, and probably his best, technical paper for the IMM about Cripple Creek, little thinking that within a year it would be the setting of his last major assignment as a mining engineer.

Winfield Scott Stratton's Independence mine, on the slopes of Pike's Peak, in the middle of the Cripple Creek complex, suddenly came on to the market and Rickard was asked to evaluate it for his principal client, the Venture Corporation of London. In doing so, he made one of the few mistakes of his career: the mine was certainly rich, but not as rich as Rickard reported it to be; he was, in short, 'salted', and Venture paid several millions of dollars more than they should have done for its purchase. Ironically, it was Rickard's brother-in-law, Chester Beatty, and John Hays Hammond, now back on the Western American circuit from South Africa, who proved him wrong.

When the news leaked out, the Independence company's shares crashed; investors in other Cripple Creek projects caught the whiff of panic, and confusion spread throughout the mining market. Pluckily, Rickard sailed for England to face angry shareholders and to defend his figures. He was certainly not wholly to blame, but he was a convenient scapegoat for those who had lost their money. Within a few months he closed his Denver office and moved to New York to become editor of the prestigious *Engineering and Mining Journal* and to begin his second career.

In fairness, it must be said that the Independence fiasco was not the only reason for Rickard's change of direction. He had already begun to tire of the pressures of his job: the long absences away from home and family, and an increasing involvement in not only the technical aspects of the properties that he was examining but in the financing of and negotiating for their purchase or sale—in fact, just the sort of situation that led to the Independence scandal.

In New York Rickard soon discovered that running a publication of the size and reputation of the *E&MJ* was a vastly different proposition from preparing at leisure occasional technical papers on subjects of his own choosing. Despite Dr Raymond's diligent coaching, he lacked practical experience and, like many others who have turned to journalism as a second career, was surprised to find its disciplines and ethics as demanding as those of any other profession. He had to learn quickly and he did so, largely because of the help that he received from Frederick Hobart, a former editor, and from a fellow IMM member, Walter Ingalls, a regular contributor, who moved into Rickard's chair when he resigned.

Rickard edited the *E&MJ* for only two years, but in that time he was already becoming as controversial a figure in technical journalism as he had been in mining engineering. He believed firmly that the urge to preach and to criticize was the essence of successful editorship. He followed a self-imposed rule not to own any mining shares, not to be a director of any mining company and not to participate in any mining promotion. He imposed the same rules on those who worked for him.

He left when he felt that his editorial independence was being threatened, and returned to the West, where he bought the *Mining and Scientific Press* in San Francisco, bringing in his cousin Edgar as business manager. Not even the great earthquake of 1906 could shake his enterprise: although his plant was demolished, he lifted it from its ashes and was soon vigorously campaigning against the many corruptions that bedevilled the city's orderly reconstruction.

Among those who followed Rickard's career in journalism with interest and admiration was the man with whom he had shared 'wildcat' reports in Australia some 15 years earlier. By 1908 Herbert Hoover had given up his partnership in Bewick, Moreing and installed himself in private practice in London Wall Buildings, in the heart of the Square Mile. There he continued his professional work as a mining consultant and began to ease himself into the world of mining finance. As he himself described it, he saw his future role as a dual one: 'determining the true share value of mines' and 'providing facilities for obtaining capital for meritorious operations'. In other words, Hoover was becoming a 'professional speculator', a middleman between mineowners who needed money for development and investors looking for potentially profitable projects to back. In this 'new look' to mining consultancy, he found a ready collaborator in Alfred Chester Beatty, who had settled in London after his career in the American West, during which he had worked with John Hays Hammond, developing mines for the Guggenheims from the icy wastes of the Klondike to the high Andes in Chile and Peru.

At about this time Hoover and several of his friends were beginning to feel the need in London of a mining paper more attuned to the quickening pace of technological and commercial development than the conservative *Mining Journal*, then beset with management problems that at times looked like threatening its survival. Moreover, critics of the *Journal* felt that far too much space was being devoted to economic and political aspects of the industry, and too little to the practical problems of mining and metallurgy.

Whether or not Hoover's tongue was in his cheek when he identified himself with this view is not clear, but he initiated an invitation to T. A. Rickard and cousin Edgar to come to London to start an independent journal 'to give the industry an honest background image to the public'. This was obviously very much in the interests of the IMM, many of whose members gave the project unofficial, but enthusiastic, support. The Rickards put up most of the money for the venture. Hoover and 29 other prominent mining engineers, nearly all of them IMM members, subscribed for the rest, and in September 1909 the *Mining Magazine* was launched.

True to form, Rickard immediately campaigned for higher standards of ethics and better management in the mining business. As in San Francisco, he forbade his staff to have any dealings in mining shares, and in the first issue he told his readers: 'It will be no part of our purpose to tell people what shares to buy and sell . . . The mining papers of the better sort do not thrive on the support of the dabbler in the margins of the Stock Exchange'.

Such pious discourse was not, however, consistent with the appearance in the same edition of the anonymous article 'Investments and Speculations', summarized as an 'appraisal of the present value of mining shares . . . contributed in good faith by a speculator unusually well qualified to form a just estimate'. Tongues started to wag when it was known that the author was none other than the *Mining Magazine*'s chief sponsor, Herbert Hoover.

Inevitably, Hoover and his editor soon came into sharp public debate: the catalyst was a speech by John Hays Hammond to the Colorado School of Mines in which he urged mining engineers to 'acquire . . . a knowledge of business methods'; the goal of mining, he contended, was 'to make a profit . . . and the engineer should not be limited to the consideration of the academic features of mining problems'.

Rickard's response was an editorial vigorously attacking Hammond for 'counsels of imperfection'. Hoover immediately went into print in support of Hammond, but, as always, the editor had the last word: 'Whether it be right for Messrs Hammond, Hoover, or other men as experienced, as shrewd, and as honourable, to engage in promotion is one question, but assuredly it is quite another matter to advise inexperienced youths, about to begin their apprenticeship, to take part in the most dangerous, if the most lucrative, of trades, and to turn their backs on the best traditions of the profession.'

The IMM, divided in its views, but intimately concerned with the question, wisely kept out of the argument. Rickard had stirred a hornets' nest and it was better not to risk getting stung: the Institution had found a champion, but it was as well to keep him at arm's length.

Rickard certainly had no wish to embarrass his friends in the IMM. He had resigned from Council before the first issue of his paper appeared, deciding it best to be in a detached position so as to be able to criticize the policy of the Institution in a friendly and, he hoped, useful way. He continued to submit technical papers for debate at the 'ordinary' meetings and, for the most part, these were accepted without question and highly appreciated. But Council felt the sharp edge of his tongue when it refused to print his paper 'The persistence of ore in depth', fearing that his contention that ore was *not*, in fact, persistent would upset shareholders of mining companies and depress the market.

Rickard insisted on a meeting with the Publications Committee to resolve the problem. Years later he recalled the incident in his autobiography: 'One of my objections was to the fact that somebody whose name I did not mention, although I knew it was the President, a geologist, had marked the manuscript of my paper for the purpose of indicating the portions that, he thought, ought to be deleted. I informed the committee that I would submit to revision by the person designated as editor, namely the secretary, but not by anyone else, for I was a professional writer and they were 18-handicap amateurs.'

In the end, the paper was accepted for presentation at the November meeting in 1914, by which time the timid ones were reconciled by the fact that the Stock Exchange had been closed on account of the war with Germany and little harm could be done. The text of the paper, and the transcript of the debate that followed, filled 190 pages of the *Transactions*—a record to that date, and rarely exceeded since.

While none could match his fluid pen, Rickard continued to strive for even higher standards in technical writing. In one paper to the IMM he declared: 'We miners are the worst of sinners in corrupting the verbal coinage minted by the masters of English prose. By our nomadic life and by our reckless borrowing of words from every country into which we penetrate in search of minerals we are continually introducing counterfeits into the currency of our English speech, until it needs careful examination to distinguish between the genuine and the spurious.'

After six years in England Rickard returned to San Francisco to resuscitate his ailing *M&SP*, summing up his time in London as 'good fun . . . and an enriching experience of men and mines in a worldwide way, for the mining finance of London has a geographical amplitude like that of no other city'. At the IMM annual dinner before he sailed his golfing friend, Fred Hamilton, paid him an unusual tribute: 'I suppose that there is hardly a man in this room who, at one time or another, has not had occasion to differ from him on some subject, and when we differ from Mr. Rickard we know it. But I am sure that there is no man here who does not recognize that no word he has ever written has rankled or left a poisoned wound, that no word he has ever uttered has been actuated by any personal or unworthy motive, or by any other desire than to present the truth as he understood it.'

Back in the States again, Rickard sold his *M&SP* to McGraw-Hill, who promptly merged it with the *E&MJ*. Four years later he was invited to become secretary of the AIME, its directors declaring that they wished to give the post the prestige that it had enjoyed during Dr Raymond's distinguished tenure of office. But, as an integral part of its operations, AIME published a monthly magazine, and a small-print clause in Rickard's agreement with McGraw-Hill prevented him from being concerned in technical journalism anywhere in North America. The restriction seemed unreasonably harsh for a man from whom words flowed so freely and who so passionately believed that the maintenance of a strong technical press was essential to the well-being of the mining profession as a whole. 'As literature is a criticism of life', wrote Rickard, 'so technical journalism is a criticism of the life of the technician . . . it has done much to stimulate the development of character in the profession and to render it articulate to the public.'

And so the great tide of articles, treatises, lectures and contributions to learned societies and professional institutions began to ebb. But Rickard, with several volumes of stories of his travels round the world already on the shelf, went on writing non-technical books, of which the most notable were his *History of*

American Mining and *Man and Metals*, published in two volumes in 1932.

Rickard always told his friends that if he were to be remembered after his death he hoped that it would be as one who had helped to improve the writing of those in the engineering profession, and to give new editors the grounding that he himself had lacked when he adopted journalism as a second career. While still learning the basics of class-journalism he published *A Guide to Technical Writing*, which went to several editions and, finally, in 1932, was reprinted and distributed to 1200 junior members of the AIME to help them in their studies. It subsequently found its way into the offices of many of the big mining companies whose staff published technical papers and into the most important professional institutions throughout the world. *Technical Writing* was never a *De Re Metallica*, but in a smaller circle it became a highly prized reference book and its message is as pertinent today as when it was first penned more than 80 years ago.

CHAPTER FOUR

Wider Still and Wider

George Seymour, first President of the Institution of Mining and Metallurgy, died in 1897. Eighty years later a forgotten drawer in the offices of the *Mining Journal* gave up a rare treasure—a collection of pen sketches that Seymour had made of nineteenth century Cornish mining characters, reflecting both the humour and stark reality of mining in those days. The *Journal* published them in a little volume entitled *The Man Machine* after the primitive equipment used to carry men up and down the shafts, and which was perhaps the forerunner of the escalator or moving stairway. The booklet was issued at the time of an international mining machinery exhibition in Birmingham, thus reviving in a delightful way the memory of the chief architect of the IMM and a century of progress in the development of mine equipment.

Seymour occupied the presidential chair of the Institution for two successive years, and remained the only man to do so until Charles Moreing at the turn of the century.

For the first ten years or so the IMM concentrated on increasing the quality and expanding the scope of its regular 'ordinary' meetings, which drew gatherings of distinction, and frequently of some considerable size, to debate matters of importance in the world of mining and metals. In this formative period the Institution was helped and encouraged by its elder brother across the Atlantic, the American Institute of Mining Engineers, in recognition of which it accorded honorary membership to its two principal founders, Rossiter Raymond and

Richard Rothwell.

There was, however, the odd occasion when relationship with the Americans was not so cordial. For example, President Walter McDermott found himself bristling with annoyance when he read a magazine article by Rothwell suggesting that the IMM had 'failed to restrict membership to those who were professionally entitled to it'. After challenging the accusation, McDermott reminded Rothwell that the IMM was a young institution, adding, 'we have not yet here a Professor (sic) Raymond to devote the energy and specialized skill to its promotion'.

Hardly had the barb been sent flying towards New York than the IMM became embarrassed by the behaviour of the salaried secretary whom it had engaged when George Ferguson ceased to act on an honorary basis. After only a year or two the official in question suddenly departed, leaving behind 'some serious irregularities' in the Institution's finances—and not a few red faces among members of Council. The books showed an unexplained shortage of £765 18s 7d, which members decided to make good by a quick, but costly whip-round.

Fortunately, Charles McDermid, who replaced the defaulter, was a man of very different character. He had worked for several years in the head office of the Iron and Steel Institute and, although he may not have been quite a 'Professor' Raymond, he was to serve the IMM energetically and well for the next 39 years.

The benefit of AIME's experience was also sought by those who planned the Australasian Institute of Mining Engineers, which came into being in 1893, just 12 months after the inauguration of the IMM. In view of McDermott's brush with Rothwell a year or two later, it is a little puzzling that in a letter to Uriah Dudley, secretary-elect of the Australasian Institute, Dr Raymond emphasized that an important factor in AIME's success was 'the absence of professional qualifications for membership . . . the only requisite for membership is practical connection, direct or indirect, with mining or metallurgy, and our associates do not need to have any connection with either'.

Dr Raymond also remarked that the AIME had found that 'the attendance of ladies accompanying members (at meetings) has been greatly beneficial'. Elaborating on this with the puckish humour for which he was famous, the good doctor added: 'At our meetings the number of feminine guests is usually about half as large as that of the men. If one-fourth I think there would be too

Dr Rossiter Raymond, co-founder with Richard Rothwell of the American Institute of Mining Engineers and an honorary member of the IMM. Both by his pen and his personality he exercised much influence on the development of the minerals industry for more than 40 years

many men subject to the restraints without compensation of their presence. In other words, the average American lady can be trusted to make three men happy at once; but if the load be increased, the factor of safety is reduced, although there are plenty of samples for which even the limit of elasticity can be determined by social machinery.'

What exactly the Australians did about their ladies is not entirely clear, but they agreed conditions of membership that represented something of a compromise between the strict rules of the IMM and the broader-based requirements of the AIME.

In South Africa, where a big concentration of mining men had been drawn together in the development of the Witwatersrand gold fields, early attempts to form an institution were frustrated—first, by the effects of the Jameson Raid in 1896, and, secondly, by the outbreak of the Boer War, which followed three years later. Both these events were linked with the enormous new wealth discovered in Paul Kruger's Republic of the Transvaal. Ten years earlier Cecil Rhodes, the 'Great Amalgamator', had rushed from the diamond mines of Kimberley to build another empire in and around Johannesburg. where he established his all-powerful Consolidated Gold Fields of South Africa. Although they paid the bulk of the Republic's taxes, the *Uitlanders*, who had flocked to the Transvaal from Britain and elsewhere, were denied any effective share in government; the English language was banned in schools and law-courts; only burghers could become members of the judiciary; and the supply of mining equipment, including explosives, was a government monopoly, often administered with much corruption.

If gold was indeed the prime reason for the war, it assumed an even greater importance when it was found that John MacArthur's cyanide process, introduced into South Africa a year or two earlier, was increasing production at a rate that was to double output in the course of the next decade.

The South African war lasted nearly three years; it cost the British 22 000 men, and the Boers not far short of 6000, as well as 4000 women and 16 000 children who died in concentration camps. It was a miserable and dishonourable end to British imperialism in Queen Victoria's 'glorious reign'; moreover, it revealed serious defects in the Army's tactics and equipment, and although the *rooineks* were the eventual victors, the struggle aroused a new national consciousness among the Afrikaner people that remains to this day.

As to the war's effects on gold mining in the Transvaal, members of the IMM were given a first-hand account by their President, Hennen Jennings, who had gone out to South Africa in 1899 to be consulting engineer of what was to become the Wernher Beit Company, which made more money than most from the early years of Rand mining. When what was eventually to become the South African Institute of Mining and Metallurgy was formed in 1894,* many of its first members naturally already belonged to the IMM; others were AIME men; a few, like Hennen Jennings, found themselves members of all three institutions—and active in all of them.

In Canada, as in the United States and Britain, the initiative for forming an association of professional mining men came from the media and, in particular, from a man of remarkable talent and energy: Benjamin Taylor Bell, editor of the *Canadian Mining Review*.

Soon after the French–Canadian government of Honoré Mercier came to power in 1890, it introduced a Bill to impose a three per cent royalty on all mines 'already alienated from the Crown'. Bell attacked the measure in his editorial columns as 'pernicious and unjust', and organized protest meetings that culminated in the formation of the General Mining Association for the Province of Quebec—with himself as secretary. The public outcry, aided by a mounting scandal that government subsidies for the railways were being diverted for party political purposes, brought the Mercier regime down and the royalty law was repealed by the Conservatives who were then voted to power.

Inspired by this success, mining societies sprang up in Nova Scotia and Ontario—with Bell as secretary of both—and in 1896 the three bodies federated, adding a newly formed association of mining engineers in British Columbia to their number. Two years later the Canadian Institute of Mining and Metallurgy (CIM) was incorporated by Act of the Federal Parliament—with none other than Benjamin Bell as its chief executive.

Unhappily, Bell's career came to an abrupt end one day in

---

*The original title was 'The Chemical and Metallurgical Society of South Africa', nicknamed 'The Cyanide Club' owing to the preoccupation of many of its members with the recently introduced cyanide process of gold extraction from the ores of the Witwatersrand.

1904 when, returning from lunch, he fell down the lift shaft of the Ottawa building which housed his *Review* offices and the CIM library that he had established there. He was only 43. As a Canadian mining historian wrote 75 years later, Bell 'never discovered a mine, never worked in one, and never owned one, but it would be hard to picture the Canadian mining industry in its early days without him'.

*   *   *

While these developments were taking place in the Empire, in London the range of IMM activities widened as the organization grew in strength and influence. In 1900 a symposium was held on international mining law, and a year or two later a committee was set up to work for greater uniformity of technical terms, weights and measures, and costing methods within the industry.

A key figure in promoting these activities was Arthur Charleton, a founder member of the Institution and its President in 1902–03, who had travelled the world before returning to London to set up a consultancy. Charleton, like Hammond and Hoover, firmly believed that technical expertise was not enough in a mining engineer—he should also be 'a practical man, a man of business'. A prolific writer, Charleton expressed his philosophy in five papers for the *Transactions* and countless articles in the technical press. More particularly, he appealed for a uniform system of accounting to enable realistic comparison of costs between different mines. Working on his suggestions, the committee evolved such a system and regularly published its details for the benefit of the industry.

By 1904 the *Transactions* had become so heavily weighted with the transcripts of papers and debates at the 'ordinary' meetings that a monthly *Bulletin* was introduced to accommodate news of the Institution's other activities and to provide a forum for members to express their views. Within a year or so it had become a publication of some substance, including contributed articles on a wide variety of topics and reports of general meetings and presidential addresses, supplementing, and in some cases overlapping the contents of the *Transactions*. In the ensuing years both its format and content have changed from to time, the most recent trans-

John Stewart MacArthur, first IMM Gold Medallist in 1902 for his part
in the development of the cyanide process of gold recovery, which
revitalized a waning industry on the Witwatersrand and doubled the
world output in two decades

formation coming with a new-look bi-monthly publication, *Minerals Industry International*, in 1989.

The twentieth century was still young when the IMM began to consider ways to mark its recognition of conspicuous services to the science and practice of mining and metallurgy throughout the world. In 1902 the Council announced plans for a Gold Medal Award. Simultaneously, Consolidated Gold Fields of South Africa presented, through Lord Harris, its chairman, a gold medal and premium for annual award for the paper of highest merit published in the *Transactions* during each session, or for researches into the occurrence, mining or treatment of minerals.

Prizes were also donated by founder-members Arthur Claudet and William Frecheville for annual presentation for the best papers by students. At the same time the IMM began to award scholarships for students taking post-graduate courses in practical work, and encouraged leading mining companies to offer jobs to those who showed most promise.

First Gold Medallist of the Institution in 1902 was, not surprisingly, John MacArthur 'as the representative of many workers connected with the gold-mining industry whose efforts resulted in the introduction and development of the Cyanide Process'. Hennen Jennings took the 'blue riband' the next year—the year in which he became President—for his work in South Africa, after which there were no further awards until 1906, when the honour went to Hilary Bauerman, an RSM and Freiberg man, who for 18 years was Professor of Metallurgy at the Royal Artillery College at Woolwich.

*   *   *

With a high proportion of its early members being graduates of the Royal School of Mines, the IMM naturally took a close and personal interest in its affairs. Unfortunately, the establishment of the school at Sir Henry De La Beche's Museum of Practical Geology in Jermyn Street was not the end of the struggle to provide proper training in Britain for those seeking careers in the mining industry. It was but the beginning of a teething period that dragged on, sometimes most painfully, for more than 50 years until a degree of stability was attained following some drastic reorganization in which the IMM played an important part.

When Prince Albert opened the doors of the school in 1851, De La Beche was able to boast a staff 'never more brilliant and gifted for scientific teaching'. John Percy was in charge of metallurgy, which, it has been said, he 'found in chaos, and left a systematic science'; Warington Smyth had mining and mineralogy; and Lyon Playfair, a young man who had caught the eye of the Queen's consort and of the Prime Minister, Sir Robert Peel, was professor of chemistry.

Everything was set for an auspicious start. The flags were put out and the staff awaited an invasion of students. But, much to everyone's astonishment, the expected flood was no more than a trickle. A nation that had vociferously demanded mining education now seemed to have lost all interest in the project. The mining districts, which had petitioned Parliament so urgently, did not contribute a single student. Edward Forbes, one of the lecturers in geology, had visualized leading expeditions of 'undaunted investigators, armed with stout hammers and sharp chisels, who would make the rocks shake and yield up their treasures for many a mile around the great metropolis'. Alas, no one seemed to want to join his band.

Of the first intake, the school had only seven *bona fide* matriculated students, together with 20 or so 'occasional' pupils—mostly soldiers from nearby barracks and, according to Forbes, 'a few ladies and philosophers whose tickets had been backed by one or other of us so as to give them free admission to all the lectures'. Indeed, it became quite fashionable for ladies and gentlemen of good society to attend the lectures, unhindered by school discipline. Playfair's first-year audience included the Duke of Marlborough, the Marquis of Tweesdale, several Members of Parliament and a few Guards officers—undoubtedly all of high moral standing, but hardly the sort of material that the school needed. Warington Smyth, who refused to style himself 'Professor' under such circumstance, did, in fact, do rather better: Hilary Bauerman was one of his pupils and his future eminence was undoubtedly due in no small part to Warington Smyth being able to give him almost undivided attention.

There were two main reasons for this unfortunate beginning. First, the aim of the school had never been clearly defined: its title of the 'Government School of Mines and of Sciences applied to the

Arts' was a pretty meaningless mouthful. Secondly, there were already worries about its future in view of a much-publicized scheme of Prince Albert and his friends to use the considerable profits of the Great Exhibition to establish a mammoth scientific complex on some 80 acres of land that stretched from Kensington High Road to Cromwell Road, bounded on one side by Queen's Gate and on the other by Exhibition Road. Much of this land was wilderness; indeed, there was a partridge shoot over that portion on which the Natural History Museum now stands.

After eight years barely a dozen matriculated students were attending the courses in Jermyn Street, compared with 68 'occasionals'. Ironically, only one section really flourished, winter evening lectures for artisans filling the theatre to overflowing: more than 600 crammed through the doors, and twice that number regularly applied for tickets. Often Prince Albert would steal in by the back door and take a seat behind the curtain, sometimes to be discovered nodding off, exhausted from attending some public function or from writing one of his laborious memoranda.

In 1855 the school suffered a further setback by the death, at the age of only 59, of its mainspring, De La Beche. Sir Roderick Murchison was already in his mid-sixties when he succeeded him—hardly the age to take up the life-work of another. However, the appointment of the new director coincided with the arrival on the staff of one who was to have a far greater influence on future developments. Thomas Henry Huxley, biologist, philosopher, a born champion of science, who was later to shake the prim Victorian world as 'Darwin's Bulldog', was just what the school needed. His adventurous background and strong personality gave the establishment a new and progressive look. The number of *real* students increased and very soon the school began to outgrow its accommodation and facilities. Huxley and some others of the staff believed that its future could only be assured by accepting a move to the bigger and better facilities offered by the developing complex in South Kensington; others, headed by John Percy, ever fearful of losing the laboratory that he had patiently and lovingly created, were vigorously opposed to any transplantation.

When Murchison died in 1871, a divided RSM trembled for its very existence. Eventually, the Government decided that the school should become an integral part of the Royal College of

Science, of which Huxley was appointed Dean, and over the next six or seven years its various departments were moved to South Kensington. Under the new scheme of things the veteran Warington Smyth continued in charge of mining until his death in 1891, when he was succeeded by one of his former students, Clement Le Neve Foster; and William Roberts-Austen, one of Percy's outstanding pupils, became Professor of Metallurgy.

This then was the position when the IMM came into being in 1892, and continued so with various oscillations until the turn of the century when the establishment of a Government Board of Education signalled a national reawakening to the importance of keeping pace with other countries in the development of higher and, more particularly, scientific education. Unfortunately, what development there had been in England was totally unco-ordinated; indeed, it came as a shock to many to discover that within a stone's throw of the Royal College of Science and the RSM, another institution, the Central Technical College of the City of London Guilds, backed by some of the wealthiest and most influential commercial companies, was offering training in subjects that overlapped the work of its neighbours.

Acutely aware that the training courses at the RSM were in need of reorganization, Professors Roberts-Austen and Foster sought the advice of the IMM, as a result of which in 1901 recommendations were made by a top-level committee, drawn from Council and headed by the then-President, Charles Moreing. Three years later, the Board of Education decided to tackle the matter in its broadest context: Hennen Jennings, who had become IMM President, Walter McDermott and Sir Julius Wernher, the multimillionaire pioneer of South African gold mining, were invited to join representatives of other interested bodies on a Departmental Committee under the chairmanship of Lord Haldane to investigate the whole problem.

Their enquiry was systematic and thorough; they compared the British methods with those of every country in Europe, in Canada and the United States. Their final report embodied the best of what they discovered, together with many specific suggestions of their own. What eventually emerged was very much a realization of Prince Albert's own vision 60 years earlier—an Imperial College of Science and Technology, open to students at home and overseas, affording the 'highest specialized instruction' and providing the 'fullest equipment for the most advanced training and research'. The report confirmed that the Royal School of Mines would retain its identity as an integral part of the new college, the governing body of which would include representatives of the IMM and other leading engineering and scientific institutions.

Although primarily concerned with events in South Kensington, the IMM also kept a watchful eye on educational progress in the Westcountry, where the three Cornish schools had amalgamated to form the School of Metalliferous Mining at Camborne. The IMM was represented on its governing body from inception, though naturally most of its members were Cornishmen. Having been called on to give evidence before the Board of Education's Departmental Committee in 1904, some of the governors hoped that Camborne would become a constituent school of Imperial College, and were disappointed when the only intended linkage was a suggestion that RSM students might benefit from 'courses of vacation work' at Camborne. This recommendation was, nevertheless, adopted and some mutual benefit was undoubtedly derived from the occasional intermingling of staff and students from both schools.

With so many local educationalists on the board of governors, it seems strange that a 'foreigner' should have been appointed as first principal, the natural claims of John Beringer, the accepted 'father' of the school, being totally overlooked. W. Fischer-Wilkinson, who moved into the chair, was a mining engineer of some eminence, but he was soon at loggerheads with his staff and resigned after a few months. Beringer was promptly reinstated, but ill health prevented him from being able to bear the full load, and he died soon afterwards.

*   *   *

With the approach of the twentieth century there was a growing feeling in the IMM that the status and influence of the Institution would be considerably enhanced if Queen Victoria might be 'graciously pleased' to grant a Royal Charter of Incorporation. Council was, of course, fully aware that Her Majesty would have little or no personal say in the matter, being then in her 82nd year and with many other more pressing duties to perform.

Protocol required that such applications be made to the Office of the Privy Council and accordingly a petition was submitted with a draft Charter in the names of Charles Moreing, the President, and Past-Presidents Joseph Collins, Samuel Cox and Walter McDermott.

The petition cited a membership of over 700, and contended that the need for Chartered status had become all the more necessary in recent years 'because London is now the commercial centre of mining enterprise both at home and abroad and British mining engineers are called upon to report upon mining propositions in all parts of the world and to supervise and carry out the work necessary for the development of the same, and large amounts of British capital and many British workmen of all descriptions are required and employed'.

It cannot be said that the petition was very well thought out, or attractively—or even grammatically—presented. Clearly, the Privy Council Office was not impressed: its Clerk wrote back pointing out that there was no mention of the Institution's financial position, and suggested that a simple registration under the Companies Act, omitting the word 'Limited', might best meet the members' aspirations.

Undeterred, the IMM continued to press its case. Moreing even persuaded the influential Duke of Somerset, with whom he had business dealings, to support the application, but His Grace's intervention did not do much good. Nevertheless, in the absence of any official contestant, the IMM considered itself still in with a chance. Then, on the very day that had been gazetted as the closing date for lodging objections, a representative of the Institution of Civil Engineers called at the Privy Council Office to ask the procedure for putting forward the ICE's views. The visit was quickly followed by a formal letter of protest and Sir William White, President, and the ageing Sir Frederick Bramwell hurried round to reinforce the Civils' objections.

As the oldest and most prestigious engineering institution in the world, the ICE was a force to be reckoned with. Born in the warmth of a Fleet Street coffee house three years after Waterloo, its history was inextricably bound with one of the great periods of British society. Thomas Telford was its first President; Sir William Cubitt and the Brunels, father and son, were among its earliest members; and—which was slightly encouraging to IMM—its first Royal Charter was granted by King George IV, barely ten years after its formation.

Behind the wording of their protest it was not difficult to detect a feeling by the Civils that the IMM was behaving rather like a cheeky schoolboy in asking for a Charter. With dignified restraint, the ICE pointed out that *every* branch of engineering, including mining and metallurgy, was represented in its 7300 worldwide membership, and it therefore saw no purpose in granting a Charter to any one branch whose interests were already well catered for.

The IMM petitioners made a quick rejoinder, refuting ICE's claims to represent them, but opposition mounted when the Federated Institution of Mining Engineers (IME), the coal mining engineers' organization, claimed that as an older body (by a mere three years, in fact) and with thrice the membership of IMM, it had repeatedly considered applying for a Charter, but had deferred doing so in the hope of effecting an amalgamation with its sister society.

To the IMM this was like a red rag to a bull, Council having frequently declared that such a move was impracticable as qualifications for membership were entirely different, and claiming that amalgamation would materially change the professional status of its members.

When it was known that the Privy Council was seeking the views of the Royal School of Mines, the IMM saw some glimmer of hope. But its friends Professors Roberts-Austen and Le Neve Foster—now both knighted for their work—found themselves unable to give their support. In fact, they made it clear that they felt most strongly that the question of a Charter should not be entertained until the IMM had agreed to amalgamate with the 'older and more important society'.

This was the last nail in the coffin and it was no surprise to Council when on 14 May 1901 a letter was received stating that their Lordships of the Privy Council found themselves unable to recommend the granting of a Charter.

Obviously thinking that this decision might have softened the IMM's attitude to amalgamation, the IME lost no time in inviting it to reconsider its objections. But Council stuck to its guns and the letter was politely acknowledged and placed on the file.

While these exchanges were going on with the Privy Council, Queen Victoria, to whom, nominally at any rate, the IMM petition had been addressed, passed peacefully away at Osborne, surrounded by her large family, including the Emperor of Germany, who had hastened to her bedside. The nation was plunged into mourning; it was said that the Queen's death came as a personal bereavement to every one of her subjects, and the day of her funeral was a day of silence. The IMM sent its condolences, postponed its annual dinner from March to October and, with the rest of the country, pondered with some little apprehension on the prospects of life under the new monarch, King Edward VII.

Obviously, it was no time to reopen the question of a Royal Charter, and throughout the first decade of the century successive Presidents appeared reluctant to initiate a new application. In 1913, however, Bedford McNeill came to the chair after 18 years of active membership, and from his inauguration members sensed that they could be in for an exciting year. McNeill's enthusiasm and good humour, coupled with a strong determination, were infectious. 'I realize I belong less to myself than to this Institution', he told his colleagues, 'and I promise you I will leave nothing undone to discharge my duties as efficiently as I am able.'

McNeill set himself two main targets: to secure bigger and better premises for the Institution's headquarters than the small suite of offices occupied in Salisbury House since 1902; and to prepare the ground for a second attempt to win a Royal Charter. Cleverly, he made the two projects work for each other.

Despite the claims of the Civils to represent the miners with all other branches of engineering, McNeill was emphatic: 'No other Institution fills, or has attempted to fill the place that we occupy, but we have no authority, jurisdiction or corporate being whatsoever. Anyone can call himself "a mining engineer", can re-date and use a report years after it was originally made, can write a report of a property that he never visits . . . can knavishly mislead the public with impunity . . . What we wish to do is to protect the public on the one hand, and on the other, secure an honourable career for ourselves.'

McNeill reminded his listeners that a Charter, while conferring rights and privileges, also carried obligations. One of the first things that they would have to do was to improve the Institution's finances. Larger offices, a bigger library and more staff were needed to cope with increasing membership and all other work that was accumulating. 'The time has arrived', he urged with some passion, 'when we should take counsel together, remembering that "Unanimity gives Strength", and petition His Gracious Majesty the King, to recognize, by the granting of a Royal Charter, the work we have already done, and to assist us in doing that which still remains for us to do.'

Once he had secured the backing of members, McNeill turned to his second project. In this, Council gave him virtually a free hand, relying on his astute business acumen and his close contacts in the 'Square Mile'. The outcome was that, aided by a gift of £10 000 from the widow of Sir Julius Wernher, the IMM was able to buy itself a new home at No. 1 Finsbury Circus and to become freeholders in the City of London.

The latter was important as it enabled McNeill to invite the Lord Mayor, Sir Vansittart Bowater, to perform the opening ceremony on 13 January 1914, the 22nd anniversary of the Institution's foundation. He was also able to get a preview of the Lord Mayor's speech and to nudge him into support for a Royal Charter. 'The object you have in view', Sir Vansittart told the 250 members who attended the opening, 'is very laudable, and I sincerely hope His Majesty will see his way to grant it to you, because everyone knows that once an institution gets a Royal Charter . . . it acts as an incentive to those belonging to the profession it represents to more readily combine for the public good.'

It now remained only for a formal application to be drawn up and submitted to King George V—more accurately, to the Privy Council. This time the petitioners did not forget to put in the financial figures: a capital of £20 000 and an annual income of £5000. Membership had increased to 2400, more than one-quarter of that of the Institution of Civil Engineers, which continued to claim that it adequately represented *all* branches of engineering throughout the Empire. As expected, the Civils again lodged an objection.

The Institution of Mining Engineers did not object: it simply applied for a Charter of its own!

Once more, the Privy Council turned to the academics for advice. At Imperial College the governors ducked a direct reply, tactfully acknowledging their indebtedness to both institutions in the organization and administration of the Royal School of Mines.

Left to make a Solomon's judgment, the President of the Privy Council accepted that there was still no chance of amalgamation between the two institutions, and on 9 February 1915 approved both applications on the understanding that the IME should concern itself exclusively with coal and iron mining, and the IMM with all other minerals and non-ferrous metals.

Which was, of course, precisely the position that had existed ever since the two institutions were formed more than 20 years earlier.

It took a month or two before the various formalities were completed and the draft Charter was eventually returned, fully approved by the Lord Chancellor. By that time Bedford McNeill had been succeeded as President of the IMM by Frederick Hatch, the geologist whom John Hays Hammond had recruited to help him in his work in South Africa in the 1890s and who accompanied him on his expedition into Mashonaland with Cecil Rhodes and Dr Jameson.

Hatch was the first to acknowledge that most of the credit for the award of the IMM's first Charter belonged to McNeill. Frank Merricks, himself a future President, described McNeill's year of office as 'one of the most momentous in the life of the Institution. His heart and soul were part and parcel of it, and the services he rendered were incalculable.' These services, incidentally, included the successful breach of the male chauvinistic attitude that the Institution—and most other similar bodies of the day—had tended to show in relation to the attendance of women at its functions. McNeill threw open the annual dinner to ladies for the first time and although there was some tut-tutting among the diehards, it was generally acclaimed as 'one of the most graceful of the many kindly acts' that he had performed for the IMM.

Dr Raymond would most certainly have approved.

CHAPTER FIVE

War Underground

But I will delve one yard below their mines,
And blow them at the moon
Hamlet, Act 3, Scene 4

At 3.10 am on 7 June 1917 the German battle lines along the Messines Ridge in Flanders disappeared in the biggest explosion of the First World War. Within 30 seconds 19 mines, containing close on one million pounds of high explosives, were detonated at key positions on a ten-mile front, most of them on a stretch of no more than 4000 yards.

The effect was devastating.

War correspondent Philip Gibbs described the explosion as 'the most diabolical splendour I have ever seen. Out of the dark ridges of Messines and Wytschaete, and that ill-famed Hill 60, there gushed out and up enormous volumes of scarlet flame, spilling over into fountains of fierce colour, so that all the countryside was illuminated by red light. Where some of us stood watching, aghast and spellbound by this burning horror, the ground trembled and surged violently to and fro. Truly, the earth quaked.'

On nearby Kemmel Hill a special lookout had been reserved for some of the chief architects of the earthquake. There was Major-General R.N. Harvey, Inspector of Mines at GHQ, son of the founder of a firm of Bristol wine importers famous for its rich brown sherry. Next to him was his right-hand man, Major Ralph Stokes, veteran of the Boer War, mining engineer of the Reef, and years later to become one of the most popular presidents of the IMM.

Huddled in his greatcoat, saying little but absorbing every detail, sat Major Edgeworth David, geologist and scientist, 'the quietest man ever to come out of Australia', and in Harvey's opinion, 'the most efficient man I have ever known'. David, who had helped to form the Australian Mining Corps when the opposing armies in Europe became bogged down in trench warfare, saw '19 gigantic red roses spring suddenly from the ground and, as their crimson petals fell apart, flames of all colours of the rainbow, ending in brilliant white, towered upwards . . . the air far and wide resounded with dull booms and roars like thunder.'

Across the Channel in Kent and Essex people stirred in their beds as the shock-waves spread. Prime Minister Lloyd George heard the explosion in London—and so did a student lying awake in his room in Dublin. What few people knew until weeks later was that the explosion was the work of the Tunnelling Companies of the Royal Engineers, manned largely by colliers and sewer-workers from the North of England, and officered by professional mining engineers, prominent among whom were volunteers from the Institution of Mining and Metallurgy.

Messines was only one battle in a long succession of bizarre and terrible struggles that took place underground amid the mud and carnage of France and Flanders. As Field Marshal Earl Haig was to remark when he unveiled a memorial to the memory of IMM men who died in the war, 'There was no truce at any time to the warfare that went on underground. . . . Every offensive undertaken by us right up to the days of the last great series of advances meant a fresh call on the energy, the industry, and the courage of those special Services upon whom the due preparation for these offensives so largely depended . . . I am glad to thank, not for myself only, but on behalf of the whole Army, this gallant body of men.'

*   *   *

On 22 May 1900, a tall sunburnt man of military bearing walked into the IMM headquarters in New Broad Street and applied for full membership. He found little difficulty in satisfying the Institution's minimum requirement of five years' practical experience in mining, for he had far more than that in South Africa and Rhodesia. But the application form stipulated that for full membership he needed to be over 30 years of age, and he was one year short. However, as Herbert Hoover had done in the same office three years earlier, he had no hesitation in declaring his seniority: he signed with a flourish, giving his address as the Salisbury Club, Rhodesia, and adding for good measure that he was a Justice of the Peace for Mashonaland, and late Captain and Adjutant of Lord Roberts's bodyguard in the South African war.

John Griffiths—later Sir John Norton-Griffiths, Bt., KCB, DSO—was, even at the age of 29, a man of remarkable character and achievement. Without formal qualifications as an engineer, he had been concerned in a variety of mining and construction enterprises in Central and South Africa. Born in Somerset, son of a building contractor, he was a scholar at St Paul's School, London, but by the time he was 17 he had left for South Africa, lured by the gold rush on the Witwatersrand. After the Jameson Raid in 1895 he joined the Mashonaland Field Force on its mission to relieve Rhodesian settlers in the rebellions of the Matabele and Mashona, and saw some lively action.

The Boer War sent him scurrying to Cape Town, where the newly arrived Lord Roberts recognized his potential and appointed him to his personal bodyguard. Thereafter, he accompanied Roberts on the campaign that culminated in the relief of Kimberley and the surrender of Cronje at Paardeberg.

Griffiths then returned to England to further his career as a mining consultant—and to obtain professional status by joining the IMM. Early disappointment in the staid atmosphere of London was followed by an exciting involvement in the building of the Benguela Railway, hardly a mining project but closely linked with the mineral development of the Congo, the brainchild of Robert Williams in opening up the Katanga for King Leopold of the Belgians. Indeed, it was Griffiths who was largely responsible for the railway *not* going to Benguela: on his way out to Africa he found the seventeenth century Portuguese settlement dangerous and unsuitable for a terminus for the line from Katanga, and he bribed his ship's captain with £100 to put in at the almost uninhabited Lobito, where there was a fine natural harbour.

With no experience of railway work, let alone in such arduous conditions, Griffiths, with a labour force of 10 000 Africans and a corps of camels to carry water and supplies, built his first 100 miles of track three days ahead of his contract. He later completed another 250 miles before a slump in copper prices hit

'Empire Jack'. After an adventurous career in southern Africa, John
Norton-Griffiths inspired the British counter-offensive to German mining
operations on the Western Front in the First World War and was largely
responsible for Allied victory in the war underground

Williams's company, Tanganyika Concessions, and brought work to a halt; in fact, it was 1931 before the link was finished, by which time the rail route to the south had been operating successfully for nearly 20 years.

For Griffiths, the Benguela Railway led to other lucrative jobs of railway construction, notably in South America, but, more important to his future role in the Great War, he took on major drainage contracts in London, Manchester and Liverpool, and learned the technique of tunnelling in clay.

By now a man of substance and social standing, he found it fitting to change his name to Norton-Griffiths and to seek a Conservative seat in Parliament, which he secured comfortably in 1910. His dedicated imperialism earned him the name 'Empire Jack'. One of his biographers described him at this time as '. . . pioneer, prospector and wildcatter—self-confident, reckless, a man of ungovernable temper, with no humility and no understanding of it in others'. Certainly his temper often over-boiled at his political meetings, where he once left the platform to strike a persistent heckler to the ground, and then continued his speech as if nothing had happened.

On the outbreak of war with Germany in 1914 he advertised in the *Pall Mall Gazette* urging 'all Africans, Australians, Canadians and other Britishers who served in Matabeleland and in the South African War, who are not connected with any existing military or naval organization, to apply to Mr Norton-Griffiths MP, 3 Central Buildings, Westminster'. From the many thousands who did so, he chose 500 tough, bronzed campaigners to form the 2nd King Edward's Horse Regiment—Norton-Griffiths's private army, the only body of irregulars to be given official blessing by Secretary of State for War Lord Kitchener, who usually had no time for enthusiastic amateurs. But Kitchener remembered Norton-Griffiths from South Africa and Egypt, and let him have his head.

However, this was to be no war of flying pennants and dashing cavalry charges: it soon became clear that it was to be a war of little movement, the opposing armies strung out in lines of trenches, sometimes little more than 50–100 yards apart, stretching from the French Channel ports almost to the Swiss border. There did not appear to be much scope for Major Norton-Griffiths's volunteers and, although he was impatient to take his regiment to France, he saw no immediate prospect of doing so.

Pondering the situation, Norton-Griffiths was reminded how army commanders tackled such problems in medieval times when military operations centred largely on besieging an enemy in a heavily defended castle or fortified town. Sieges could go on for months, sometimes for years, and often the only way of ending them was for the attackers to tunnel under the foundations of the walls and collapse them with burning brushwood, or with gunpowder when it became available.

Surely, thought Norton-Griffiths, the present situation was not much different; the war in France was a siege war and it would be won by the side that could evolve the most effective siege tactics. As a mining man he would like nothing better than a chance to blow up the enemy's lines. What was more, he had the very men for such a job—small-tunnel miners working on his contracts in the sewers and drains of England's northern cities. His 'moles', or 'clay-kickers', as he called them, were well used to working silently with the minimum of equipment. Officered by professional mining engineers, they could be formed into quasi-military companies to undermine the enemy at strategic points and fire their mines when least expected.

As early as November 1914 Norton-Griffiths put up a scheme to the War Office, begging permission to take a small party of men to France to make a reconnaissance. His letter was politely acknowledged and placed on a file marked 'Moles' and the contents were sent to France for the comments of the Commander-in-Chief of the Expeditionary Force, Field Marshal Sir John French.

More than a month went by without a reply. Norton-Griffiths fussed and fumed. Then the Germans themselves prompted the answer. On 20 December three mysterious flares arched into the sky over the German lines near Festubert, on the French–Belgian border. Next moment a loud rumbling noise spread along 1000 yards of Allied trenches held by an Indian brigade. The ground beneath the soldiers' feet shuddered and then split asunder with the simultaneous firing of ten German mines.

Shocked and dazed by the violence of the explosion and knowing not its cause, those Indians who had not been instantly blown to pieces or horribly maimed, threw down their weapons and took flight, pursued by machine-gun and mortar fire. Waves of German troops then raced across No Man's Land and occupied their positions without loss. The effect on the morale of the

Indians—and on other troops as the news spread—was catastrophic: some units refused to stay at the front and a few days later the whole Indian Corps was withdrawn to reserve.

Field Marshal French immediately called for retaliatory mines to be fired—by the Royal Engineers, who were already overcommitted and without the labour and back-up organization that military mining requires. In the following January the Germans fired more mines at Festubert and a week later at St Eloi, where soldiers of a Yorkshire regiment reeled back in confusion under heavy fire after their trenches had been blown.

By now heavy rains and snow of the first winter of the war added to the misery of the entrenched troops. Faced with continued bombardment by shell fire, swept with machine-guns and picked off by snipers, they lived in incredible filth, tormented by lice and rats, which gorged on the flesh of their dead comrades. Even so, the Tommies made the best of it. But to be forced to fight an enemy they could not see, and had no means of resisting, was a new form of frightfulness: almost any physical distress was better than waiting passively to be blown to pieces by German mines.

At last Norton-Griffiths received the summons that he had been waiting for and hurried to the War Office to see Kitchener. 'He showed me', wrote Griffiths in his diary, 'some of the urgent despatches that had been coming in from Lord French. They showed that unless some means could be found of checking German mining some sections would have to be withdrawn from the line. Kitchener then asked me to elaborate my ideas for counter-mining. I told him the only thing I could suggest would be to use my "Moles".'

'What on earth are "Moles"?', demanded Kitchener.

Norton-Griffiths seized a fire shovel from the War Office grate, flung himself to the floor and demonstrated how a 'mole' or 'clay-kicker' worked with his feet to operate a scoop-like tool and send the earth under his body for disposal by a companion behind him.

Kitchener was impressed. 'Get 10 000 immediately', he ordered.

Norton-Griffiths did not think that there were that number in the British Isles and, in any case, he told the Field Marshal, he would need to go to France to make sure that ground conditions were suitable for such an operation.

'Then go', said Kitchener, and turned to his desk.

This was the sort of reaction that the irrepressible entrepreneur understood. That evening, with two of his expert
tunnellers, he was on his way to find out.

Next morning, Saturday, 13 February, he walked into the office
of the Engineer-in-Chief at St Omer, repeated his demonstration
to astonished staff officers and sent his experts to examine the
nature of the clay soil on the battle front. By the following
Tuesday he was back in London, reporting his findings to Lord
Kitchener. On Wednesday he was in Liverpool closing down his
sewer-driving contracts and offering his employees alternative
jobs on the Western Front. On Thursday he appeared at Royal
Engineers Headquarters at Chatham with a first draft of 18 men,
who were attested, clothed and transformed into army sappers
within a few hours. On Friday night he returned to France with
his men; he arrived at Béthune on Saturday—and remained to
start them at work on Monday.

It may have been a 'static war', but Norton-Griffiths set it
moving. He astounded staff officers with the speed and purpose of
his activities. Years later General Harvey described his movements during the formation of the first five Tunnelling Companies
as 'meteoric'. 'He was', he recalled, 'provided with a mandate from
GHQ which enabled him to visit all units containing officers and
men who had mining experience, and to select from them
personnel for the new companies. He did this with unfailing
energy and enthusiasm, combined with his persuasive powers
and irresistible good humour. He used to claim that his
experience in lobbying in the House of Commons was of untold
value when he was up against a Commanding Officer who very
naturally objected to being robbed of his best men . . . but
Norton-Griffiths always got his way . . . he was here, there and
everywhere, holding parades, selecting officers and men, dashing
across to England to collect recruits and conducting them
personally to the Channel ports at any hour of the day or night, to
their final destination, occasionally finding time to look in on the
Engineer-in-Chief to report progress.'

Even to those troops who were unconnected with the mining
project, the sight of the galloping Major careering up and down
just behind the battle lines in his wife's two-ton chocolate-
coloured Rolls Royce, which he had commandeered for military
duty, was something of a tonic. Even General Harvey, a stickler
for discipline, found his own family background a help in turning

a blind eye to the cases of wines and spirits that Norton-Griffiths invariably carried in his car to soften up any hostile company commander.

'But then he would do', chuckled Norton-Griffiths. 'It was good for business.'

*   *   *

As soon as war broke out in 1914 the IMM Council gathered to consider ways in which the Institution could best help the national effort. The War Office was asked if any special corps of mining engineers was contemplated. Council was assured that such a body would not be immediately necessary, but if the occasion should arise the IMM's offer 'might be utilized'.

A vital opportunity to be first in the field in underground warfare was thereby lost, and the Germans, their mining schools much more attuned to military requirements than the British—some, like Freiberg, were run strictly on military lines with uniformed staff and students—had a six-month lead over their opponents.

The IMM accordingly made it clear to members that those who wished to volunteer for service should apply to join units of their own choice. Within a few months more than 300 members had joined up, many of them leaving responsible jobs overseas and travelling thousands of miles to stand in line at recruiting depots or to be drafted to officer-training establishments.

When, therefore, Norton-Griffiths breezed into the Finsbury Circus headquarters in February 1915 in search of recruits for the Tunnelling Companies, he found that many potentially valuable men had been widely dispersed among various branches of HM Forces. With the help of Charles McDermid, the IMM secretary, he was able to trace some to their units and persuade the authorities to release them, but it was a tricky, time-consuming business and, with the Germans becoming increasingly efficient in their mining operations on the Western Front, time was not on the British side. At least, the IMM was now alerted to the urgency of the situation and from 1915 onward members asking for advice were put in touch either directly with Norton-Griffiths or with the appropriate department at the War Office.

If Norton-Griffiths's sewer-workers could be whisked away to France and made into uniformed sappers in the space of a week, it was not surprising that it took only a little longer to deliver the officers who were to lead them into battle. The experience of Arthur Lumb, a Harrow boy and a Royal School of Mines graduate of 1910, was typical of that of very many other members of the IMM.

The outbreak of war found Lumb in West Africa, where he worked for the Mineral Survey of Southern Nigeria, under its director, Sir Albert Kitson. Arriving back in England on an April weekend in 1915, he checked in at the IMM office and was quickly sent on his way to the War Office. The staff major who interviewed him was really only interested in one thing. 'We are trying to send out one officer a week to the Tunnelling Companies', he said. 'You will be next on the list. Can you leave on Monday week?'

Slightly surprised, Lumb replied that he was ready to go, but emphasized that he had no military training of any kind. 'Oh', said the major, 'don't worry about that. You are going out to engineer, not to fight. Come and see me again on Wednesday.' Lumb duly reported, was medically examined, attested and commissioned all in one morning, and told to report to Chatham barracks the following week for final instructions. The Easter weekend was coming up and Lumb had a mining report to write for his former employers, to see his Liverpool directors, and buy his uniform and equipment.

'Just one more thing', said the major while Lumb's mind tried to grasp all that he had to do, 'I wonder if you would mind taking a small draft of men with you?'

It was at that point that 2nd Lieutenant Lumb's troubles really began. Fortunately, he had a cousin, a regular colonel, stationed at Chatham, and on his arrival there he made haste to contact him. Lumb's cousin sat up all night coaching him in military procedures and etiquette and, as dawn broke, delivered him to the parade ground and bade him farewell.

'There I found myself standing in front of my small draft which, to my alarm, consisted of 120 men', recounted Lumb later. 'The men were all miners from the Midlands, whose ages ranged from 20 to 60, and whose sole training had been three days at Chatham.

'A regular sergeant of some 20 years' standing then appeared and, giving me an imposing salute, said he was reporting for orders. I had been told I would be expected to march off at the head of the company to the railway station but, not wishing to make a fool of myself or let down the prestige of Chatham, I acted on a brainwave. I returned the sergeant's salute as best I could and said: "Look here, Sergeant, I hold you responsible for getting these men to Southampton. You will walk in front; I shall walk behind to see that there are no stragglers."

'At Southampton, the sergeant shook me warmly by the hand and cleared off. I then had to look around among the men to see if there were any NCOs. I found a solitary lance-corporal, who had been in the Territorials for six months, and told him he was to take charge of the party.

'A large transport, packed with troops, was on the point of leaving so, with the corporal's help, I got the men in line two-deep and marched at the head of them from the station to the ship's gangway, the corporal bringing up in the rear. As I approached, the ship's captain, surrounded by a bevy of military staff officers, was on the bridge and very impatiently shouted at me through a megaphone: "Come on, sir, you are holding up the whole ship." For the life of me I could not think of the orders to get the men into single file and up the gangway. By this time the captain was becoming really peevish and the faces under the red hats were showing both anger and derision. The corporal, too, was stumped for the right order but, seizing the men one by one, he pushed them up the gangway. Such a simple solution had never occurred to me.

'When we disembarked at Le Havre, I was marching at the head of the party along the main road when I suddenly saw approaching a large funeral cortège. I had no idea what to do when, fortunately, I caught sight of an intervening side street, up which I marched the whole party in the nick of time. When the procession had passed, we right-about-faced and proceeded on our way.

'On another occasion, when reaching a hill in Rouen, I saw several of my men getting off a bus at the top. They thought this was better than walking and, as War Office instructions were just to get them out there, I did not consider that this called for any disciplinary action.

'After two or three days we finally reached a village behind Ypres, where a company was awaiting my detachment before moving to the front line. With the exception of two men, who had got off the train to look for food and had been left behind, my party was intact. I thought I had done rather well, but when we were paraded before the company commander he roundly abused me for arriving late, which I felt to be grossly unjust, and for losing two men. Being weary and cross, I muttered something uncomplimentary. This was overheard by the sergeant major, and then there was more trouble . . .'

A few days later Lumb was in the trenches west of the infamous Hill 60, and stayed there for 32 days without relief. The two front lines were no more than 50 yards apart and shelling and sniping went on all the time: the batman who fetched his supper from the canteen was shot before he could reach him. When off duty from the front Lumb and his men were continually being sent for, particularly at night, by agitated infantry officers to investigate noises thought to emanate from German tunnellers. After this first taste of war, Lumb had two days at HQ before being sent back to Hill 60 and remained in the line for a week before coming out for 48 hours, and back again in the trenches for another long spell.

'It was small wonder', reflected Lumb, 'that after a few months of this life, many officers and men were almost fit for a mental home. The older men, in particular, could not stand the pace and most of those over 50 were finished in six months.'

Lumb was one of the lucky ones who survived. He took over command of his company—No. 175—and won the Military Cross and a mention in despatches. After the war he returned to Africa, where his work took him to the Ivory Coast, Liberia, Sierra Leone, the Gold Coast and, finally, back to Nigeria. He was responsible for the first survey of the Marampa iron ore deposits after they had been discovered by Dr N.R. Junner, the Sierra Leone geologist who also found one of the first diamonds in the country, opening it up for vast alluvial mining.

*   *   *

The scale and tempo of military mining in the 1914–18 war has seldom been realized other than by those intimately concerned in the operations. Within a few months of the first bewildered miners arriving in France—some fully expecting to be taken to work by bus from billets safely behind the lines—a force of 25 000 men was raised, embodied in 25 Tunnelling Companies of the Royal Engineers. These companies included a considerable number of South Africans, who were later joined by special units brought over from Canada, New Zealand and Australia.

The Germans, having taken the initiative in the war underground, forced the British to fight defensively in the early stages, intercepting and destroying the enemy's tunnels and wearing down his attacks in every way possible. From an undisciplined rabble the tunnellers quickly became responsible for the protection of the whole British front against underground raiders. Vast areas of No Man's Land, and even beyond the lines, became riddled with mines and galleries. Hundreds of men were buried alive in their efforts to counter German raids on British trenches, and hand-to-hand fights to the death took place in the darkness as opposing diggers broke into each other's tunnels.

It was a war of initiative and improvisation that, amidst the horror and carnage, sometimes had amusing results. One IMM member, an officer in a Tunnelling Company, won himself the name 'Push-pipe' Martin for a novel idea to surprise the Germans. Frustrated by the slow and wearisome task of driving tunnels big enough for men to crawl through, he devised a plan to push a pipe, filled with explosives, forward beneath the enemy lines and fire it when it was in place. He and his men got to work one night and made even better progress than they expected. When dawn broke, the pipe was seen protruding several feet into the air, bending back ominously towards the British lines!

It soon became apparent that operations could not be allowed to continue to be directed by enthusiastic amateurs and the British High Command decided to regularize the position. General Harvey, a soldier of great experience, a man of strong character and untiring energy, was appointed from the Engineer-in-Chief's office to take charge as Inspector of Mines, with Major Ralph Stokes of the IMM as his chief assistant. The two had a common bond in that they had both fought in the Boer War and, indeed, Harvey stayed on in the Transvaal for several years after the war to work for the civil government. More importantly, perhaps, Harvey hit it off with 'Empire Jack', for whom there was still much to do.

One of the major problems that concerned them was the choice of explosive with which to charge the British mines. After experimenting with gunpowder and a variety of other mixtures ammonal was found to be more than three times as powerful as any other, easier to handle and more effective in the local clays. But ammonal was little known in the army and staff officers who were asked their opinion of it had hurriedly to consult their subordinates. One corps commander, having seen a requisition for ammonal, sought an explanation from, among others, his chief medical officer, who reported that 'ammonal is a compound drug extensively used in America as a sensual sedative in cases of abnormal sexual excitement'; it was not, he added, a medical issue to Corps HQ and 'so far no cases have occurred indicating the necessity for our administering the drug'.

As explosive charges became more and more powerful, casualties from the gases that were left behind assumed serious proportions. One company had 16 men killed, 48 badly injured and 86 slightly affected by gas poisoning in the space of a month; another had 12 killed, 48 seriously ill in hospital, and 60 other cases in a similar period. As most of these men were skilled miners, whose places it was almost impossible to fill, such wastage had a sharp effect on the capabilities of the underground forces. Norton-Griffiths made a lightning tour of the British coal fields, collecting Proto-sets and other lifesaving gear, and in course of time a comprehensive mine-rescue system was set up on the Western Front.

There was also a call for canaries and white mice for detecting gas underground. A staff officer visiting a sector of trenches in which a Tunnelling Company was operating was emotionally moved when he saw a canary chirping happily in a cage, hung outside a dugout. 'What nice chaps these miners are', he remarked to his aide, 'they even bring their pets to war with them.' But the canaries suffered casualties, too, both above and below ground. One escaped from its cage and fluttered into a tree in No Man's Land; a sniper was called to despatch it for fear that it would arouse enemy suspicions that an attack was eminent, but he found the target far too small and eventually bird—and tree—had to be demolished by mortar fire.

Listening devices to monitor the enemy's movements underground were also in demand. Again, Norton-Griffiths rose to the occasion by raiding the London Metropolitan Water Board for 'listening sticks', used for detecting leaky water mains, and these were widely employed until the French geophone—described as 'a cross between a doctor's stethoscope and the long ears of a donkey'—became available. Later, more sophisticated instruments were evolved.

Slowly, by the courage of the 'clay-kickers' and the skill of the professional mining engineers—the hard core provided by the IMM—the German underground offensive was checked and the British tunnellers were able to move over to the attack. The 'moles' burrowed deeper and deeper, laying more heavily charged mines beneath the enemy lines. Tactically, the war took on a new and more deadly dimension; planning became more scientific and long-term, culminating in the extensive preparations for the vital Battle of Messines.

The Messines–Wytschaete Ridge was no more than a spur of ground running ten miles or so across Belgium, partly encircling the village of Ypres, but, because of the flatness of the surrounding land, it was an important military acquisition.

Between Ypres and the neighbouring village of Cormines a single-track railway had been laid before the war; during its construction soil had been removed from a cutting through the Messines Ridge and piled into three separate dumps beside the track. The largest of these was Hill 60, so named simply because it was 60 metres high.

The Germans had held the ridge and the three dumps since 1914 and, although many bloody attempts were made to dislodge them, they remained in a seemingly unassailable position, free to fire at will into the lines of the British 2nd Army, occupying the lower ground in front.

In midsummer 1915 a Tunnelling Company started a drive from 200 yards behind the British lines towards the garrison on Hill 60. The 'moles' called it the Berlin Tunnel, figuring that they would eventually come up in the German capital! Quite independently, another company, commanded by IMM member Captain Cecil Cropper, a tough metal-mining man from Cumberland, was aiming a four-gallery attack on Messines from another direction.

It was then that Major Norton-Griffiths came bustling around this sector and immediately foresaw the immense possibilities of a combined effort to 'earthquake' the whole ridge in support of a major offensive planned to be made on this front in July 1916. At first the generals would have nothing to do with it, and it took all Norton-Griffiths's powers of persuasion to make them change their minds. Only when he promised that the scheme would save thousands of British lives and that 'our soldiers will be able to walk to the top of the ridge smoking their pipes', was he given the go-ahead.

Months of preparation followed: miles of tunnels were driven by the 'clay-kickers', and mines, more powerful than any previously exploded, were laid under enemy positions ready for the great attack. Then came anti-climax. Bogged down on the Somme, British Commander-in-Chief Douglas Haig ordered the Ypres offensive to be postponed. For a whole year the mines lay, fully charged and encased in waterproof bags, under the Messines Ridge. If the enemy had discovered them, or if even one had been prematurely exploded, the whole operation could have been ruined. In the event it remained one of the best-kept secrets of the war, though there were anxious moments, especially when the Germans raided the British trenches and for several days occupied a dugout immediately above one of the mining shafts.

Of the 22 mines laid, 19 were fired at zero hour on 7 June 1917. The German garrison was stupefied; men who a month or two earlier would have fought to the last, lifted their hands in despair. The extent of their casualties was never accurately known. Ten thousand prisoners were taken on the first day of the British advance, but thousands more Germans just ceased to exist, torn to shreds by the terrible blast that lit the sky for 60 miles and sent the townspeople of Lille tumbling in panic into the streets. One mine alone killed 1000 soldiers of two crack German battalions.

Yet the greatest consequence of the mines was not the number of enemy killed but the effect that the explosion had on the survivors. Everything that Norton-Griffiths had promised came true in those dreadful ten seconds of hell on earth. Not until the British infantry passed beyond what had been the first German lines did they meet any resistance. Without the mines, a frontal attack on such a heavily defended position could have cost 50 000 men.

Perhaps the highest tribute to the Tunnellers' handiwork came from the German General Erich Ludendorff, who wrote in his memoirs: 'We should have succeeded in retaining the Messines Ridge except for the exceptionally powerful mines used by the British . . . the demoralizing effect of the explosions was simply staggering.'

CHAPTER SIX

Three of a Kind

In the records and memorabilia of those who fought the war underground the names of three men constantly recur: Stokes, David, Gurrey. A study of their experiences and behaviour stamps them as exceptional, even among that relatively small band of specialists in which most were unusual and many remarkable.

Two of them, Stokes and Gurrey, were mining engineers and members of the IMM. The third, David, was a geologist, one of the most brilliant scientists of his day but, although closely associated for much of his life with both the IMM and the Australasian IMM, was never officially a member.

Brigadier Ralph Shelton Griffiths Stokes served with distinction in three major wars, spanning nearly half a century. He won the Queen's Medal in the Boer War, and by the time he joined the 8th Army in the Western Desert 40 years later his battle-dress also carried the ribbons of the DSO and MC, awarded for his work with the Tunnelling Companies between 1914 and 1918, and the OBE for his part in the Archangel Campaign of 1918–19.

Twenty years after Archangel he was at Narvik, but few medals were on offer for that disastrous operation, which most historians agree was undertaken more for political purposes than for military necessity. Indeed, both of Britain's major armed excursions into the Arctic have been condemned as 'blunders' in concept, and 'failures' in result; and, looking back on them in an article written when he was over 90, Stokes could not help but reflect that behind each lay the dominating influence of Winston

Churchill.

Despite his outstanding military service, war for Ralph Stokes was little more than an occasional interruption to a successful mining career that occupied more than 50 years; in fact, for much of his army life he was able to pursue his calling, to the great discomfort of the enemy, especially in France and Flanders in World War I.

In contrast, the Boer War was more in the nature of a boyish adventure. Stokes was born and educated at Windsor until one day in 1899 he vanished from his tutor's care and was not heard of again until he turned up in Cape Province. There, he enlisted as a trooper in the prestigious Paget's Horse, in which his elder brother was already serving, and was drafted to one of Lord Methuen's columns in West Transvaal.

War on the South African veldt was a very personal affair and, despite its hardships, Stokes fell in love with both the life and the country. Seventy years later, he found that his memory was sharper for names and incidents of that war than for events of the two world wars. 'Many personalities stand out vividly in my mind from those days on the veldt—from Methuen, our General, to Trooper Rose of lime-juice fame', he once told an interviewer. But he could not be persuaded to set down his own adventures; he would talk of others and the part that they had played, but seldom of himself. The most that could be got from him was that his most terrifying experience was when his horse was struck dead by lightning when he was standing beside it.

Not surprisingly, Stokes became fascinated with the life of the gold miners on the Witwatersrand, and as soon as war ended in 1902 he got a job with Crown Reef as an assistant surveyor, and continued to serve the mines of the Corner House group intermittently for the next 57 years. At first, he found little encouragement from the mining houses for young men whose education had been interrupted by the war. and he seized the opportunity to broaden his experience by writing on mining affairs for the *Rand Daily Mail*: this led to a world tour and the publication of his book entitled *Mines and Minerals of the British Empire*.

Stokes rejoined the Corner House group in 1907 to work underground at Robinson, then the premier gold mine on the Rand, and later became chief surveyor and then underground manager at Crown Mines. In 1912 he left for North America to become a field engineer for the International Nickel Company.

The outbreak of the Great War in 1914 found him in Alaska, but he managed to reach the trenches in Flanders as a sapper before the end of the year. As soon as Norton-Griffiths appeared on the scene he became heavily involved with the Tunnelling Companies. His underground experience on the Reef was invaluable and his promotion was rapid.

Stokes kept a full and meticulous account of every operation in which he was involved: several inches thick, his diary remains today one of the most valuable records of the war underground. Once, his company drove a tunnel beneath the enemy lines, branching out into smaller galleries, each of which was charged with explosives for maximum effect. Before the mines could be fired, a hostile tunnel was detected, heading across the British system. Hasty retaliatory action could have ruined the whole operation, but Stokes calculated that if the Germans were allowed to continue, their gallery would pass just overhead.

Huddled together in the darkness beneath No Man's Land, he and a fellow officer and IMM colleague, Laurence Hill,* listened for two days as the Germans scraped their way a few feet above them: so close were they that their conversation and laughter could be heard. Next day came the silence that usually preceded violent action. In the nick of time Stokes blew the German tunnel, and the main attack on the enemy lines was launched according to plan.

For much of his service in France Stokes was Number 2 to the Inspector of Mines, General Harvey, but he was seldom to be found at GHQ and spent most of his time moving about the British lines, giving help and advice to the Tunnelling Companies, never hesitating to become the guinea pig for any new tactics or devices to harass the enemy. His technical work for the Battle of Messines was a major contribution to its success.

After Messines he was given control of mining for the British First Army, but was not with them long before being appointed engineer for an operation with the curious code word 'Elope', the only hint of its purpose being that it involved some demolition work 'in a distant field'.

The 'field' was certainly distant, and of considerable dimension: it occupied over 30 000 square miles of forest in Archangel, a

*OC military tunnelling, Malta, World War II—Chapter Ten.

cold and bleak territory, traversed by rivers, ice-bound for half the year. The objective was to save from enemy hands what remained of a vast stock of ammunition and supplies shipped for the then disintegrating Russian army and to prevent German attacks on Allied shipping.

Whether or not the Archangel 'intervention' was the mistake attributed to it in later years, Stokes saw the campaign as 'unique in the novelty and diversity of its components: an enemy upon whom no war had been declared . . . spies and agents behind our lines . . . operations under a British mandate from discordant Allied powers . . . a long Arctic winter of intense severity . . . a summer cursed with plagues of mosquitoes and other flies . . . bloody mutinies amongst local battalions, and insubordination among Allied troops . . . air reconnaissance and bombing hampered by ice, snow and swampy runways'.

He was glad when it was all over and he could get back to civil mining. In London he joined the IMM and headed for South Africa to become superintendent of mines for De Beers, serving eight years at Kimberley before rejoining the Corner House in 1928 as consulting engineer. In those post-war years he never forgot his old friends of the Tunnelling Companies: he set himself the onerous task of compiling a register of all officers who served therein and laid the foundations for an old comrades' association, with branches in four countries, that continued to thrive right up to the outbreak of the Second World War.

In 1936 the IMM notified him that he had been awarded the Consolidated Gold Fields of South Africa gold medal, and in the following year he was appointed President of the Chemical, Metallurgical and Mining Society of South Africa—later to become the South African IMM.

In August 1939, when he was nearly 57 and war with Germany seemed again inevitable, he returned home determined to rejoin the British army. He arrived on 8 September and reported personally to Chief of the Imperial General Staff General Ironside, who had been his commanding officer in Archangel. General Ironside looked at him critically. 'Stokes', he said, 'you're five days late!'

A few months later he again found himself bound for the Arctic, this time as engineer to 'Rupert Force', a combined British, French and Polish corps assembled to drive the Germans out of Norway—or at least to capture Narvik to offset the humiliation of

Brigadier R.S.G. Stokes served in three major wars and became one of the IMM's most popular Presidents in 1954. He spent most of his mining career with the Corner House group

the Allies 'missing the bus' further south along the Norwegian coast.

The word went round among the sappers that they were being led by a man with only six years' military service—two in the Boer War and four in World War I. But his pride in the corps, his understanding of sapper problems and his unflagging energy soon endeared him to all ranks. One who served with him in Norway had two special memories of him—his insistence on testing a new Arctic sleeping bag by personally spending a night out in it in the snow, and his perpetual and unnerving habit of crimping detonators to fuses between his teeth, which he laughed off as an old South African mining trick.

Like Archangel, 'Rupert' too was a failure—and Winston Churchill was provoked to anger and irrational criticism. Stokes inclined towards a more objective appraisal, which concluded that 'a direct assault on Narvik was impracticable, especially for troops not trained for amphibious operations or snow warfare, and inspired by a tradition, while glorious, was not noted for its flexibility'.

At the end of the war Central Mining appointed him chairman of its oil holdings, Trinidad Leaseholds; he also became the corporation's technical director and in this position played an important part in the acquisition of the Harmony gold mine, which became one of the largest of the Corner House group.

Even when he retired to England in the 1950s Stokes retained his seat on Central Mining's board, and began to busy himself with the affairs of the IMM. When he became President of the Institution in 1954 he had to choose between addressing members on his wartime experiences or the wisdom that he had gained from 50 years of mining. He chose mining, and his dissertation on the problems and future resources of the Witwatersrand mines is a classic.

Both in war and in peace the men who worked for the 'Brig', as he was popularly known, found him a brilliant and understanding leader. His ABC of behaviour in dealing with any matter was quite simple: its requirements were to be Articulate, Brief and Courteous. Stokes himself combined all three with a high degree of professionalism that earned him a place in the front rank of mining engineers of the twentieth century. With his natural charm, humour and humility he was certainly one of the best loved.

*   *   *

THREE OF A KIND

Lieutenant-Colonel Sir T.W. Edgeworth David had no 'cordal appendages' from the IMM, nor from the Australasian IMM, within whose orbit he spent most of his working life. If he had they could have been something of an embarrassment to him for he could already write—but seldom did—the letters KBE, CMG, DSO, FRS and D.Sc. after his name. And David was never one to let the tail wag the dog. No account of the war underground between 1915 and 1917 would be complete without acknowledging his contribution to its victory; similarly, any reference to the early history of mineral exploration and discovery in the Australian continent that failed to record his achievements would ignore a man who for nearly half a century dominated its geological science with a benevolent mastery.

Tannatt William Edgeworth David was born in a Welsh rectory in 1858 and it was his father's wish that he should follow him into the church. But the boy David had other ideas. At Oxford his education was interrupted by illness, and while convalescing he made a round trip to Canada and Australia in a sailing ship. Returning to Oxford, he attended Professor Joseph Prestwich's lectures on geology and continued his studies at the Royal College of Science, where he took his degree in 1881.

He was barely 24 when he was off on his second voyage to Australia, this time to join the New South Wales Geological Survey, of which he later became director. He virtually discovered the great coal fields at Maitland, and his account of their survey to a packed audience of local residents was his first experience as a public lecturer and led to his appointment in 1891 to the chair of geology and palaeontology at Sydney University. It was at Sydney that he produced the most enduring part of his work as a teacher: his enthusiasm and his gift for making geology a living subject inspired generations of students to pursue a study for which the greater part of Australia was then an unknown field.

In 1897, on behalf of the Royal Society, Professor David led a scientific expedition to the coral island of Funafuti, 500 miles north of Fiji, and his conclusions gave striking support for Charles Darwin's theory that coral atolls had grown progressively on slowly sinking platforms. In contrast, he took an increasing interest in glaciation and by 1906, when he travelled by way of India and Europe to attend an international geological conference in Mexico, he had become a leading authority on ice ages, which he made the subject of his address to the congress.

It was thus with an established reputation that David was picked by Ernest Shackleton to head the scientific staff of the British Antarctic Expedition, which set sail in the *Nimrod* in 1907. It was never intended that the professor should be a member of the land party, but David argued his way ashore and set up a winter station on the ice. The following year he led the first party ever to climb the treacherous glacial volcano Mount Erebus, which towers 13 000 ft high. Impressed by this achievement, Shackleton put him in charge of an attempt to reach the South Magnetic Pole. The four-month journey, in which David and two companions dragged laden sledges more than 750 miles across the ice plateau and back to the waiting *Nimrod*, has passed into the annals of polar exploration as an epic of courage and endurance.

When in August 1914 the British Association for the Advancement of Science decided to go ahead with a conference in Australia, despite the outbreak of war in Europe, David contributed much to the success of the occasion, not least by his example of tactful behaviour towards delegates from what had suddenly become enemy countries. His public insistence that 'all men of science are brothers' led to his investigation by the New South Wales Government. But David was a staunch patriot. With Ernest Skeats, his opposite number at Melbourne University, he took the lead in urging the Federal Government to form an Australian Mining Battalion when the opposing armies found themselves bogged down in trench warfare. It was no part of the plan that David should go with them, but he managed to wangle himself a commission and arrived in France with his men in the spring of 1916.

David's original idea was that the battalion should work as an integral part of the Australian Corps, but General Harvey insisted—and rightly so, as David agreed—that the Australians, like British and other Commonwealth tunnellers, should come under his command as Inspector of Mines, and the force was accordingly split into three companies plus a repair and maintenance unit.

This left David's role in some doubt. Harvey, as he admitted later, had not at this stage realized the value of an experienced geologist. For his first few weeks, therefore, David spent his time wandering as a freelance along the British front—very much as Stokes had done—giving specialized advice wherever it was needed. In this way he became almost as well known to the tunnellers as Norton-Griffiths, careering along the shell-pitted roads in his wife's Rolls Royce. Despite his uniform, he was always 'The Professor' to the troops, readily recognized by his slightly bent shoulders and flowing white hair. In an attempt to disguise his age he grew a regulation moustache of the 'worn-out toothbrush type', and was surprised when it came out a dark brown and everyone accused him of dyeing it.

Once, during the early days, he was in the La Bassée–Loos area to study unpredictable rising and falling of icy water, which was making operations miserable for the troops. He walked round one night close to the enemy lines with Major Leslie Coulter, one of his young Australian company commanders, and another officer. Suddenly a flare spluttered into the sky, illuminating the three men brilliantly. Immediately there was a crack of bullets, one of which whipped between Coulter and David. 'The Professor' wrote home to say what happened next: 'Coulter moved quickly up to my right, which somewhat irritated me, and although no words were spoken, we executed a kind of waltz or *schottische* around one another in the moonlight until at last I succeeded in re-establishing our original marching order.' He had earlier complained that the other officers seemed to regard his life as more important than their own—a point of view he dismissed as 'tommy-rot'.

David's freelance wanderings came to an abrupt end one day when, in order to make an examination of the Vimy Ridge strata for the British First Army, he decided to go down a 100 ft deep disused well. He descended cross-legged on a board set across the rim of a bucket, but at little more than 20 ft the windlass collapsed and sent him hurtling to the bottom. Peering down into the darkness, his horrified companions were able to make out that he was still alive, and lowered a doctor to give first-aid.

Despite several broken ribs, a deep scalp wound and severe internal injuries, David was hauled to the surface, his legs dangling through the loops of a rope. Once he shouted to the men at the top to stop for a moment so that he could examine a stone in the brickwork that might give information important to his mission. When at last they got him out he refused to go to hospital before thanking the doctor and each one of his rescuers. When General Harvey visited him a few days later he found him eager to explain by a complicated mathematical process that his survival was 'proof of the theory of the parallelogram of forces'.

On David's return to duty Harvey had him posted to GHQ, where he could keep an eye on him, having at last realized that he had on his staff one of the world's leading scientists, whose geological expertise was a vital factor in winning the war underground. David was closely involved in all the final preparations for the Battle of Messines and proud of the fact that of the eight Tunnelling Companies involved, two were of his own raising.

'An hour's conversation with David', wrote Harvey several years later, 'was like a breath of fresh air amid the stale and unprofitable discussions which were necessarily based on incidents of the war. His charm of manner was equal to his depth of knowledge of all things scientific, and his eyes had the most humorous twinkle, which always showed itself when replying to some leading question.'

Only once during his war service was David on record as displaying anger or even annoyance. During a tunnelling operation his men discovered the well-preserved remains of a fossil mammoth. Unfortunately, the Germans attacked and occupied the ground. David wrote in his diary: 'The beastly Boche has gone and captured my mammoth fossil, blast him! But I've been to the Engineer-in-Chief and he has promised to get it back.' The ground was duly recaptured, but not before the Germans had recognized their prize and carted off the remains, leaving a note of thanks to the Australians for doing all the hard work.

But there was compensation for David's disappointment. Returning to Australia after the war, his last great scientific triumph came in 1928—eight years after he had been knighted—when he discovered in the rocks of the Mount Lofty and Flinders range perfectly preserved animal remains, dating millions of years earlier than anything previously classified. When he died in 1934 he was given a state funeral. So great were his achievements in the world of science that in a long obituary in *The Times* there was room only for a single paragraph about his war record. But the tunnellers, not only of his Australian companies but all who served in the war underground, never forgot their kindly 'Professor'.

*   *   *

If anyone had suggested to Donald Gurrey when he left England to join the tunnellers in 1915 that, with the war still raging, he would be helping to reconstruct the French coal mines in the Pas de Calais, he would have dismissed the idea as ridiculous. He would have also discounted any suggestion that within 18 months he would be sharing Christmas festivities on the Western Front with German troops, whom he would use his best endeavours to kill within minutes of their return to their own lines.

But war can play strange tricks on a man.

Francis Donald Gurrey—Donald to his friends—had the benefit of a classical education at Malvern College, followed by a course at the Royal School of Mines, where he took his degree and became a student member of the IMM. He left, intending to specialize in metal mining, but after only a short spell in the Cornish tin mines he joined Warncliffe Colliery in Yorkshire. There he worked under George Blake-Walker, a pioneer of coal-face mechanism, and gained one of the earliest colliery manager's certificates to be awarded—No.18.

From Warncliffe, he moved in 1912 to Kent, his native county, where he was under-manager for the sinking of a 3000 ft shaft at the Snowdown Colliery: it was troublesome ground, but the experience gained was of much value when he later became involved in the rehabilitation of the Nord and Pas de Calais mines, where conditions were similar.

Early in 1915 Gurrey felt that he could make a more positive contribution to the war effort than sinking shafts in Kent and, through the IMM office, he contacted John Norton-Griffiths. 'Just the man we want', said 'Empire Jack', and within 10 days he was 2nd Lieutenant Gurrey of a Tunnelling Company in a waterlogged trench near Armentiers in France.

In places the enemy line was less than 150 yards away. 'We sank pits in spongy clay 20 ft deep', he recorded. 'German mining became extremely active, but never seemed to be intelligently pursued . . . German officers appeared not to go underground and left this to their subordinates . . . we approached their workings on many occasions and then everything depended on who blew his mine first. The Prince of Wales was OC Trench Pumps and did good work on his bicycle.'

One of the highlights of Gurrey 's early experience came when, in taking over a sector from the French at the side of the

Captain Donald Gurrey. For half an hour or so on Christmas Eve 1916, he and his men exchanged friendly greetings with the enemy. Then the shelling began again . . .

Béthune–Lens road, it was found that enemy galleries were already under the British line. 'My section was ordered to sink down on top of them and fire before they did', said Gurrey. 'This was accomplished in rapid-working shifts. Using light coal-mining picks to minimize noise while digging in solid chalk, we sank a shaft 20 ft deep and drove a horizontal gallery 40 ft long. We came so close to the Germans that we could hear them talking, laughing and singing. I am sure they heard us too, but we got our mine off first.'

In December 1916 a picket of sappers arrived with a boring machine to work in the clay area near Givenchy, where Gurrey and his company were then operating. After some difficulty it made good progress towards the enemy line, and on Christmas Eve a mine was fired at the end of the tunnel.

What followed next was described by Gurrey as a 'shining tubular bridge', which 'left the ground about 20 yards from our parapet and ended up in a shell-hole 15–20 yards from the enemy. We then heard cheers and laughter from the Boche, who seemed to think it was a fraternity gesture. Anyway, after some bomb and grenade work by both sides, we saw the enemy advancing slowly over the top with hands outstretched.

'We exchanged cigarettes, cigars and rum. I spoke three languages—French, Spanish and Afrikaans—and was able to understand that the Boche thought it was some kind of Christmas joke, for there was much guttural laughter.

'After half an hour the Germans returned to their own lines, and this was followed by hymn-singing by both sides, each joining the other lustily whenever they knew the tune. For 30 minutes or so there was silence. Then the war began again.'

It was about this time, when fighting was going on around the important *Mines de Béthune*, that two elderly French mining company directors would creep into the British trenches to ask about the state of *Fosse No. 8* just behind the German line, and the general situation in their mining area. Incredibly, the French were still drawing coal from one of the shafts, using compressed air to drive their winding engine.

'The Frenchmen asked us if we could man an outpost at the pit bottom of *Fosse No. 8* as they were afraid of enemy attention', explained Gurrey. 'This was done by a small party from No. 17 Tunnelling Company, but they were mostly Irishmen with a habit of singing boisterous choruses down the pit which were clearly heard at the bank. Next day there was silence: they had all been gassed by the enemy.

'Later, two French army officers from the *Corps de Mines* asked if, on my next leave to England, I would report on the plight of the French collieries to the War Office and urge the necessity of an early start to the rehabilitation of their shattered mining industry. The opportunity occurred in the autumn of 1917 when I went to the War Office and was referred to Brig-General Sir H. Osborne Mance, who was responsible for military railways and roads.'

From then onwards things moved quickly. General Mance, a powerful personality and brilliant organizer, recognized the importance of Gurrey's report and a meeting was arranged with Lord Derby, Secretary of State for War, who ordered Gurrey's attachment to General Mance's staff, and appointed him Technical Liaison Officer to the French Government.

'So', wrote Captain Gurrey, 'after two and a half years of warfare, I was out of the trenches, leaving behind five fellow officers and 30 of my sappers in the cemeteries of Maroc and Noeux les Mines.'

Gurrey found an office at 66 Victoria Street and, in cooperation with the *Groupement de Houillères Evahies* and British consultants, started a programme to reconstruct the French mines. His first task was to dewater the flooded pits. Like Norton-Griffiths, he was a persuader and improviser. When suitable sinking pumps could not be found in England, he got them from Sweden; he prevailed upon a reluctant Admiralty to let them have pipes; and when a hoist was needed for an underwater camera, he made one from the chassis of an Hispano-Suiza car, captured from 'Little Willie', the Kaiser's son.

It is not clear exactly how long Gurrey worked for the French Government, but in 1921 he established himself in Paris as a consulting mining engineer to promote the sale of British mining equipment. Seven years later he was co-founder, with the Mining Engineering Company of Sheffield, of Cie Meco Paris and built up a thriving business throughout France.

Forrest Anderson, a pioneer of the Scottish mining equipment company Anderson Strathclyde, who had a long business and personal relationship with Gurrey, found him friendly and helpful, but initially 'rather a formidable character'. 'His military bearing and appearance, his energy and decisive approach to affairs were very impressive', says Anderson. 'He was always in a hurry, except when discussion with clients called for patience. He was continually sending telegrams, but to whom and where I am not quite clear. He loved driving his Voisin car—always with the hood down. When travelling he wore a blue beret, and I copied him, for it was a convenient headgear, particularly in an open car. With his tall figure and his beret, he was a *kenspeckle* person, easily recognized by a great variety of people. He was not averse to a little showmanship and when he visited us at Motherwell he still wore his beret, and was the focus of many a look as he passed through the shops, where he was always referred to as "The Frenchman".'

Gurrey's command and understanding of the French language was impressive—but it did not fool the French. His mining assistant, a Frenchman of character and temperament, who almost worshipped him, told Forrest Anderson that his chief was easily recognizable as an Englishman. Anderson asked what was the tell-tale trait. 'It is obvious', replied the Frenchman, 'he *walks* like an Englishman!'

When the Germans again invaded France in 1940, Gurrey got out his ancient Voisin and drove with his wife to St Jean de Luz, on the Atlantic coast, close to the Spanish border, where they were lucky enough to be taken off by a British destroyer. For most of the war they lived in the Staffordshire village of Chebsey, where Donald continued to work for the British end of his business. As soon as peace came he was back in France to help get the mines working again, repeating in some respects his task during and after the 1914–18 war. He steered his company through 20 years, including some difficult ones, extending his interests into Spain, as well as becoming involved in copper mines in Mexico, phosphate in Morocco and manganese in Algeria.

In 1965, he decided to spend the last years of his life in his vineyards in the south of France, leaving his son Patrick to run the business. His death in 1976 was a loss to both British and French mining. Britain had rewarded his war service with the DSO and Military Cross; France gave him the Croix de Guerre and made him a Chevalier de la Légion d'Honneur. The IMM accepted him as an associate member just before he left for France for the first time, and accorded him full membership in 1934.

*   *   *

It would be a fitting end to the story of the IMM miners of the Great War to be able to record a similarly peaceful twilight to the turbulent life of John Norton-Griffiths, the man who did more than any other to ensure the winning of the struggle underground. But for 'Empire Jack' his days of violence were not over with the Battle of Messines. Formalization of the activities of the Tunnelling Companies, under the direction of General Harvey, reduced the need for the sort of services that he could provide. As soon as he realized that he was becoming redundant, he returned to England—without even seeing the Messines mines blown—explaining to his friends that he felt he was neglecting his Parliamentary duties.

Promotion to the rank of colonel and the award of the DSO did not really provide the sort of recognition that he deserved, or wanted. He looked for new excitement, and he found the promise of it when he was sent for by British Military Intelligence and told of Allied fears of a collapse of resistance by Romania, which was coming under heavy enemy pressure. If the Germans succeeded in taking over the country, they would win a prize of 7.5 million tons of grain and 1.5 million tons of fuel from the Ploesti oil fields. The Russian revolution of February 1917 had virtually opened the gates for the Germans, and the situation was becoming daily more serious.

Griffiths was asked if he would attempt the destruction of the oil industry if the Romanians refused to carry out a 'scorched earth' programme. He agreed, and asked only one concession—to be allowed to take his former batman with him. They travelled out through Sweden and Russia—at just about the same time as Ralph Stokes was landing with his men at Archangel. In Romania he found a disintegrating government more inclined to hand the industry over to the Germans than to destroy it.

Aided by the prevailing chaos, Griffiths set about his task. With flaming petrol, with blocked drill-holes, with acid to rot boilers, with smashed machinery, he carried out an orgy of destruction over 200 square miles. In a few sleepless days and nights he achieved £50 million worth of damage—and the Romanian oil industry went out of production for months.

On his return to England Griffiths was knighted and his war honours were added to with three further mentions in dispatches, the Legion of Honour, the Order of St Vladimir and, perhaps a little ironically, the Grand Star of Romania.

He then addressed himself to the reconstruction of his old firm. By the end of the war he had built slipways at Middlesbrough, a dry dock at Dublin, enlarged the Tyne shipyards, and created Catterick aerodrome. He now appeared to be at the peak of his success, with many and powerful friends, with wealth and social position at his command. But the complexities of business and finance began to tell against his entrepreneurial methods, and his affairs wallowed in poor administration, badly chosen subordinates and disastrous investments. Then a contract for heightening the Aswan Dam in Egypt gave promise of restoring his fortunes. It did not work out that way: cumulative errors and unforeseen difficulties brought him to the brink of ruin.

In a last ruthless gesture he took a boat, rowed to the middle of the Aswan lake and shot himself.

Perhaps his most appropriate epitaph was penned by Keith Middlemass in his book *The Master Builders*: 'He was the expression of all that characterized the empire builders of the Edwardian era . . . In an ideal world Norton-Griffiths should have been a *condottiere*, a guerrilla general . . . it was his fate to blunt his energies in the service of a hard master, international finance, and to emerge disillusioned and drained by the circumstances of his life, with customs and habits which the world had made archaic.'

CHAPTER SEVEN

Linking the Family

The Institution of Mining and Metallurgy emerged from the stress of the Great War stronger and more firmly established than before.

Paradoxically, its recovery was more rapid than that of the industry which it represented: several years were to pass before mining activity in the member countries of the British Empire was able to match the pace of its pre-war development. The war had brought to light a chaotic state of affairs in the organization and distribution of the Empire's vast mineral resources and a pathetic lack of information as to where precisely its most important production fields and processing plants were located. The IMM took a leading part in attempting to improve the situation by instigating the establishment in London of the Imperial Mineral Resources Bureau 'to collect and co-ordinate information . . . to stimulate its dissemination and to advise upon measures for protecting and extending the mining and metal industries in the manner best calculated to promote the national safety and welfare'. The Institution also helped to promote a Bill in Parliament 'to safeguard the nation against a recurrence of enemy alien influence or control in the non-ferrous mineral and metal industries', and kept a close watch on all other legislation affecting the industry and those who worked in it.

Despite the strain on the Institution's resources and the difficulties of travel, the series of 'ordinary' meetings, at which technical papers were read and discussed, was unbroken, though attendances were inevitably much smaller. Even the annual dinner was still held, and if fewer seats were occupied and the menu was less attractive, the enthusiasm of those able to take part was undiminished.

For the IMM the highlight of its affairs during the war had been the award in 1915 of the coveted Royal Charter and a move to new headquarters in premises befitting its growing influence and prestige. The Institution had become accepted and recognized in the City, its offices occupying a key position in Finsbury Circus—a locality already the home of several of the big international mining companies and consultancies. More than anything else, the major part that the IMM had played in recruiting officer material for the Tunnelling Companies of the Royal Engineers had led to a better appreciation by the Government and the public of the important position occupied by the Institution and similar professional bodies in promoting the national interest.

For these and many other developments achieved within the constraints of four years of war the IMM had largely to thank Charles McDermid, its secretary since 1900. McDermid collaborated closely with Norton-Griffiths in the latter's insatiable quest for mining engineers for the war underground in Flanders. Griffiths repeatedly tried to persuade him to take a commission in one of the Tunnelling Companies, but McDermid always refused, partly because the thought of masquerading as a soldier when thousands were being slaughtered nauseated him and, more importantly, because he felt that once in uniform his opportunities of helping the war effort, and his Institution, would become seriously reduced. So busy was he in this period that he temporarily exchanged his home in Westerham, Kent, for a house in Ladbroke Square, West London, in order to be able to put in even longer hours at the office, despite German air raids on the capital, which were becoming increasingly frequent and violent.

McDermid's value to the Institution in the war was generously acknowledged by his employers, often in the inflated language that those called upon to propose votes of thanks at annual meetings felt it appropriate to apply to such occasions. Thus, Harry S. Denny in 1915 likened him to 'the sturdy Eddystone . . . [that] stood through all weathers and vicissitudes of fortune, above the ebb and flow, as a familiar and trusted symbol of integrity and a tower of strength'. In more restrained terms, another member declared: '. . . he is, of course, more than a member of staff, more than the secretary of the Institution, for he is himself an institution'.

And indeed he was. Personal contact was essential in holding the IMM together at a time when communications were so difficult, and McDermid provided the focal point on which relationships were centred. He had friends in all governmental ministries concerned with the prosecution of the war. When, for example, Harold Titcomb turned up one day in 1917 with some revolutionary ideas of expediting the war, McDermid at once put him in touch with Walter McDermott, a founder member of the IMM and its sixth president, and Frank Harbord, both of whom were then attached to the Ministry of Munitions.

Titcomb, one of the more remarkable American mining engineers of his time, had been an IMM member for some years, having moved to London from the States in 1910 at about the same time as the arrival in Britain of Alfred Chester Beatty, with whom he had graduated from Columbia School of Mines and later shared a series of exciting adventures in the American West. From personal experience he knew that the great iron works of the Ruhr, supported by the nearby coal fields, were the main source of Germany's strength and power for war, and he was anxious to interest the British authorities in bombing them.

McDermott and Harbord took Titcomb to the Iron and Steel Institute in Victoria Street and introduced him to its secretary, G.C. Lloyd, who agreed to help him compile production data of the enemy's iron industry and prepare maps and plans of the principal plants. For three months Titcomb worked almost every day, and often through the night, on his report, which, after many frustrations and delays, eventually arrived on the desk of Glaswegian shipowner and industrialist Sir William Weir, who was also the Minister for Air. Weir, who was later to become chief architect in building up British air power between the wars, was already fighting off demands for an Admiralty-controlled air arm and persuading Lord Trenchard to develop the Royal Air Force. He sent for Titcomb and looked at him critically across his desk. Titcomb's as yet unpublished diary takes up the story.

'Sir William told me that he thought the scheme was a good one, but it would take time to get together a force to make such an attack. He asked my opinion of how the matter might best be handled.

The war memorial at IMM headquarters. The original, designed by P.N.
Nissen, inventor of the Nissen hut, was unveiled by Field Marshal Earl
Haig in 1921; many years later it was stolen from Portland Place, but a
copy was made

"Sir William", I said, "you are an engineer, are you not?"

"I am", he grunted.

"So am I. Can I speak to you as one engineer to another, or
must I address you as Chief of the Air Force of Great Britain?"

"You can speak to me in any damn way you please", replied
Weir.

'So I said, "Why in hell don't you bomb, for example, this plant at Saarbrucken?" And I stubbed my finger on the map and referred him to my report and the production figures.

'I went away greatly impressed with Sir William Weir and encouraged that something might be done, but even I was unprepared for the speed of events. Within a week the British newspapers reported that the German iron works at Saarbrucken had been successfully bombed. Later, I learned from my friend Lloyd at the Iron and Steel Institute that production from that plant had fallen to about one-third of what it had been before the bombing.'

The IMM lost 126 of its members in the Forces during the war, many of them killed while serving with the Tunnelling Companies. When Council decided to honour their memory, Charles McDermid persuaded an old friend, P.N. Nissen, inventor of the Nissen hut and of an ore reduction process that also bore his name, to design a memorial. Nissen had served with field companies of the Royal Engineers and was closely in touch with the Tunnellers throughout the war. He produced a fine work in bronze and malachite, depicting an officer of the Tunnelling Companies in the act of firing a mine with an electric exploder, the model set upon a plinth on which a roll of honour was inscribed.

This was the memorial unveiled by Field Marshal Earl Haig on 24 November 1921, when the 'Last Post' and 'Reveille' were sounded by trumpeters of the Honourable Artillery Company. It was adapted for 44 Portland Place and rededicated there on 11 November 1957, the names of IMM members who lost their lives in the 1939–45 war being added to the roll of honour. The bronze was later stolen by vandals and its 1978 replacement now stands in the entrance hall of the Institution's headquarters.

*   *   *

Reflecting on the successes and failures of his illustrious career, the Duke of Wellington once remarked: 'Next to losing, the worst thing is winning'. Britain and her Allies won the Great War; it is debatable whether they won the peace.

The Empire that emerged from the four-year holocaust was weakened by the loss of one million men—the 'flower' of the population, the sort of men who in peacetime would have been making a major contribution to their countries' continued development and prosperity—and its material resources were severely strained. More than three-quarters of those killed were from what was euphemistically known as 'the mother country'. India, Australia and Canada each suffered more than 60 000 dead: Indian troops caught the full blast of the Germans' horrific first assault with mines on the Western Front; thousands of Australians and New Zealanders fell in the ill-conceived expedition to the Dardanelles; Canada put half a million men into the fight out of a total population of eight million; even Newfoundland lost more than a thousand inhabitants of its rugged and sparsely peopled territory.

In these and other British 'possessions' the war inevitably produced a spirit of . ᵗⁱ⁻ nalism, a feeling that grew in intensity as time went on, sowing the seeds of political change. Despite this, the Empire gathered its strength and continued to hang together for quite a long time yet—in some countries longer than even the more ardent imperialists had dared to hope.

On the credit side, the war underlined the fact that although in many cases it lacked organization and coordination, mining development in the Empire over the past 80 years had made it largely independent for minerals. Moreover, almost every country in the world had come to depend on the British Empire for at least some minerals necessary for its industrial development.

The IMM made it its business to ensure that these facts were recognized in the right quarters—not merely in its own interests but to help to ensure that the position was maintained and strengthened as a matter of national security.

Frank Merricks, an engineer who had travelled the world extensively in the latter part of the previous century before settling down to consultancy work in London, pressed home this point when making his IMM presidential address in 1920. The fact that he had worked closely with the Ministry of Munitions throughout the war ensured that his words would not pass unnoticed. 'It is surely', he remarked, 'a just cause for pride that a small country like England, herself one of the richest mineral countries . . . should have developed an Empire that has attained so unique a position in regard to mineral production, a business which, I venture to assert, has done more to populate that Empire and knit its peoples in a bond of loyal fellowship than any other

Frank Merricks. Under his Presidency in 1920–21 the IMM agreed to share its offices with the IME; services were united under one secretariat though each institution retained its own identity. The arrangement continued until 1954

industry that could be named.'

Merricks went on to make a masterly survey of the current position throughout the Empire, drawing attention to the new opportunities for prospecting opened up by the great advances in land and air transport during the war. 'In both Australia and Canada', he told his audience, 'there are vast stretches of altogether unexplored country, which may contain enormous mineral wealth, great tracts of valuable agricultural land, awaiting the survey of the pioneer by aeroplane. The motor lorry and the railway train will not be long in following the flying man, should he find gold or lands of any sort of golden promise. A loan of, say, £1 million, raised in Australia or Canada, and devoted exclusively to the finding of new mining fields by, and for the benefit of ex-soldiers, might in a few years yield its providers a quite handsome revenue, and would certainly betoken gratitude to those brave men.'

Finally, Merricks appealed to the governments of all Empire countries to take advantage of the experience gained in the war and set up committees of technical advisers—such as had already been introduced in New Zealand—so that 'the brains and practical knowledge of the ablest men of affairs throughout the Empire may be always at her service', and he pledged the cooperation of the IMM in any scheme to achieve this purpose.

On the domestic front, the resettlement into civil employment of IMM members returning from the war went on quicker than had been expected, or, perhaps more correctly, less slowly than had been feared. Although the Institution could obviously not become a fully fledged employment agency, it maintained an appointments register and kept in close touch with key departments of the Ministry of Labour and with mining companies headquartered in Britain. It also pressed the companies and, where appropriate, overseas governments, to revise pre-war salary scales of engineers and metallurgists to bring them into line with higher living costs and the depreciated value of money.

The immediate post-war years also saw the first positive moves towards a closer union between Council and members abroad, and a draft constitution for overseas committees was drawn up after talks with visitors from Canada, Australia, South Africa and India.

Total membership in the early 1920s was around the 2450

mark, of whom fewer than 1000 had registered addresses in Britain: in fact, the proportion of overseas members was even greater than these figures might suggest as many of those with 'permanent' United Kingdom addresses spent most of their time abroad.

Council was always in some difficulty when seeking to increase overseas membership, appreciating that most of those who worked abroad were also necessarily members of local sister institutions and thereby liable to pay more than one set of fees. Wherever the main allegiance of members lay, the wide geographical separation of the world's major mining fields meant that they could meet together but rarely. In Canada, for example, the important mining provinces of Ontario and British Columbia were 2000 miles apart; in Australia the principal groups of members were in Western Australia and New South Wales; in India there were three groups of roughly equal strength—in Burma, Bengal and Mysore State; and in Africa pockets of membership dotted the continent from the West Coast, through the Congo and the Rhodesias, to the gold fields of the Transvaal.

In these circumstances the importance of the Institution's *Transactions* assumed a new dimension. However desirable it was to encourage personal contact with and between its members, Council accepted that its principal means of communication with those in distant parts would have to continue to be through the distribution of reports of technical papers and discussions, together with other printed material issued from time to time. From the earliest days of the IMM's history, the *Transactions* had been enriched by contributions arising from the experiences of its members. who together had probed most corners of the world where mineral resources were known to exist. Their accounts were to become of permanent value to the profession. Collectively, they were the very lifeblood of the Institution and Council was determined that the flow should continue in even greater strength.

The spirit of cooperation and unity engendered within the Institution during the war overflowed into its relationship with outside bodies, especially in regard to its old rival, the coal mining-related Institution of Mining Engineers. For years the two institutions had operated very much at arm's length, the IMM repeatedly rejecting all suggestions for amalgamation or a closer working relationship. Members of both institutions had been

thrown together in the war; they had fought side by side in the
trenches, often as fellow officers in the Tunnelling Companies, as
a result of which the misconception that some IMM members had
of IME men being 'black-faced scallywags' had undergone
considerable change.

When, therefore, in the latter part of 1920 the IME made a
further tentative approach to discuss the possibilities of closer
association, it did not receive the same sort of rebuff that had
greeted previous overtures. In fact, as Frank Merricks announced
at IMM's annual dinner in the following April: 'This open-hearted,
broad-minded action on their part was much appreciated and
welcomed by us, and I am happy to say that in the space of a very
short period several meetings of representatives of the two
councils have taken place, resulting in working arrangements
being agreed upon between the two institutions. These
arrangements provide for each institution retaining its identity . . .
the Institution of Mining Engineers will be housed in the new
House of the Institution, and the library and other services will be
united under one secretariat, headed by our secretary, Charles
McDermid.' A joint advisory committee was constituted and
questions common to the two institutions were to be referred to it.

He continued: 'The fact that only a few months ago there were
two mining institutions in London with a combined membership
of over 6000, who were to all intents and purposes friendly
strangers, was a regrettable state of affairs. The fact also that at
the end of these few months it has been possible to remove that
barrier, and to bring the two institutions together on the lines I
have mentioned, must, I think, be considered a fine and notable
achievement.'

If, as a result of these arrangements, the IME expected to
exchange its offices in Victoria Street, Westminster, for the IMM's
prestigious 'House of the Institution' in the City, it was
disappointed, for no sooner was the ink dry on the agreement
than a property company turned up with a scheme for
redeveloping Finsbury Circus and made an offer for the IMM
freehold. Council insisted that no offer could be considered
unless it provided for the reinstatement of the Institution in
another building with at least equal, and preferably larger
accommodation.

The developers subsequently offered Cleveland House, a gaunt
looking building at 255 City Road, with twice the floor space and

three times the ground area of the Finsbury Circus offices. Council found the facilities at Cleveland House 'eminently suitable', though its distance from the existing headquarters at the centre of London's mining community—15 minutes' walk and five minutes by bus or train—was somewhat of a disadvantage. But the terms were attractive—a cash payment of £20 000 and an 88-year lease at a 'peppercorn' rent—and the offer was accepted.

In May 1921 both institutions moved in, and by the following year had reached such an harmonious working relationship that it was decided to celebrate with a grand banquet at the Guildhall, to which the Prince of Wales was invited as guest of honour. The Prince warmly commended the arrangement as 'making for greater efficiency in the very important national work with which the institutions are concerned', as well as providing material economic advantages. The Prince accepted honorary membership of both institutions and Sir John Cadman and Savannah Speak, presidents of the IME and IMM respectively, each became an honorary member of the other's institution. It was an evening of good fellowship and self-satisfaction—a particularly momentous occasion for Mr Speak, who, it will be remembered, had represented the younger element of mining engineers at the IMM's inaugural meeting in 1892 and now, 30 years and a distinguished career later, had achieved his institution's highest office.

Honorary membership was a privilege that neither institution bestowed lightly. When in 1929 Herbert Hoover became President of the United States—15 years after he had ended his mining career—the IMM Council decided to make him an honorary member. To the surprise of many the decision was vigorously opposed by secretary Charles McDermid, not because Hoover had falsified his age in his original application for membership but because of a highly unsavoury dispute in which Bewick Moreing, and Hoover personally, had been involved in the early years of the century over the control of the Kaiping mines in China. The case went to the High Court of Justice, from which Hoover eventually emerged successfully, but not without some nasty stains on his professional character. McDermid felt that Hoover's behaviour in this affair had put him out of the running for honorary membership and he persuaded Council not to go ahead with the invitation.

The Hoover case undoubtedly contributed to a general tightening up between the two world wars of the qualifications demanded for all grades of IMM membership; the rules were constantly re-examined, more closely defined and stringently enforced. Exhaustive enquiries were made to ensure that candidates fulfilled requirements in regard to both professional attainments and personal character: everything possible was done to ensure a high standard of technical efficiency and integrity, sometimes at the cost of rejecting quite a considerable number of applicants.

At the same time the IMM kept a watchful eye for evidence of unprofessional conduct among its members and few years passed without reprimands being handed out to some 'black sheep' found to be guilty of fraud, of deliberately reporting excessive mineral values of properties under their examination or of unauthorized and incorrect use of the Institution's initials as guarantees of competence. Even so, Hugh Marriott, a former President and ex-officio Council member, felt that the Institution was not doing enough. In a book entitled *Money and Mines* he asserted that the IMM's usefulness would be greater if it paid as much attention to a member's character as to his professional competency. 'It [the Institution] possesses a power of expelling members guilty of unprofessional conduct, but this power is rarely exercised', he wrote. 'The question that really has to be faced and decided is whether the Institution exists to maintain and improve the status of the mining profession as a whole, performing the same services for its members as the Law Society does for solicitors and the General Medical Council for doctors, or whether it exists to promote and protect the selfish interests of its members like a trade union.'

Council reacted indignantly to this attack from within, and demanded a withdrawal of the offending passage. But Mr Marriott was unrepentant, claiming, like so many critics who come under challenge, a 'misreading' of the words in question.

Among several milestones reached by the IMM in the first ten years of peace after the First World War was the establishment of its Benevolent Fund. Edward Riley, a prominent member for many years, who died in 1914, left the Institution a legacy of £2000, which Council unanimously decided to use to get the fund started, adding to it an amount of £543 8s 1d, the balance of an account to relieve hardship suffered by families of members who had been killed in the war.

This project had been the dream of successive Councils for

many years, Robert Gilman Brown told those attending the annual general meeting. He spoke from personal experience, having been a member of the IMM for 30 years, the second American citizen (after Hennen Jennings, in 1903–05) to become President, and one of a distinguished band of 'old boys' of Columbia School of Mines who made their home in Britain and helped open up the mineral wealth of the Empire.

*   *   *

Although the IMM and the IME kept strictly to the terms of their 'common law' marriage and did not interfere in each other's affairs, living as they did under one roof, they could not be entirely indifferent to each other's problems.

For all connected with Britain's coal-mining industry the 1920s were a traumatic period. Faced with a major economic slump and the removal of wartime controls on production, colliery owners were unable, or unwilling, to consider miners' demands, even for as little as an extra two shillings a shift; employers maintained, in fact, that wages should be lowered and set locally instead of by national negotiation with the unions.

A series of stoppages and lockouts put the industry in a turmoil, which culminated in the TUC calling out all its members for Britain's first general strike, starting at midnight on 5 May 1926. A great middle-class army at once rushed to the assistance of the establishment: stockbrokers, barristers, businessmen and undergraduates realized boyhood fantasies as they climbed onto the footplates of strikebound trains, behind the wheels of buses, and into the cabs of lorries, loaded with supplies. Good order and essential services were thus largely maintained, and the mood of the country was captured by the secretary of the MCC when he loftily told a reporter: 'As far as we are concerned we have no intention of allowing cricket to be interrupted.' Within ten days the strike crumbled and the embattled miners were left to fight on alone.

A Royal Commission was set up and the IME was among the many bodies invited to give evidence. With much public feeling on the side of the coalface workers, the IME took the opportunity of condemning some widely held misconceptions, and expressed the resentment of British coal-mining engineers of a popular belief that the industry was 'carried on with a general want of humanity and insufficiency of technical skill and scientific knowledge'.

The IMM could do little more than sympathize with its sister institution, though it did publicly declare itself strongly opposed to the state ownership of the coal-mining industry—a view emphatically endorsed by the Royal Commission.

*   *   *

It is not clear who it was who first had the idea to hold an Empire Exhibition in London in 1924. Some say it was the Prince of Wales but, although he accepted office as its President and took a close personal interest in the project, there is little evidence that he contributed anything like the inspiration of his great-grandfather, Prince Albert, who conceived the Great Exhibition of 1851. Whoever it was, the idea was a good one, a badly needed tonic for the great family of nations, still struggling to re-establish itself after the pressures and privations of war. True, a quarter of the world was still coloured red on the map, schoolchildren still had a holiday to look forward to on 24 May and everyone sang 'Land of Hope and Glory' just as boisterously as in Victorian times, but it was somehow beginning to have a hollow ring.

The IMM Council was quick to recognize that an Empire Exhibition would offer a golden opportunity to launch a project on which it had been pondering for some time. At the 1921 annual dinner Frank Merricks, who enjoyed an exceptionally eventful presidential year, gave the first hint of Council's thinking when he suggested that it might be possible to 'link up the various mining institutions of the Empire under one imperial federation'. By doing so, the mining profession would be able to speak with one voice, and with such 'united power would exercise great influence on matters affecting the mining industry . . . its president could be drawn from one of the federated institutions . . . and a special meeting held in his country'.

Prophetic words indeed. Then, at the memorable Guildhall dinner in the following year, Sir John Cadman, speaking on behalf of both the IME and the IMM, made a more positive declaration: 'We are taking steps to invite sister institutions in the British Isles and throughout the Empire to join with us as equal partners in forming an Empire Council of Mining and

Metallurgical Institutions. It will not be, unless I am greatly mistaken, a mere debating society. It will be a body linking up all the men of our profession throughout the British Empire in a concerted effort of practical achievement.' Then, turning to the American Ambassador at his side, he added that he hoped that 'such a scheme may find favour amongst the engineers of your great country and ultimately embrace all English-speaking mining and metallurgical engineers . . . That, in my opinion, is a tremendous and auspicious development.' Sixty-five years were to pass before Cadman's vision of American participation became reality, but at least the seeds were sown.

From then on there was exceptional activity in the joint secretariat at Cleveland House under its tireless workhorse Charles McDermid, who accepted the possibility that he would finish up—as indeed he did—as honorary secretary of the imperial body. Cooperation was secured from the Mining Association of Great Britain, the scientifically orientated Institute of Metals, and institutions looking after the interests of petroleum technologists, and engineers in all branches of the iron and steel industries.

It was then but a small step to give substance to the plan by arranging a first congress during the Empire Exhibition at Wembley in the spring of 1924. Invitations went out to all the overseas institutions, and technical papers were invited for delivery and discussion at a four-day congress in Conference Hall Number One, the very centre of the Exhibition, which, as King George V was to declare at its opening, was to present 'a picture of our commonwealth of nations, a vivid model of the art, architecture and industry of all races under the British flag . . .'

Lord Long of Wraxhall, a former Colonial Secretary, chaired the meetings at which no fewer than 40 papers were presented, a programme made possible only by dividing sittings into four concurrent sections devoted, respectively, to mining, petroleum, iron and steel, and non-ferrous metals. In this way time was made available for a garden party at Goldsmiths' Hall in the City, a reception at the Royal School of Mines and a Guildhall dinner.

It was even possible to have an afternoon to look round the Exhibition. Naturally, mining occupied only a small part of the space in most pavilions, though there was a notable exception in the Malayan building, in which it assumed an almost preponderant importance.

But the big attraction, not only for the mining men but for the public at large, was a full-scale model of a coal mine, appropriately located, as one correspondent astutely noted, between the Palace of Engineering and the Amusement Park, 'for it partakes many of the characteristics of both its immediate neighbours'. To call it a 'model' was, however, somewhat misleading as visitors could go 'underground' and inspect the actual conditions at the coalface where such a large section of Britain's industrial workers toiled for so little. A full range of surface equipment was also on show—headgear, winding engines, air compressors, ventilating fans, coal-handling and cleaning plant, and in the nearby Mining Hall a collection of models spelt out the history and development of the industry since earliest times.

The highlight of the Congress for the mining institutions came when the resolution 'that the official delegates . . . acting upon instructions from the councils of their respective institutions, hereby constitute themselves an Empire Council of Mining and Metallurgical Institutions' was unanimously and enthusiastically adopted. The resolution went on to outline the constitution and the objects, powers and function of the Council. At the Guildhall dinner that evening, when Prince Arthur of Connaught was guest of honour, Lord Long of Wraxhall, publicly announced the Council's formation when proposing a toast to the mineral and metal industries of the Empire. Emanuel Shinwell, then Britain's Secretary for Mines, responded and was thus first to congratulate the Empire institutions on their initiative and wish them well.

Everyone went away feeling that the whole event had been highly enjoyable and entirely successful. Among them was Dr A.C. Wallis, President of the Canadian Institute of Mining and Metallurgy, and on his return home he persuaded his council to agree to host a second congress in Canada in 1927. In 1930 a third congress was held in South Africa on the invitation of the two local constituent institutions. It was to be Australia's turn next, but world depression in the early part of the decade ruled it out, and by the time economic conditions started to ease new war clouds were beginning to gather.

The Canadian congress, centred on Ottawa, was notable for a resolution, which the IMM had initiated several years earlier, calling for a full-scale review of mineral resources of the Empire, and the South African event for a recommendation to have the findings of such a review coordinated by the Imperial Institute, which subsequently formed a special committee for the purpose. Ottawa also came up with an idea to establish the Empire Council in a special building in London that would house the headquarters of all the British-based member institutions. Quite a lot of work went into inspecting sites, obtaining building estimates and other relevant information. The project even won the support of the Prince of Wales, who continued a lively interest in the affairs of the mining institutions, and an option was taken on a site in Westminster. But the scheme floundered when it was discovered that costs would be no less than £150 000—and it was well-nigh impossible to raise that sort of money at the time.

The IMM, never completely happy with Cleveland House, had better luck when it began to cast around for alternative accommodation for itself and its IME lodgers—and to raise the necessary money to enable it to do so. When George Winter Gray came to the presidency in 1933 he very astutely suggested that advantage might be taken of the current high price of gold, which had swollen the profits of the big mining companies. His suggestion was followed by the creation of an endowment fund and a tactful approach to the companies in question that here was a worthy cause that they might feel moved to support. In a short space of time there was nearly £50 000 in the kitty. Unfortunately, base-metal producers were not enjoying the same prosperity as their gold-mining friends—quite the reverse, in fact—but the IMM soon had enough money in its pocket to go house-hunting.

By this time the redevelopment of Finsbury Circus had been completed, and a self-contained suite of offices was available for rental on the upper ground floor of Salisbury House, the building that the Institution had vacated 14 years earlier. IMM took the suite on a 21-year lease and, together with the IME headquarters team, moved in December 1934. It took a bit of time to find a buyer for the Cleveland House lease, but eventually things were satisfactorily settled.

CHAPTER EIGHT

Case Study: The Copperbelt of Northern Rhodesia

In the two decades between the world wars the Copperbelt of Northern Rhodesia, present-day Zambia, became the fourth largest producer of the red metal internationally, and a few years later could claim to be the most heavily concentrated copper mining area in the world.

Nowhere, at any time, has the impact of professionalism on mining development been more dramatic than in this narrow strip of land that runs for some 70 miles along the border between Zambia and the Katanga province of Zaïre, the former Belgian Congo and once the private African empire of King Leopold II.

That the area had much evidence of being rich in copper had been apparent to European prospectors in the dying years of the nineteenth century, but it was not until the arrival some 20 years later of a new breed of professional mining engineers, metallurgists and geologists that vast tonnages of mineral-bearing rock could be classified as 'ore', and the commercial potential of the region fully realized, despite its location in an otherwise barren, inhospitable and distant land.

In the great transformation that followed, from desolate bush to thriving industry of world importance, members of the IMM played a significant part, together with similarly qualified engineers from the United States and all parts of the British Empire, notably Canada and South Africa. The development of the Copperbelt was, in fact, very much a product of that closer association between the world's professional mining men and their institutions which inspired those who conceived and planned the Empire Mining Congress of 1924.

*   *   *

For several hundred years before the coming of the White Man Africans had been mining copper in various parts of the continent south of the Equator, their production reaching a peak with the introduction of a new and superior culture by the builders of the mysterious city of Zimbabwe, the precise origins of which are still being argued over by archaeologists and anthropologists.

By the nineteenth century, the Zimbabwe empire had long since perished, though copper was still traded by Arab slavers to both the east and west coasts. Livingstone wrote of meeting a caravan in 1868, its slaves struggling through the bush with five tons of the metal. But by the time the first European prospectors arrived in the Congo and along the upper reaches of the Kafue, one of the main tributaries of the Zambezi, the Arab influence, and with it copper trading, had declined almost to vanishing point, though some tribesmen still carried on their craft, mining and smelting in time-honoured fashion to produce tools and weapons for domestic use.

Central Africa's potential as an important source of world copper supply was recognized by the European powers in the 1880s when they scrambled for possession and carved up the continent between them under the watchful eye of Germany's Iron Chancellor. Though as eager as any to establish a political and commercial position, Britain had learned that empire-building could be difficult and costly. The Government therefore readily agreed to Cecil Rhodes's request for a Royal Charter for his British South Africa Company, thereby placing the risks of empire-building in the hands of the company's shareholders rather than those of British taxpayers, and effectively giving the directors a blank cheque to explore, develop and administer an area almost the size of Europe.

Rhodes did not wait for the formalities to be completed before sending emissaries north across the Limpopo and Zambezi rivers, and one of his agents obtained the first of a series of mineral concessions from Lewanika, Chief of the Lozi, before Rhodesia was annexed in 1890. The Lozi, a powerful tribe in what is now the Western Province of Zambia, claimed large areas of the territory to be under its jurisdiction—a circumstance that was to have considerable bearing on the subsequent disputes about the ownership of the country's mineral resources, which the BSA, or 'Chartered' Company retained until the eve of Zambian Independence in 1964.

The treaties with Lewanika were not immediately honoured, much to the disappointment of the chief, who had been led to expect the protection of Queen Victoria against such traditional enemies as the Matabele from the south, as well as other benefits that never materialized. His misgivings were not allayed by the arrival of European prospectors from one of the numerous subsidiaries of the Bechuanaland Exploration Company, formed by Edmund (later Sir Edmund) Davis, an Australian, who, like Rhodes, went to South Africa for his health and rapidly became one of its successful entrepreneurs.

By the end of the century prospectors were tramping over large tracts of country north and south of the Kafue, leaving behind strange names to mark their unsuccessful claims—North Star, True Blue, Wonder Rocks, Crystal Jacket, Lou-Lou, Sugarloaf, Beehive—while to the east Rhodes's agents were obtaining concessions from African chiefs between the Luapula and Luangwa rivers, and as far south as present-day Ndola. When in 1899 George Grey arrived from Bulawayo with a party sent by Scottish engineer Robert (later Sir Robert) Williams to prospect along the Congo border, Africans led them to old copper workings at Kansanshi, just inside Northern Rhodesia.

Encouraged by these results, Williams applied to King Leopold for mining rights for his Tanganyika Concessions Company, rights that were, in fact, granted as a result of a classical blunder by the Belgians. The geologist Jules Cornet had already surveyed many of Katanga's ancient copper mines; his report was considered of great scientific value, but he failed to recognize the commercial importance of his discoveries: he could not, so to speak, see the copper for the mines.

It was not until 1901 that Northern Rhodesia showed its first real promise of workable minerals. Tom Davey, consulting engineer of one of Edmund Davis's companies, lost his way in the bush in rain and gathering darkness and eventually found

himself beside a kopje, or rocky hillock, which, when he attacked
it with his hammer, produced fragments of lead- and zinc-bearing
rock. He pegged the 'Rhodesia Broken Hill', naming it so because
of its geological resemblance to the famous Australian mine.
Thanks to the arrival of the railway from the south in 1906, the
property was developed without too much delay, giving some
substance at least to Cecil Rhodes's dream that mining would
help to finance his 'all red' route to Cairo.

*   *   *

Of greater long-term significance than Davey's find was the
discovery in 1902 of copper outcrops north of Broken Hill by
William Collier, another of Edmund Davis's employees. Collier, a
Dorset man, was typical of those early non-professionals who
pioneered prospecting on the great plateau between the Zambezi
and the Congo. Youngest of a large family, he had emigrated soon
after his 18th birthday and in 15 years in Africa he had been
prison warder, farmer, policeman and soldier as well as
prospector. Tough, resourceful, self-reliant, he was wholly
devoted to the free life of the bush.

The land that Collier now explored was one of contrasts and
surprises. High enough to take the fire out of the tropical sun, it
sprawled pleasantly in winter beneath clear blue skies; in
summer it was hot and moody with violent thunderstorms and
torrential rain. Most of the country was covered with forests,
studded with tall, red anthills, through which the young Kafue
and its tributary streams tumbled among the rocks. The main
inhabitants were animals—elephant, buffalo and antelope of
almost every variety. There were some people living along the
streams and in clearings in the forest, but they had been so
constantly raided by their more powerful neighbours, in league
with Arab slave traders, that there were now not many of them
left. The most striking features of the land were its stillness and
its silence.

To reach this wilderness from Bulawayo, 600 miles to the
south, took Collier three months of torrid travel. After making
contact with Davey at Broken Hill, he struck north, and in
several villages through which he passed he noticed that the
people used small pieces of malachite to treat their sores and

wounds. But when he asked them the source of this 'medicine' they looked frightened and ran away. Collier discovered that the supplies were controlled by an old Arab trader who was determined to enjoy the considerable profits of his business without interference from white prospectors, and had forbidden the villagers to have any contact with them. But one evening an old man crept into the firelight of Collier's camp and asked if he would shoot some meat for him as he was too weak to hunt. Scenting the possibility of information, Collier agreed and when dawn broke the two set out together.

For two days the hunt continued. They did not go very far for the old man was indeed slow and feeble. At last, by the Luanshya river, he could go no further, but he told Collier that if he continued upstream he would come to an open space and there he would find 'what he wished to see'. Collier moved up river and as the sun began to set he came upon a herd of roan antelope feeding on a clearing by the bank. He shot a bull, and when he walked up to his kill he found that the rock on which it lay was stained green with copper. Nearby were some shallow depressions from which the villagers had clearly taken malachite, but there were no big workings such as Grey had discovered at Kansanshi and among the hills of Katanga.

Next morning Collier walked a little further up the river. He shot a rietbok, and there he found another clearing and another outcrop. Following this swath through the forest for a couple of miles, he saw that it bent sharply back to the river in the shape of a giant hairpin to the spot at which he had shot the roan. He pegged a claim on each arm, calling one Roan Antelope and the other Rietbok.

Then, a local tribesman appeared and offered to show Collier 'a real copper mine'. He led him a few miles to a kopje in thick bush and there in its heart was a great gash from which malachite had been extensively worked. It was, said Collier, 'a spectacular sight'. He named it Bwana Mkubwa—'Big Master'. Later he found some pegs at Chambishi left by George Grey's party on their way to Kansanshi three years earlier; the pegs had just missed the orebody and Collier staked new claims at the end of them.

Collier's discoveries caused a flurry of excitement and activity. Kansanshi was developed as Northern Rhodesia's first commercial copper producer in 1908; the Sable Antelope mine, west of Lusaka in the Hook of the Kafue, began in 1911; and Bwana Mkubwa went into production in 1913. But the little boom was short-lived. Investigation of a multitude of other old workings showed that the ancients had abandoned nearly all of them as worthless, and a closer look at Collier's newly found outcrops on the Luanshya river revealed only lean oxide ores not worth the cost and trouble to exploit. Dreams of another Katanga were shattered. Only Broken Hill with its lead and zinc was proving really viable.

Even the BSA Company was running into financial difficulties; the responsibilities of colonial administration were becoming increasingly burdensome, and moves were begun to persuade the British Government to take over the territories, which it eventually did—Southern Rhodesia in 1923 and Northern Rhodesia in the following year. Shrewdly, Chartered insisted on retaining its mineral 'rights' and, realizing that the efforts of small companies and individual adventurers were getting nowhere, decided to offer exclusive prospecting licences over large areas to companies that could show that they had the professional expertise and finance to carry out systematic exploration. It was a decision that was to have a profound effect on the future of both the BSA Company and the country.

*   *   *

Among those who followed closely the developing situation in Africa was the American-born mining engineer, Alfred Chester Beatty, who had gone to live in London after a highly successful career in the United States and Mexico. With such men as Daniel Jackling, Pope Yeatman, Henry Krumb and Seeley Mudd, he had helped to pioneer the development of the American 'porphyries'—massive deposits of copper-bearing rock, hitherto uneconomic to mine by conventional underground methods because of the low average grade of the ore. Family tragedy and ill health drove him to settle in England in 1911, but Herbert Hoover, an old friend, rekindled his interest in mining and in the first year of the war Beatty began a second career by forming Selection Trust, destined to become one of the great mining companies of the world.

Looking to the Rhodesian field, Beatty took particular note of

Edmund Davis's efforts to develop Collier's find at Bwana Mkubwa, where progress was hindered by metallurgical problems. To help to solve these difficulties Davis had engaged as consultants a company called Minerals Separation, holders of the patents of the flotation method of concentrating copper ore—an invention that had played a big part in the profitable mining of North America's porphyry deposits—and which was to become one of the keys to unlock the riches of the Copperbelt. Working with Minerals Separation on the Bwana Mkubwa problem was W. G. Perkins, an American metallurgist whose office was on a floor below Beatty's in London Wall Buildings, a few hundred yards from IMM headquarters at Salisbury House. Perkins was glad to discuss his experiments with Beatty but, more importantly, he introduced him to another American, Preston K. Horner. Both Perkins and Horner were IMM members.

A thick-set bundle of energy and enthusiasm, Horner had been general manager of Union Minière's mines in Katanga before being forced to resign when the company insisted that only Belgians should hold the top jobs. While in Katanga, Horner had come into contact with William Collier and soon after leaving Union Minière he made a trip into the bush northwest of the Ndola boma to inspect the Roan Antelope prospect and adjoining claims at Nkana. All these copper oxide discoveries were still generally regarded as useless, running from 3 to 5 per cent oxide copper, compared with grades as high as 15 per cent sulphides being mined over the border in the Congo. Yet Horner had a hunch that they were worth further investigation. He found a ready listener in Chester Beatty, who, even at that early stage, had begun to consider the possibility that Rhodesia's lean oxide ores could well overlie deposits of more easily treated sulphides.

As a result of his talks with Horner and Perkins, Beatty formed a syndicate to re-examine mineral claims in Northern Rhodesia and to search for new deposits. By the end of 1922 he had persuaded the BSA Company to give him prospecting rights over 50 000 square miles and Rhodesia Congo Border Concessions (RCBC) was formed to carry out the work.

The task that RCBC set itself was enormous. The concession, extending along the Congo border from the eastern end of Katanga to Angola in the west, was the size of England: it had no roads, it was crossed by only one railway, and most of it had not even been surveyed, let alone prospected. In the early days,

Raymond Brooks, its American-born general manager, had no professional geological staff and his headquarters were simply a tent at Ndola. He worked on the theory that any outcrop that had distinguishing characteristics, such as green stains of copper or zinc or lead colorations, had probably been seen by some local people. Brooks sent his parties out in pairs: an experienced bush prospector, accompanied by a younger man who had generally received some schooling in engineering. The prospector recruited and directed a gang of 20 or 30 African helpers. The 'engineer' ran traverses with a prismatic compass and a bicycle wheel fitted with a cyclometer, made records of each day's activities, mapped discoveries and collected samples for assay. It was systematic exploration—but it was not 'scientific'.

In this way the existence of at least three big copper deposits was firmly established. First, William Collier, now a member of the RCBC team, led the way to the discovery of Nchanga in a swamp northwest of Chambishi, where he had hammered his pegs into the ground 20 years earlier. Next, James Moir, a Yorkshireman only 40 years old but already wrinkled by the African sun, sent in bags of green-stained moss from the banks of the Mufulira stream, and lived to see one of the world's biggest copper mines developed on the site of his discovery. Then, north of Nchanga, James Williams, a product of Camborne School of Mines, found traces of copper among the red earth of a giant anthill beside which he rested while shooting guinea fowl. True, it remained for 30 years merely a number on the survey map, but today, as Konkola, it is one of the Copperbelt's six big mines.

*   *   *

Prospecting such a huge and desolate area with teams led by Europeans, who frequently fell victim to malaria, blackwater fever and the many other hazards of the bush, was a heavy strain on RCBS's resources, both in manpower and money, and by the mid-1920s funds were beginning to run out. To bolster the company's position Chester Beatty suggested to his partner, Edmund Davis, that the Anglo American Corporation of South Africa might be invited to join their endeavours. Beatty and Davis shared common interests with its founder and leader,

Ernest (later Sir Ernest) Oppenheimer through diamond mining—Beatty in what was then the Gold Coast and Davis in the Congo and Angola.

Oppenheimer responded by sending his American consulting engineer Carl R. Davis and his brother-in-law Leslie Pollak to Northern Rhodesia. As a result of their optimistic reports he decided to give his support, on a single and important condition—that Anglo American should take over the technical handling of all field operations. Eventually, the South African group gained financial control as well.

It was this development, perhaps more than any other, that marked the advent of professionalism into the Northern Rhodesian mining scene. Although primarily concerned with gold and diamonds, Oppenheimer was ever alert to the possibilities of expansion into other fields, and from his Johannesburg headquarters he had access to a hard core of qualified and experienced men capable of applying their skills to almost any facet of mining engineering and mineral exploration. As early as 1926 he gave orders for an aerial survey of the Northern Rhodesian concessions—one of the first, if not the first, occasions on which aerial photography was used in the search for minerals—and prospecting in the field by well-trained and properly equipped parties was begun.

The big impetus came in the following year when Oppenheimer appointed Dr J. Austen Bancroft as his consultant on copper affairs. Bancroft, of whom it was once said 'combined with his great scientific ability a most convincing air of his own infallibility', had been Professor of Geology at McGill University in Canada, and his arrival in Northern Rhodesia heralded a period of intense activity. As Carl Davis reported to Oppenheimer in June 1927, '. . . we are working on a definite policy in the engagement of young geologists and technically trained men as Dr Bancroft has unusual facilities for obtaining men of this type for our work'.

The difference between Bancroft's methods of prospecting and those of RCBC's Raymond Brooks was not only a difference in style but in the basic concept of objectives. As Brooks himself explained: 'We in RCBC started out to find mines, wherever and however they occurred, having no preconceived ideas as to where they would be found or in what kind of formations. The other [geological] system was conceived on a basis of searching for formations that might contain mines and on the interpretation of engineers in the field and at headquarters as to whether there were any.'

At various times Bancroft had up to 200 professional geologists and prospectors operating over a huge area, surveying and mapping by systematic parallel traverses at close intervals. As many as 16 diamond drills were in operation at any time and 100 miles of test pitting were excavated. It was the largest single exploration project for mineral resources carried out anywhere until that time.

Despite a somewhat patronizing and, on occasions, disparaging attitude towards Brooks's unprofessional old-timers, it must be stated that Dr Bancroft discovered no new mines. The most significant outcome of his work was that it confirmed Chester Beatty's long-held belief that the wealth of the Congo border deposits lay beneath the overhanging layers of lean oxides, in rich and more easily treated sulphides at greater depth. He was thus able to prove large reserves of ore—as distinct from 'mineralization'—at Nchanga, Nkana and, finally, at Konkola, the mine that was at first named after him, and these three properties, within a mile or so of each other, secured for the Anglo American Corporation its share in what was soon to become one of the world's biggest metal-mining fields.

*   *   *

Chester Beatty did not need Joe Bancroft to tell him that his theories about the source of Northern Rhodesia's copper wealth were correct. He himself had already proved them beyond all reasonable doubt at least two years earlier. An unrelenting individualist, he did not relish the prospect of playing second-fiddle to Ernest Oppenheimer, even though he had been largely responsible for introducing him to the Rhodesian scene. So, with the advent of the South African contingent, Beatty decided to pursue his own path in Central Africa.

Although exploration in the larger part of the border country remained reserved to RCBC and the Bwana Mkubwa Company, in both of which the Anglo American Corporation now had virtual control, Beatty had noted that many small claims, taken out by early prospectors, were still held by some of the older unsuccessful companies in Edmund Davis's group. Lunching with Davis in London one day in 1925 he raised the matter with him and as a result obtained for Selection Trust options on some 30 of these claims, including William Collier's discoveries at Roan Antelope and Rietbok on the Luanshya river. To re-investigate the prospects, Beatty picked Russell J. Parker, a 28 year-old American who had made a name for himself in the Congo diamond fields.

Even before leaving England, Parker had formed a theory that what Collier had found were the weathered tips of a great inverted arch of copper-bearing rock. At Luanshya his first inspection strengthened his belief that earlier prospectors had failed to notice a gradual increase in the grade of ore as they dug deeper into the earth. Descending an old shaft, Parker noticed that it had been discontinued just below a level at which the green oxidized ore petered out. He cleaned away the bottom of the shaft and took samples. When assayed they were found to contain sulphide ore at 4 per cent copper. As Beatty had suspected, the lean oxides that had discouraged explorers for a quarter of a century gave way at depth to sulphides that could make the project viable. The old prospectors had missed riches by only a few feet.

It was now time for Beatty to bring in his own experienced men from Selection Trust to follow up Parker's discovery. To lead them he chose William Selkirk, a tough, blunt-spoken North of England engineer with nearly 40 years' experience, mostly overseas. Selkirk—later a generous contributor to IMM's Benevolent Fund—sailed for Africa with Thorold F. Field, a partner in the American finance house Case Pomeroy, which had agreed to back Beatty's venture if it looked to be viable. Field, a grandson of Cyrus Field, the man who laid the first Atlantic cable, was also a talented engineer, a chubby ever-smiling character—in direct contrast to his austere travelling companion. By April 1926 Selkirk and Field had seen enough at Roan Antelope to recommend a programme of drilling and shaftsinking to explore its orebody at a cost of £27 000.

It took some time to import the necessary machinery north of the Zambezi and haul it by ox wagon 20 miles through the bush from the railhead at Ndola, but soon after the beginning of the summer rains everything was ready. Believing that the deposit would turn out to be extensive and comparatively uniform,

Selkirk planned to drill between the two outcrops at intervals of 1000 ft—a new technique in copper development. On this basis the first hole was critical. Selkirk and Parker were confident that it would show sulphide copper, but they knew that unless it proved to be of good grade and in great quantity it would not pay to mine it.

With the drill down to 500 ft Parker asked the driller what was coming up. The man shook his head. 'Not much, just plain shale.' He handed Parker the last core. Despondently, the American looked at the dull rock but, as routine had to be followed, he took a split half to the assay office at nearby Bwana Mkubwa for testing.

Then came the surprise. The sample ran 3.87 per cent copper sulphide and indicated an orebody 36 ft thick, 500 ft beneath the surface—good payable ore.

Hardly believing the news, Parker raced back to Roan Antelope to give instructions to the drilling team to put down a second hole. Then he and Selkirk took another long look at the remaining half of the core. Parker scratched the grey 'shale' with a pen-knife and saw that its fine particles sparkled in the dying sunlight. The sample was impregnated with the sulphide chalcocite, grey just like the shale, but its silvery specks indicated the end of a long and arduous search, and the beginning of what was to become the country's first big metal mine.

*   *   *

News of the first successful drill-hole at Luanshya, followed by equally encouraging results from the rest of the programme laid down by Selkirk, created much excitement in the mining world. Everything pointed to the discovery of a large and rich copper mine, and to the likelihood that deep drilling of other known deposits with similar geological characteristics— including those which Dr Bancroft had begun to investigate—could result in similar finds. Northern Rhodesia had revealed a unique type of copper occurrence in which true values were masked by deceptively poor-looking outcrops. All surface showings in the territory suddenly took on an entirely different complexion. The big copper rush was on!

Above, work
starts on shaft-
sinking at Roan
Antelope; left,
Mufulira's first
'general office'
of mud, poles
and thatch.
After more than
50 years of
operations the
mine is still one
of the world's
big copper
producers

Chester Beatty immediately secured further concessions along the banks of the Luanshya river to cover the whole of the local ore-bearing formation, and in June 1927 Roan Antelope Copper Mines was incorporated under his chairmanship.

Meanwhile, in the adjoining Nkana Concession, Dr Bancroft's men, spurred on by the Roan results, were busy testing the Nkana mine at depth in the sulphide zone. So absorbed were they that they paid little attention to the rest of the concession, which covered nearly 2000 square miles and included several known outcrops. Beatty had surprisingly little difficulty in obtaining rights to prospect the whole of the area, save that in which the drilling teams were presently working.

To finance this new exploration Beatty organized a syndicate called 'Mineralize Venture'. Russell Parker was put in charge of prospecting with a team of geologists headed by Anton Gray, one of Beatty's top field men. Their first job was to map all geological structures of the same type as at Roan. Every yard of the vast concession was covered between July and December 1927—a remarkable achievement in country where outcrops of rock were few and far between and where torrential rain towards the end of the period made the work especially difficult. Of the most promising sites it was decided to concentrate deep drilling at Mufulira, where five years earlier James Moir had found copper-stained moss on the banks of the stream, and at Chambishi, still marked by pegs that George Grey and William Collier had struck many years earlier.

The first hole at Mufulira intersected sulphide ore averaging 9.4 per cent copper, and by the end of 1929 reserves of 40 million tons at 4.68 per cent copper had been established. At Chambishi 25 million tons averaging 3.46 per cent copper were proved. The prospects were exciting, but there were signs that the world was heading for economic depression and it was too much to hope to raise enough money to open up three major mines in a remote country with no infrastructure. Further work on Chambishi was therefore deferred in favour of the greater potential of Mufulira.

*   *   *

When Beatty formed his Roan Antelope Company in 1927 he had

the financial backing of Thorold Field's Case Pomeroy Company of New York, but much more important to the long-term future, not only of Roan but other developing companies in the group, subsequently consolidated as Rhodesian Selection Trust (RST), a substantial shareholding was taken by the American Metal Company (AMCO), a small but enterprising United States firm with origins going back to the feudal German states of the eighteenth century. Otto Sussmann, one of its senior directors, was an old friend of Beatty in his days in the American West and when, on a visit to South Africa, he heard of the successful drillings, he travelled north to see what was going on.

Sussmann was so impressed that he cabled his associates in New York to buy what shares they could on the London market. Later, two other AMCO engineers, Arthur D. Storke and Philip Wilson, arrived in Northern Rhodesia to endorse Sussmann's assessment of the mine's potential, and AMCO made increasingly large investments. It also provided—often on a 'lease-lend' basis—much of the high-level technical expertise necessary for development.

While, therefore, in the early days of the Copperbelt the Anglo American faction drew its professional strength from South Africa, the Beatty enterprises depended largely on the United States for technical skills, though as time went on English-trained engineers—most of them graduates of the Royal School of Mines or Camborne, and with IMM membership certificates—dominated the professional staff.

Rivalry in the field between the two teams of prospectors was intense, but seldom unfriendly. At top level, Chester Beatty and Ernest Oppenheimer rarely met, and when they did it was in London as Beatty feared that his health would not stand the rigours of a journey to Africa: in fact, he never saw any of the Copperbelt mines that were developed under his control. Oppenheimer responded to Beatty's formation of RST by registering his own Copperbelt group, Rhodesian Anglo American (Rhoanglo); its directors were overwhelmingly British—'British' in those days, of course, including South African—whereas the RST board was two-thirds composed of American nationals.

This was a situation which Oppenheimer most heartily disliked. 'The anxieties of the diamond industry', he wrote soon after the formation of Rhoanglo, 'have convinced me of the necessity of a leadership in the Rhodesian copper world that can

not only assert authoritatively our position with regard to
producers outside the Empire, but that can also bring pressure
on individual producers within our own area, the control of which
may have passed into other hands.' Oppenheimer would have
dearly liked to solve the problem by an amalgamation of interests,
preferably under his control but, if necessary, under a third
party, possibly The British South Africa Company. But Beatty
would have none of this, believing that such an arrangement
would soon result in puppet government by the Anglo American
Corporation.

The two groups therefore continued along their separate paths,
though the American influence in the Beatty camp became almost
an obsession with Ernest Oppenheimer. As an immigrant, first to
England and then to South Africa, his German–Jewish origins
tended to make him 'more British than the British'; he felt that he
had a duty to his adopted country to build up its industries and
to expand British influence to the north in the traditions of Cecil
Rhodes. He regarded Beatty, who had not yet become a
naturalized British citizen, as a 'foreigner' and he continued to be
highly critical of his American backers, conveniently forgetting the
financial origins of so much of his own South African enterprises,
enshrined in the very name of his group, and having no qualms in
accepting Newmont Mining as a Rhoanglo shareholder because,
as he said, 'it was essential that we should have on the technical
side some large American group interested'.

Matters came to a head in 1929 when it became known that
the Guggenheim brothers, for whom Beatty had been consulting
mining engineer for much of his career in North America, had
been securing options for their giant American Smelting and
Refining Company to develop the highly promising Nchanga
orebody, near Nkana—a project in which both the Rhodesian
groups had big interests. Oppenheimer was greatly disturbed. If
the Guggenheims should gain control of Nchanga and if, as
rumoured, capital was being attracted to the Beatty companies
from the United States at an ever-increasing rate, the balance of
power in the Copperbelt would be tilted decisively in favour of the
Americans.

Oppenheimer's imperial spirit was outraged and he decided to
raise a public outcry. In Britain he found instant support at the
highest level. Stanley Baldwin, the Prime Minister, had lately
become concerned in efforts to make the British Empire self-

sufficient in copper, cobalt and other strategic materials, and had called for advice from Sir Auckland Geddes, a former Ambassador to the United States, and now chairman of the Rothschilds-backed Rio Tinto Company, operators of the oldest copper mines in the world in southern Spain. Geddes quickly brought Rio Tinto and Rothschilds into alliance with Oppenheimer's interests and had little difficulty in finding other partners, including The British South Africa Company, to form a consortium, the so-called 'Council of Nine', to make a successful counter-bid to finance the development of Nchanga. 'British' control having been achieved, Oppenheimer consolidated all his Rhodesian mining interests in a new company, Rhokana Corporation, formed in 1931—and strengthened his minority holdings in most of Chester Beatty's companies as well.

Thus, it came about that control of the Copperbelt mines became divided. On the one side were the Beatty companies, the Rhodesian Selection Trust group, operating the Roan Antelope (Luanshya), Mufulira and, later, the Chibuluma and Chambishi mines. On the other side Oppenheimer's Rhokana Corporation had control of Nkana, Nchanga (Chingola) and, later, Bancroft (Konkola). The position remained thus for the next 40 years—until 1969, when the newly independent Government of Zambia brought all the mines under state ownership.

*   *   *

By 1939 the pioneering period was over. Between them, the two groups were employing 2600 Europeans, headed by some of the most highly qualified and experienced mining engineers to be found anywhere in the world, and ten times that number of Africans. A great community had sprung up around the mines with the arrival of employees' families, government officials, workers on the railways, in the stores, and in secondary industries attracted by the mines. Where, less than a dozen years earlier, there had been little more than empty bush, there were now modern towns, their inhabitants—black and white—enjoying amenities of good housing, hospitals and recreation that many more mature communities would have found difficult to match.

On the outbreak of World War II production from the mines was running at 250 000 tons a year. Without such a major contribution of strategic material, Britain's war effort would undoubtedly have been gravely handicapped. 'In Rhodesia we have only one problem', the patriot Ernest Oppenheimer wrote to his son Harry in April 1942, 'and that is to produce the maximum quantity of base metals . . . only when the war is won can we think again of profits'. Moreover, the industry had already passed the stage of being a purely extractive one: at Nkana an electrolytic refinery for the production of wirebars had been in commission since 1935, and not long after the war practically all Copperbelt output was in similar form. This in itself called for new professionals and new expertise.

It is well to remember, too, that none of the great industrial development in this part of Africa would have been possible without the introduction of professionalism to solve a problem that was as great and as complex as the search for copper and the construction of viable mines. The possibilities of large-scale European settlement along the Rhodesia–Congo border appeared extremely slim in the early days because of the prevalence of malaria, typhoid, blackwater fever, bilharzia and other tropical diseases. The old prospectors had tended to be philosophical about health hazards: they took quinine with their whisky at sundown and when the quinine ran out they doubled the whisky dose and put up with anything that broke through the defences. In this way the old-timers managed to build up a resistance, but it was a different story when pale-skinned, delicately nurtured recruits, fresh out from England, started to arrive in large numbers. Railway clerks at Cape Town would jokingly advise passengers disembarking from Union Castle ships not to bother to buy return tickets for the Copperbelt, and, indeed, it did prove a one-way trip for large numbers of immigrants.

When Chester Beatty realized the gravity of the situation he arranged for an investigation by Sir Malcolm Watson, director of the Ross Institute of Tropical Medicine and Hygiene in London. Watson had already helped Beatty with a similar problem encountered by his diamond companies in West Africa, basing his work on the theory that certain mosquitoes transmit malarial parasites from one human being to another; he had therefore attacked the disease by eradicating the mosquitoes' breeding grounds.

In a similarly brilliant campaign on the Copperbelt the malaria rate dropped from 105 per 1000 in 1929, to 14.6 in 1932, and the

European death rate was halved in little more than 12 months. Within the next few years malaria became a rare disease within the townships and, with proper precaution the likelihood of it being contracted, even in the neighbouring bush, became quite small.

As time went on, old rivalries between the two groups disappeared and mine managements worked together harmoniously, except for occasional differences in policy handed down by their respective boards of directors. This process of ever-increasing cooperation was largely generated by the fact that both groups continued to attract to their staffs large numbers of IMM members, together with members of associated institutions in South Africa and other parts of the old Empire.

In this way the two groups became united in almost every respect; there were no secrets between them; officials visited each other's properties, shared technical information and exchanged views on how common problems might be tackled and resolved. A local IMM section was formed and flourished until post-independence politics and Zambianization programmes diluted its membership; it was finally disbanded in 1975, some of its survivors joining a Mining and Metallurgical Division of the Engineering Institution of Zambia.

There are few parts of the metal-mining world today where it would be difficult to find someone who gained at least part of his experience on the Copperbelt; some have attained the highest eminence in their profession; others have moved on into boardrooms to assume even wider responsibilities in the direction of affairs of modern mining enterprises.

As for the pioneers, their achievements are enshrined in the archives of the IMM and in the honours that have been conferred upon them from time to time. Among them, Sir Alfred Chester Beatty, the acknowledged chief architect of the Copperbelt, received the Gold Medal of the Institution in 1934 and was elected to Honorary Fellowship 31 years later; Sir Ronald Prain, his successor as chairman of RST, became an Honorary Fellow in 1956 and a Gold Medallist in 1968; Carl Davis (1945) and Dr Bancroft (1955) won 'golds'; and the geologist Anton Gray was elected Honorary Fellow in 1965.

The Copperbelt was thus not merely a landmark in the development of world metal mining. It was equally an important milestone in the history of the IMM, and a practical outcome of that spirit of cooperation engendered between it and other kindred institutions at the Empire Congress in 1924, and which continues to find expression in what, since 1979, has been known as the Council of Mining and Metallurgical Institutions.

CHAPTER NINE

Case Study: The Mine in Yugoslavia

Few young men could have had a more romantic start to their careers between the two world wars than those who joined the staff of Trepca, the developing lead and zinc mine in the ancient state of Serbia in Yugoslavia.

To reach Yugoslavia with speed and certainty in those days there was no alternative but to catch the Simplon Orient Express from Paris, and thence travel in the greatest comfort and luxury through France, Switzerland and Northern Italy, crossing the border at Trieste, then plunging eastwards into the Balkans through Zagreb and Brod to Belgrade.

In Belgrade there was usually just enough time to check in at the mining company's city office and snatch a glimpse of the Danube and the historic 'white fortress' before returning to the railway station to continue southwards across Serbia to the Trepca mine headquarters at Zvecan, in the valley of the Ibar river. The local service was, alas, in sharp contrast to the Orient Express. Though less than 200 miles, the journey often took more than 12 hours, the lignite-burning steam locomotive belching out clouds of sooty smoke that swept through the train, to mingle with the strong smell of garlic that peasant-passengers consumed in large quantities. There was no restaurant car; food and drink could be bought, if one was lucky, at the many small intermediate stations, each thronged with people wearing the different and picturesque forms of national dress distinctive of the many races and religions of the Yugoslav people. For any young man who had never before been out of England it was an exciting, if somewhat bewildering experience.

Most of those who headed for Trepca from London between the mid-1920s and the outbreak of war in 1939 were members of the IMM—several of them still student members—and together they played a major part in laying the foundations of what was to become the biggest lead–zinc mine in Europe. When the Germans invaded Yugoslavia in 1941 they seized the property and continued to work it until shortly before the district was freed by Partisans in 1944. The new Yugoslav Government, headed by Tito, brought all mines under state ownership, and in course of time Trepca and its satellites became the nucleus of a workers' combine that is today one of the country's largest industrial undertakings, with 20 or more mining-related activities scattered throughout the land and employing 25 000 people.

*   *   *

Like the Copperbelt of Northern Rhodesia, the story of Trepca is one in which professional geological and engineering skills, opportunism and financial expertise combined—with a certain amount of luck—to create an industry that, more than 60 years later, is many times more important to the country than when it was launched.

In Central Africa the practice of metallurgy began with tribesmen who learned to smelt the green-stained rock that they recovered from outcrops and anthills to make tools, weapons and utensils; the raw material of their industry became exportable only when Arab traders exploited their enterprise. In Yugoslavia, 'the land of the south Slavs', the history of mining goes back at least two thousand years to when alluvial gold was produced in Macedonia, some of which, it is said, helped to finance Alexander the Great's march to India. But mining on the grand scale had to await the arrival of the Romans, who for close on 400 years worked rich deposits of gold, silver, lead, copper, antimony and iron in the land that they called Illyria. Attila the Hun put an end to the Romans and their metal industry, and when the Barbarians departed the Slavs moved in from the north and eventually became the dominant race of the region.

For several hundred years the Slavs were too busy with their tribal wars to concern themselves with minerals, and it was not until the fourteenth century that mining was resumed under the Serbian dynasty of the Nemanyas. Production reached a peak in the reign of Stevan Dušan, its most outstanding leader, who not only extended the frontiers of his kingdom into Greece and Albania but invited experienced Saxon miners—the 'professionals' of the day—to help to expand his minerals industry. The Saxons successfully attacked the Kopaonik Mountains, at the southern end of which Novo Brdo became the royal mint and 'the fairest city in all the Balkans', and developed extensive workings over a large area around Zvecan.

Serbia's 'golden age' ended with the invasion of the Turks, and after the famous Battle of Kosovo in 1398 the enemy quickly overran the whole of the Balkan peninsula. For the next 500 years there was little mining of significance; the Turks banned the export of all metals, but tried to force miners to keep up production for domestic uses. Most of the skilled Saxons fled and the mining art declined, though never entirely disappeared. Meanwhile, the Turks were being slowly driven back by forces of what emerged as the Austro–Hungarian empire, and towards the end of the nineteenth century they had been virtually expelled from the Balkans except in Albania.

With the departure of the Turks, the Serbs were able to re-establish their own independent kingdom—and so did the Montenegrins, the Croats, the Slovenes and others of the old tribes. Soon there was talk of some sort of union between them and the idea finally crystallized in 1918 when Nikola Pašić, as head of the Serbian government-in-exile on the island of Corfu in the First World War, persuaded leaders of Croatia and Slovenia to put their names to a declaration to form a united kingdom as soon as the war came to an end: it was, in effect, a birth certificate for the future of Yugoslavia.

But unity was still a long way off. Pašić and his colleagues returned home to find the peasant Slavs stirred to rebellion under the influence of the Russian Revolution; moreover, the Croats and Slovenes had been looking for a form of federal government, with a large measure of autonomy for each of the participating states, whereas the Serbs, strengthened by having absorbed neighbouring Montenegro, pressed for a centralized government with most of the power in their own hands. Pašić eventually succeeded in forming such a government, but he never managed completely to pacify the Croats, and by 1926 he was too frail to go on trying. Having been Prime Minister—of Serbia and Yugoslavia—21 times and Foreign Minister on 17 occasions, the old man was showered with gifts on his retirement—among them a package of documents giving him title to exclusive mineral prospecting rights over hundreds of square miles of southern Serbia.

At the age of 81 Pašić could not have found such a present particularly exciting, but his son Radomir, who had already shown himself an astute opportunist, recognized the potential. Even before his father died a couple of years later, Radomir contacted Thomas Landell-Mills, a British mining consultant in Belgrade, and despatched him to London to seek expertise and financial backing for a professional examination of the area. Familiar with Selection Trust's mining interests in Central and West Africa, and in Siberia, Landell-Mills made an early visit to Chester Beatty's office in London Wall Buildings. Intrigued by the possibilities, Beatty sent John Dunn, his consulting engineer and brother-in-law, to Serbia to make a preliminary survey. Although Dunn found the countryside largely snow-covered, he saw and heard enough to make him confident to begin negotiations with the Pašić lawyer in Belgrade for an arrangement for Selection Trust to prospect two concessions covering a wide area of mountainous territory centred on Zvecan and, if successful, to launch a British company to develop the resources—with, of course, generous terms for the Pašić family.

When the winter snows began to melt in the spring of 1926 Beatty sent out a small prospecting party, headed by Harold Titcomb, his old classmate at Columbia University—and the man who persuaded Sir William Weir to open a new dimension to the First World War by bombing the German steel works in the Ruhr (Chapter Seven). A mining engineer with the highest professional qualifications and experience, Titcomb set about the task in his usual methodical manner. He based himself at the little town of Kos Mitrovica, on the Ibar river, where the boundaries of the two concessions met and which was already linked by rail to the main route between Belgrade and the Greek port of Thessaloniki, a useful line of communication should the project develop successfully.

To provide themselves with shelter Titcomb and his men built two log cabins in the local style on a hillside overlooking the town, stuffing the cracks with mud to keep out the cold winds: they slept in one, and in the other they set up a glass model* on which a three-dimensional diagram of any orebody found could be traced as the work progressed. The team got around on horseback and on foot; there were few motor vehicles even on the main roads, and oxen and water buffalo provided transportation in much the same way as they had done for centuries.

The main prospecting work was concentrated at Stari Trg, or Stan Trg, meaning 'old market place', perched on a hilltop 3000 ft high, five miles from Kos Mitrovica. Stari Trg had obviously been a centre of much activity by early miners; relics of their work were strewn all around, and geological conditions suggested a mineral deposit of some size. But at first no worthwhile discovery was made, despite systematic probing with modern equipment that had been hauled up the mountain.

Here, as in the Copperbelt, historical study and scientific prospecting were to combine to provide the key to unlock the riches. Chester Beatty himself insisted that the discovery of what was to become the Trepca mine was due more to 'theological appreciation' than geological expertise, though his friends suspected that his tongue was in his cheek when he explained what he meant. 'I told my men', said Beatty, 'to remember that the miners who worked there in the early days were Saxons, devout Catholics who never went underground without first praying in a chapel. All our prospectors needed to do, therefore, was to look for the ruins of small churches, and beside them they would find the remains of the shafts that led into the mines . . .'

Despite his own professionalism, Beatty had a strong belief in this theory. As Titcomb worked on the mountainside, his chief made a personal study of local history and engaged an eminent Yugoslav professor to search the archives in Dubrovnik, the old city of Ragusa, which had been the controlling centre of early mining in Serbia. From these studies there emerged a dossier of details of the most important production areas in the country in Roman and medieval times.

Sure enough, at Stari Trg the remains of a Saxon church were discovered. Nearby were some old opencast workings and,

*Titcomb's glass model is still preserved by Yugoslav engineers at Trepca and is on show to visitors.

beneath them, the mouth of an ancient adit that had been filled in with earth and rock. The entrance was attacked with pick and shovel and very soon lead–zinc sulphide was revealed in such quantity that it was decided to put down a diamond drill-hole from surface. Titcomb, usually so cautious, was excited enough to promise his team a bottle of champagne for every metre of ore in the borehole, expecting two or three metres at the most. In fact, the drill passed through 80 metres of mineralization—and the mess drank champagne for many nights to come. This was the first contact struck with an orebody that, even after the removal of six million tons over the next 12 years, still showed reserves of 10 million tons, at only a slightly lower grade, when the Germans invaded in 1941.

Titcomb's experience at Stari Trg occurred within a few weeks of the day when, 5000 miles away in Central Africa, Russell Parker, also working for Selection Trust, excitedly examined the core of oxide copper ore brought up 500 ft alongside the Luanshya river. The formation of Trepca Mines Limited in December 1927 followed the incorporation of Roan Antelope Copper Mines in Northern Rhodesia earlier in the same year. Rarely before, or since, have two metal mines of such size and importance been discovered and developed simultaneously by one company in such widely different parts of the world.

Despite the high degree of professionalism that was brought to bear on both operations, each owed some measure of its success to sheer good fortune. For Trepca it was lucky that the discovery was made so early in the prospecting programme for, while further extensive exploration was carried out over this and other concessions totalling more than 2000 square miles, nothing approaching the size of the Stari Trg deposit was ever found. Selection Trust later acquired three smaller properties in the vicinity—Kopaonik, Zletovo and Novo Brdo—and although separate companies were incorporated to develop them, they were later merged with Trepca to form one of the biggest metal-mining enterprises that the Balkan states had ever known.

*   *   *

Among those who caught the Belgrade-bound Orient Express at the Gare de l'Est in Paris in the summer of 1929 was a young

Royal School of Mines graduate, D.J. (Jim) Rogers, then a student member of the IMM, later to become its 70th President.

Of English–Scottish parentage, Jim had been brought up in Ireland, and after schooling in Kent spent a year or two at the Chelsea Polytechnic, where he took a degree course in geology before going on to study engineering at the RSM. There he caught the eye of Professor Alfred Brammal, a consultant to Selection Trust, who, on Jim's graduation, put his name forward as a candidate for a job with the development team in Yugoslavia.

Jim was enthralled with the luxury of the Orient Express—the panelled carriages, the exquisite cuisine and the sleeping cars fitted with everything to ensure comfort and convenience, including a little hook over the bed for a gentleman to hang his gold pocket-watch. He could not, however, understand the insistence with which he had been bidden by everyone whom he had met at Selection Trust headquarters not to wander through the train during the journey. From James Whitehouse, the managing director; Gilbert McPherson, the consulting engineer; Tom Bradford, the company secretary; right down to the clerk who handed him his tickets, the instructions were the same: 'On no account leave your coach'.

Even accepting that this was his first time abroad, Jim felt that these instructions were excessively cautious. Perhaps his past was catching up with him? It was true that he had had a few wild frolics at the famous Chelsea Arts Ball, once as the back legs of a horse whose front end was occupied by his artist friend Terence Cuneo, painter of royal occasions; and again, in similar partnership, as a bull at a gala evening of the Society of British Artists, when their cavorting incurred the displeasure of Dame Laura Knight, who was endeavouring to make a speech. Whatever the reason for his employers' close injunctions, Jim found no occasion to disobey, but on arrival at Zvecan he sought an explanation from Peter Hatch, who had been one year his senior at the RSM and was now a member of the Titcomb team.

The reason, said Peter, was that London office feared a recurrence of an incident on the train a few weeks earlier. Soon after the Express left Paris, a new Trepca recruit had met a truly marvellous girl; they dined together as the train sped across France and, later, the young man, seeking a more intimate acquaintance, made his way to her compartment, clad only in pyjamas and dressing gown. Unfortunately, when he emerged with the first streaks of dawn, he was astonished to find that his own carriage had disappeared. The train had divided in the night and, instead of passing into Yugoslavia, he was now on his way to Rome, without money, tickets, passport or luggage—in fact, with nothing but what he stood up in, his pyjamas and dressing gown. To make matters worse, Anglo–Italian relationships were a bit brittle at the time; the British were having trouble with Mussolini and it was little consolation to know that the Duce was succeeding in making the trains run on time. It was nearly a fortnight before the young man eventually reached Belgrade, still in his night clothes, having caused much trouble to the British Consulate in Rome and the Foreign Office in Whitehall, to say nothing of embarrassment and consternation among executives at Selection Trust's London office.

By the time Jim Rogers arrived at Trepca no more than 18 months after Titcomb's successful borehole, the hitherto deserted countryside had become alive with bustling development. The Stari Trg orebody had proved a fine example of a replacement deposit of sulphide ore in limestone. The minerals were originally in solution deep in the earth, under great heat and pressure. The solution was forced upwards into the overlying zone of limestone, part of which was carried away and the minerals deposited in its place. Most of this deposition was along a steep incline where the limestone was in contact with volcanic breccia. Owing to the nature of the formation, the orebody was highly irregular in shape, but this encouraged the developers to expect mineralization to continue at great depth, as deep, in fact, as the limestone extended.

By September 1928, 2000 metres of underground development, and very nearly the same amount of diamond drilling, had been completed. In each of the adits drifts were driven along the limestone–breccia contact; from them, at intervals, crosscuts were made into the ore. The extension of the orebody in depth was explored by diamond drilling from within the adits, and the same method was used to carry out secondary development, holes being bored horizontally and on the incline to probe any isolated zones of ore that may have been missed by drifting and crosscutting.

Problems arose with diamond drilling because of the friable nature of the ore and the presence of large fissures and cavities in the rock in which the drills were boring. The difficulties were tackled by a system of groove-sampling. Alongside the drill-hole a small drift would be dug, just big enough for a man to crawl in and chisel away at the side until he broke through into the drill-hole. He would then cut out a small continuous groove of ore, usually about an inch wide, for assaying.

Jim Rogers remembers that in his first few weeks Harold Titcomb decided that all crosscuts were to be re-sampled with a much larger groove: 'My colleagues and I spent many hours crawling in these tiny tunnels with hammer and chisel, chipping out the samples. Years later, as a prisoner-of war in Germany, I found this experience highly useful in attempting to cut escape tunnels, but at Trepca, with so many exciting things going on, it was just too tedious. Like everything else he did, Titcomb set a high standard: he insisted on examining every groove we cut, criticizing those that went over the prescribed outline, or where it looked as if we had taken too much of the softer material and too little of the harder stuff.'

By mid-1929 development work on four main adits between the 865- and 760-metre levels had outlined an orebody 350 metres long and of widths up to 50 metres. The deposit was estimated to contain 1.75 million tons of ore at an average grade of 12 per cent lead, 11 per cent zinc and 3 oz of silver per ton. Drilling below the 760-metre level indicated that there were more big tonnages still to be found. The physical characteristics of the ore were such that mining costs were likely to be low and, at current metal prices, it was reckoned that the mine could be worked profitably at a rate of 150 000 tons of ore a year.

In London the Trepca company directors decided to go into production, and a public offer was made for £400 000 to prepare for mining and to erect a concentrator and other necessary plant.

First, the five miles of mountain track from Kos Mitrovica to Stari Trg, over which ox-carts had hauled all the development equipment, were upgraded to carry heavy motorized transport. At Stari Trg workshops, stores, offices and other industrial buildings were erected, and houses were built for the workforce. The concentrator was sited in the Ibar valley at Zvecan, and delivery of ore was by a giant aerial ropeway, strung out from the mine four miles across the hills. Serbian villagers who were becoming accustomed to a rapidly changing environment now saw their countryside festooned with pylons supporting the cables from

Jim Rogers (IMM President 1969–70) demonstrates rescue equipment to
King Alexander of Yugoslavia (left) at the opening of Trepca in 1930.
Three years later, almost to the day, the king was assassinated in
Marseilles, and in 1935 Marko Jurjevic (centre) of the mine staff was
shot dead in his office by a disgruntled miner

which huge kibbles dangled their way across the mountain. The skyline was further crisscrossed by lines taking electricity to the mine from a power plant alongside the concentrator. So much was going on that villagers found it was becoming difficult to pick out the ruins of the hilltop castle above Zvecan where, according to local legend, the Serbian emperor Stevan Dušan had murdered his father before seizing the throne six centuries earlier.

By the summer of 1930 the mine was ready to start production just four years after the first discovery of the orebody. Chester Beatty decided on a grand opening and refused to be put off when world depression sent metal prices tumbling and there appeared little prospect of early recovery. The guest of honour was Yugoslavia's King Alexander, who, in the previous year, in a dramatic attempt to bridge the ever-widening gap between rival political factions in Croatia and Serbia, had proclaimed a royal dictatorship. The occasion was remarkable for a number of reasons, including the sight of the official party going underground in top hats and frock coats. With King Alexander was his cousin Prince Paul, who was to become Regent in the critical days before the country's invasion by the Nazis in 1941. On the British side was the 'promising young diplomat' Nevile Henderson, who later, as Ambassador to Berlin, played a major part in the vain attempts by the Chamberlain government to prevent a second world war by appeasing Hitler's Germany.

'Those of us who had worked on the mine's development', says Jim Rogers, 'were glad to have Chester Beatty among us, particularly as this was the first (and only) time he visited any of the mines that he created after leaving the States to base himself in London before the First World War. He lunched in our mess and clearly enjoyed himself, telling us that if we thought the most important man on a mine was the manager, we were wrong: it was the cook! I noticed that Bill Campbell, our mine superintendent, looked down his nose at this remark, and I don't think the general manager, A. S. Howie, was much amused either.

'After the official ceremonies we retired for our own celebrations, but soon after dark we were alerted that something odd was happening in the 750 adit. We rushed down to find that our ubiquitous Albanian workers, and their friends from many miles around, were loading ox-carts with our stores, particularly timber and railway lines. Apparently they thought that now the King had been and seen it all, we would have no further use for such things, and were very disappointed when we told them to put them all back.'

*   *   *

Wherever British mining men have taken their skills, even in the most distant and inhospitable parts of the world, they have usually managed to carve out for themselves a plot that 'is forever England'. Trepca was no exception.

The expatriate staff was a blend of worldly-wise experience and the enthusiasm of a new generation of engineers, not long out of their mining schools and universities, and for most of whom the mine represented their first overseas job. In the 15 years in which management was under British control there were rarely more than 20 names on the expatriate payroll, including administrative officers as well as the engineering and other technical staff. They lived in a small, self-contained community—company-built bungalows, set about with flower beds, lawns and orchards, for the senior people and their families; and, for the single men, a two-storeyed mess and clubhouse with basic social and sports facilities.

In no way, however, did this 'garden city' insulate the staff from either the workforce or from the inhabitants of the surrounding countryside, who must surely have been among the most cosmopolitan in Europe at that time. There were Orthodox Serbs; Serbs from Montenegro, who were quite different in culture and temperament; Catholics from Croatia, Slovenia and Dalmatia; Albanians, who were mostly Moslem; and White Russians, refugees from the Revolution, who worked mainly in the concentrator and in the offices. The labour force, 4000 strong at its peak, included men of all such ethnic origins, and many more. In such circumstances relationship with management was surprisingly good; in fact, it was not until the mine had been in production for eight years that there was any major industrial dispute, and when it came it was engineered by the outlawed Yugoslav Communist Party, headed by a man named Josip Broz, better known later as Marshal Tito.

'Many of the Albanians', recalls Jim Rogers, 'were fair-skinned and blue-eyed, often moustached and bearded. They were strict Mohammedans. They carried knives and most of them smoked from silver filigree-decorated pipes or cigarette holders. They had a reputation for being bandits and they certainly had that air of fierce independence found in such mountain people. In contrast, their womenfolk were dressed in black from head to toe; nothing could be seen of their faces, or even their ankles for that matter.

'We had a few Turks—most of our nightwatchmen were Turks—conspicuous in their brightly coloured baggy trousers and tasselled fez. Then there were dark-skinned gypsies, who kept very much to themselves; their women were not veiled and looked most attractive in flowing skirts of all colours. Of clear, if not dominating, importance were the serious-looking Christian Slavs, their sombre attire accenting the diversity of dress, religion and race in our small community.

'Finally, the White Russians. Soon after I arrived in Trepca there was a farewell party for H.H. Boyes, the first mine manager. We held it on a lovely warm evening on a flat patch of land in front of the mess. Many of our Russian workers had been Cossacks, famous for their horsemanship. To the wild music of a balalaika band the Cossacks gave us the sort of show that one normally sees only at the circus; even the horses seemed to catch the mood of the evening as they galloped past at breakneck speed, their riders swinging on their backs, performing every conceivable trick of horsemanship by the light of the burning torches.'

Inevitably, nationalistic and political tensions sometimes overflowed among the local people with tragic results. Once, Serbs ambushed and killed a visiting representative of a British rockdrill company while he was being driven to Zvecan by car. The victim had apparently been mistaken for a Croatian official believed to be favouring his countrymen in allocating jobs. The Croat was later shot dead in his office by another Serb; the murderer fled to the hills, which still abounded with bandits and outlaws, but in a great manhunt, in which many of the expatriate staff took part, he was pursued and brought to justice.

*   *   *

None of the expatriates at Trepca could have failed to be conscious of what Jim Rogers has described as the 'tremendous feeling of history' in the environment in which they lived and worked. Both above and below ground there was much evidence of cultures going back for centuries, and of the ancient skills of the mining craft.

'At Stari Trg', says Rogers, 'we found that the early miners had rightly surmised that the ore extended below the opencast workings. They made strenuous efforts to get to it, but were frustrated by a massive zone of silicified iron pyrites, close-grained and incredibly tough. Even our compressed-air drills were quickly blunted when we attacked it. Here, we found several probing tunnels, so narrow that they must have been driven by dwarfs or children. In contrast we also came across a tunnel near the entrance to the 760-metre level that was much larger and obviously dug in a different age. A visiting expert declared it Roman in origin.'

When exploration teams turned their attention to other smaller concessions in the neighbourhood on which the company had options, they discovered even more extensive relics of ancient mining. At Kopaonik in rugged mountains northeast of Trepca no fewer than 1500 pits had been sunk, some to nearly 1000 ft, in a strip of land no more than a couple of miles long and half a mile wide. An immense amount of labour must have been employed to win the lead–silver ore, of which at least one million tons had been excavated.

Beatty's men drove a main adit into the side of Belo Brdo—the 'White Mountain'—and found payable ore. Development was begun in 1937, the material being swung down the mountain by ropeway in the same way as at Trepca, and sent to the concentrator at Zvecan. In winter, when Belo Brdo was snow-covered, the staff had to ski down the slopes, or travel on the ropeway—strictly forbidden at Trepca—first packing the kibbles with straw to protect themselves from the extreme cold.

In the Zletovo concession, to the southeast in Macedonia, the little town of Kratovo, built on the inside slope of an extinct volcano, had been the centre of mining in both Roman and medieval times. Exploring one ancient adit, the modern prospectors found its chiselled walls lined with niches to hold miners' lamps, and at the far end they came across the figure of a man carved into the rock. The features were distinctively Roman. When Chester Beatty heard of it he sent word that the carving was not to be disturbed, and thereafter referred to it affectionately as 'my consulting Roman mining engineer'.

Novo Brdo, city of Serbian princes and the richest mining

centre in the Balkans in the Middle Ages, had, like Kratovo,
shrunk to a village of no more than 200 inhabitants. Here, the
Turkish invaders had been resisted longer than anywhere else in
Serbia, but its garrison was finally subdued, its leading citizens
put to death and its young people carried off as slaves. Huge
heaps of ancient slag were found along the river banks, but it was
evident that the Romans and Saxons had left little for modern
miners, and future operations were confined to Trepca and the
smaller Kopaonik mine. Lead and zinc concentrates from the
central plant at Zvecan were railed to the Greek port of
Thessaloniki and thence shipped to Antwerp for conversion into
metal. Towards the end of the 1930s it was decided to build a
lead smelter alongside the concentrator. It proved too late to
benefit the British owners, but its 400-ft chimney stack still
dominates the valley of the Ibar river.

*   *   *

With the exception of a few Americans, the expatriate technical
staff at Trepca from 1926 to 1941, when the mine was evacuated
in front of the German invasion, were of British stock, with a
strongly Scottish accent, particularly among the older and more
experienced men.

A.S. Howie, who went out as technical manager to take charge
of the development work, grew up the hard way in the Scottish
coal industry before getting a job in Peru with Cerro de Pasco, the
American copper mining group. Rebecca West, on a visit to
Trepca for her classic story of Yugoslavia, *Black Lamb and Grey
Falcon*, aptly described him as 'a Scotsman of the toughly delicate
type'. As general manager from 1929 he was responsible for all
operations under Trepca control, including the satellite mines,
and it was largely due to him that the project developed so
quickly and successfully, his ability as an administrator proving
perhaps even greater than that as a mining engineer. He 'died
with his boots on' in 1938, having caught pneumonia after
emerging one day from the oppressive heat of the mine into the
cold mountain air.

Two other Scots who had worked with Howie in Peru gave him
good support. Bill Campbell, a bachelor who lived in a modest
bungalow and kept bees as a hobby, was regarded by the younger

engineers as a bit of a martinet, but he was a meticulous mine superintendent and kept a tight hold of everything that went on underground. James Jackson, the other ex-Cerro Scot, had been in charge of Selection Trust's Tetiuhe mine in Siberia before being transferred to Trepca, where he found it a relief to work with congenial Yugoslav labour after the Russians, whom he described as sullen and neither able nor willing to work. In 1936 he was given the job of opening up the Kopaonik mine, which he did with speed and efficiency, and he became mine superintendent at Trepca when Campbell retired in 1938.

Peter Hatch was one of three young mining engineers engaged to help Harold Titcomb in the early exploration of the Stari Trg area. A son of Frederick Hatch, President of the IMM in its Royal Charter year in 1915, he had followed a family tradition of contributing to the Institution's *Transactions* and as early as 1931, while still a student member, wrote a paper on check sampling of diamond drill-holes at Stari Trg—an operation in which he was intimately concerned. Described by a contemporary as 'an instinctive engineer of high competence', he returned to his native South Africa after the war to work for Selection Trust and played a major part in the development of the Bikita mine, just over the border in Rhodesia, and famous for its lithium and various rare minerals, some of them unique.

Charles Forgan, another RSM and IMM man, joined Trepca as a geologist in its development period. He remained at the mine until evacuation, by which time he had become assistant general manager to Pat Page, an American who had been recruited first to oversee the building of the concentrator and then stayed on as superintendent of the plant.

When Page moved into the general manager's chair in 1938 he was succeeded in the concentrator by a tubby, short-sighted man of equable disposition who, as a young chemist, had originally been engaged to assay mineral samples during the exploration. S.W. (Bill) Bailey was the very last person whom colleagues would suspect of getting mixed up in clandestine operations, but when war with Germany became inevitable he slipped away from the mine to join a cell of British secret agents working in Belgrade. A fluent control of the Serbo–Croat language and an intimate knowledge of the people of the country helped make Bailey invaluable for an undercover job. As a member of SOE he was later parachuted to the headquarters of General Mihailović, the

Yugoslav Cetnik commander, in an attempt to get him to resolve his differences with Partisan leader Tito, in order to preserve a united front of resistance against the Germans.

*   *   *

By the time Britain declared war on Germany in 1939 Trepca had become one of the most important lead–zinc mines in the world outside the United States. Now its future was in grave jeopardy. In answer to an appeal from the British Legation in Belgrade, backed by a personal message from Chester Beatty, most of the staff stayed at their posts. While the majority of Yugoslavs were in sympathy with the Allies, the Government needed desperately to improve the country's own defences. Neither Britain nor France was in a position to help. Ironically, the Germans were willing to supply arms, but only in exchange for raw materials that would enable them to produce more military equipment.

British diplomats did all they could to dissuade the Yugoslavs from dealing with the Nazis, but it soon became obvious that some sort of compromise would have to be made or the mines would simply be taken over by the Government. Eventually, the British Legation approved an arrangement which gave Yugoslavia 70 per cent of all production, leaving Trepca free to send the rest to Britain—if it could get it there.

All this time the country was on a knife edge between war and peace. On 25 March 1941, after intense German pressure, Prince Paul, who had come to power as Regent for the son of the assassinated King Alexander, signed an agreement with the Axis. Immediately, there were angry demonstrations: Prince Paul and his government were overthrown and the 17 year-old Prince Peter was appointed to the monarchy.

Hitler's reaction to this rebuff was swift and terrible. On Sunday, 6 April—Palm Sunday—he unleashed his Luftwaffe to carry out 'Operation Punishment'. Belgrade was ruthlessly bombed and German troops moved across the frontiers from Hungary, Bulgaria and Romania. At Trepca Pat Page called his management team together and urged them to get their families away by the one safe route remaining through Greece.

Twenty-four hours later, word came that the Germans had

captured Skopje and were moving towards Kos Mitrovica. Page had no alternative but to hand over the mine to the local Yugoslav military commander and to arrange the evacuation of the remaining British staff. At dawn next morning, a party of 12 left in two cars for the Adriatic coast, hoping that the British Navy would be there to rescue them. The ships never came, and after a few days and nights of uncertainty a patrol of Italian motorcycle troops swept into the village in which the refugees were resting and took them prisoner.

They were flown to Italy, placed under the protection of the American Embassy, and then sent to a sleepy spa near Perugia to be lodged in one of the town's best hotels. They stayed for five weeks, living on good food and good wine, and pleasantly looked after. In fact, when after five weeks they were told that they were to be sent on through Vichy France and into Spain and Gibraltar for repatriation, the local population turned out to shower them with gifts and wish them goodbye.

One of the first acts of the Yugoslav Communist Government at the end of the war was to nationalize the country's mines, and all that the former owners could hope for was some measure of compensation. Eventually, after 12 years of continuous negotiations, they had to be content with £1 million, to be paid in instalments; in fact, it was not until December 1957 that the final payment was made.

Clem Richardson, a lifelong member of the IMM, and among the escaping party of 1941, has since told of a return visit that he made to Trepca with Charles Forgan* at the invitation of the mine management in 1976: 'He [Forgan] was greeted with a history of his work in Yugoslavia in the form of reports and plans he had made of the mines of the Trepca group and of prospects and other properties he had visited, together with a résumé of their present position. It was astonishing to see how accurate his predictions had been, and he was bombarded with requests for his technical opinions on and prognostications for properties he had not seen for 35 years . . .'

There would appear to be no doubt that the professional expertise on which Trepca had been built was well founded.

---

*Charles Bradley Forgan, a Fellow and Council member of the IMM, died in April 1980.

CHAPTER TEN

Into Battle Again

'We all know that modern warfare, whether in the air, or on the sea, or on land, necessitates the use of metals and minerals in far greater quantities than ever before. The present consumption of the British Empire is much larger than the highest figure recorded in peace-time, yet, with few exceptions which are not serious in relation to the whole, sufficient supplies have been forthcoming . . . with the outstanding exception of oil, nearly all these supplies are produced within the Empire, but it is not so well appreciated how recent is the growth of the mineral industry that has made this possible; nor how severely limited our supplies would have been without it.'

So said Edward Clifford when he came to the Presidency of the Institution of Mining and Metallurgy early in 1941—a time when Britain was preparing to take the offensive after throwing back the mass raids of the Luftwaffe, which were to have been the prelude to Hitler's invasion.

Giving IMM members a bird's-eye view of the state of the metals industry, Clifford went on to detail both world and Empire production of the most important minerals in 1913 and 1938, the years immediately preceding the two world wars. Global production of every mineral, except iron ore, had shown an increase. The relative position of the Empire during the 25-year period had improved remarkably in some cases, and the outbreak of the Second World War had found it in a strong position for practically every major base metal.

In copper, the outstanding events had been the discovery and development, almost simultaneously, of the orebodies in Northern Rhodesia and the Frood nickel–copper deposits in Canada, the combined annual production of which was around half a million tons—five times the Empire output of 1913. Production of lead and zinc had doubled to one million tons, by far the greater part due to the Sullivan mine in Canada. World production of aluminium had increased sevenfold to nearly 600 000 tons, but although the Empire was well endowed with both bauxite and low-cost hydroelectric power, its share was no more than 15 per cent of the total output of a material of ever-increasing strategic importance.

On the face of it, except for aluminium, these figures were impressive, but a more critical analysis than it was possible for Clifford to make at that time may not have produced a picture so encouraging. No one doubted that the Empire's mineral resources were sound; what was questionable was whether the British Government had taken full advantage of the position.

In an attempt to solve a highly unsatisfactory state of affairs at the end of the First World War the British Metal Corporation was set up under the management of Oliver Lyttelton, later Lord Chandos, to protect future supplies. By the late 1920s BMC controlled large resources of lead and zinc, but very little copper. Chester Beatty had suggested that the balance might be adjusted by the Corporation making a substantial investment in the developing Roan Antelope mine in Northern Rhodesia, but, as Lyttelton was to record in his memoirs years later, 'I failed to persuade the board to accept, and by far the greatest opportunity of the century was missed as every figure and estimate given by Beatty was either fulfilled or exceeded as time went on'.

At every opportunity between the wars, IMM as a professional body, and members of Council individually, did all that they could to encourage Government to make adequate provision for metal supplies against a national emergency. Little headway was made. Deaf to the warnings of the 'warmonger' Winston Churchill, and convinced that Hitler was not a threat to world peace—despite seeing most of Eastern Europe disappear under his heel—the Chamberlain Government clung to a policy of appeasement blindly believing that war was just not a possibility and that Hitler was a man with whom they could do business.

In the months that followed Chamberlain's meeting with the

Führer in Munich in 1938, Lyttelton pestered the Government to buy more copper, but while Germany built up big reserves, Britain did nothing. Finally, after much pressure, a number of departments were introduced in the Ministry of Supply to regulate the country's requirements. Lyttelton was appointed Controller of Non-Ferrous Metals, and arrived at his desk to find that Britain had only 7000 tons of copper in stock. Contracts were immediately signed with all Empire producers to secure the whole of their output for the Government at fixed prices for the duration of the war, and within 12 months the armament factories were gobbling up thousands of tons of metal every month. Britain's supplies of copper—and other strategic base metals—were ensured, but it was a close-run thing.

The problem of maintaining overseas metal supplies in times of transportation difficulty prompted the IMM to impress upon the Government the urgent need to re-examine the reasons for the decline—almost to extinction—of Britain's own metalliferous mining industry, which had flourished up to the middle of the previous century, and to consider how it might be revived. In a memorandum to the Ministry of Supply some positive suggestions were made, emphasizing that the problem was so urgent that it should not be regarded entirely from the standpoint of profit.

'An active metalliferous mining industry is of far greater benefit to the nation, and to the particular district [in which it operates], than the revenue accruing from taxation of the industry.' The IMM memorandum went on: 'In the past this country has built up overseas, both within and without the Empire, metal mining interests of vast importance which are of the utmost value to the nation, not only for their products, but also as markets for the machinery export trade. It will not be possible to maintain the position of this country in world-wide mining enterprises unless the supply of British mining engineers is kept up. If the domestic industry is allowed to die out—and it assuredly will do so if remedial measures are not taken—there will be no non-ferrous mines in Britain wherein mining engineers and miners can be trained.'

The importance with which the Institution viewed this problem was underlined by the appointment of two of its most senior and professionally experienced members to give evidence before the Ministry's committee for non-ferrous ores—Robert Annan, a Past-President, and J. Allen Howe, soon to become President for two

consecutive war years. Howe died in 1952, but Annan lived fo
another 30 years, until he was 96—long enough to see a
considerable revival of United Kingdom metal mining in the
1970s, especially in the Westcountry, followed, alas, by ye
another decline.

*   *   *

With the exploits of the Tunnelling Companies of the First World
War kept alive for 20 years by a vigorous old comrades
association, it was no surprise to the IMM when word came from
the War Office that it proposed to form a Company on the same
lines as those which operated between 1915 and 1918 and would
be glad to have names of those who might be available for
service.

The request did not carry quite the same degree of urgency as
in 1915 when John Norton-Griffiths virtually hijacked large
numbers of IMM members to officer the units of 'clay-kickers' that
he formed at the behest of Lord Kitchener to counter the
Germans' initiative in mine warfare on the Western Front.
Nevertheless, there was immediate and considerable response to
the Government's invitation, the volunteers including several who
had played a leading part in the first war underground.

Chief among the Great War veterans was Ralph Stokes, who
had hurried from South Africa as soon as he considered war to be
inevitable and put himself at the disposal of the Chief of the
Imperial General Staff, General Ironside, who had been his
commanding officer in 1918. Another was Laurence Carr Hill
member of a famous family of mining engineers whose name is
linked with the Rio Tinto mines in southern Spain. Laurence won
the DSO and MC and was three times mentioned in despatches
for his work with the tunnellers in Flanders. John Bell Simpson
had flown with the RAF in the First World War before entering
Camborne School of Mines, since when he had mined in South
America, in the Kolar gold fields in India, and in West Africa,
before returning to London to report for military service within a
week or two of Ralph Stokes's arrival.

The 'new boys' included Jim Rogers, who had moved on to
South Africa from Yugoslavia, and A.R.O. (Bill) Williams, who
worked on the Reef for Consolidated Gold Fields and later on the

rehabilitation of Kansanshi, Northern Rhodesia's first copper mine on the Congo border, which had been abandoned in 1914. Rejoining Gold Fields, Williams was in Toronto at the outbreak of war in 1939, but, determined to join the Royal Engineers, he sailed across the Atlantic in an American ship, 'lit up like a Christmas tree', to return to England to enlist.

Almost all the officers—other than 'regulars' of the Royal Engineers—of the first Tunnelling Company (No. 170) formed at the end of 1939 were members of the IMM. They came together at Chatham Barracks, where they were hurriedly trained in basic military disciplines, commissioned and uniformed. A photograph from the IMM archives, taken in January 1940, shows the nucleus of the Company, including Stokes, Simpson, Rogers and Williams—all of whom were to become Presidents of the Institution over the next 30 years, following Laurence Hill (not in the photograph) who occupied the chair in 1950–51.

As other Companies were created, the services of more members were called upon by the War Office. In all, some 225 IMM men fought with the Engineering units of the Imperial Forces during the war, many of them as tunnellers, who served in every rank from the lowest to the highest. Once again, the Institution became a busy recruiting centre and a committee was set up to deal with appointments and many other matters brought before it by the Army authorities. Most of the work fell on W.J. (Bill) Felton, who had taken over as IMM secretary on the retirement of Charles McDermid in 1939.

For members of No. 170 Company, who went to France early in 1940, it was soon apparent that their work would be very different from what the tunnellers had been called on to perform in 1915. Although the 'phoney war' was still dragging on in Western Europe, the Germans had already dramatically demonstrated in Poland and the other countries they had overrun that, despite the 'impenetrable fortresses' of the Siegfried and Maginot lines, this was to be no siege war. Trench and mine warfare had gone as surely as the days of bows and arrows. This was to be a war of rapid movement, dominated by aircraft and tanks: the blitzkrieg had changed the whole concept of human conflict in the twinkling of an eye. This did not necessarily mean that there was no work for the tunnellers. The development of aerial warfare meant that only beneath the surface of the earth could one be completely safe from attack. Accordingly, No. 170

Ten members of the IMM are in this picture of 170 Tunnelling company RE, taken at Chatham in January 1940. Left to right, front row, 1, A.R.O. Williams; 2, A.S.W. Wood;* 4, R.G.S. Stokes;* 5, G.M. Edwards; 8, R.T. Brandt; back row, 1, G.A.P. Moorhead; 2, T. Pickering; 5, D.J. Rogers; 8, J.E.A. Paterson. Inset, left, J.B. Simpson (* denotes service also in the 1914–18 War)

Company spent most of its time in France, not in pushing mines beneath enemy emplacements but in excavating for military headquarters, underground operations rooms, casualty stations and stores for ammunition and other supplies. It was unexciting, laborious work in that first winter of the war when the main enemy was boredom—and the bitter cold.

Then suddenly, on 10 May, everything was changed when the Germans launched their big attack—a four-pronged assault through neutral Holland and Belgium to draw off the best of the British and French troops, followed by the main thrust across the Ardennes, the Nazi troops unsportingly pouring through a gap in the Maginot line to race towards the Channel, pivoting north to entrap the Allies. It was a classic example of the new concept—deep penetration of fast-moving Panzers with close and terrifying support from the air—a concept, as Liddell Hart observed, 'as revolutionary as the use of the horse . . . the longbow, the musket and the [artillery] gun'.

What happened to No. 170 Company in this great encirclement is graphically described by Jim Rogers in his book *Tunnelling into Colditz*. In the absence of a front line, the Company had been digging air raid shelters for Army GHQ under a fortress that had been a school of correction for young ladies at Doullens, in the Pas de Calais.

'We were still mining away when the German Blitz on France began,' he writes. 'We had army communiqués which told us that something big was going on. The only action we took was to man the ramparts with machine-guns against air attack, which never occurred, though some low-flying aircraft came over going at a tremendous speed and howling like banshees. Convoys of vehicles passed through the town, mostly French and all moving westward. We started to get stories about the advancing Germans, about the horrors of dive-bombing and the irresistibility of German tanks and guns.

'In spite of all these alarums and excursions, we continued with our digging activities as if nothing was happening. However, after a few days the powers-that-be saw the amber light and we left Doullens by road for Arras and, two days later, went on to Boulogne by train right to the quayside. Unfortunately the last boat had gone and so, willy-nilly, we became part of the defence force of the area . . .

'Soon someone realized that, as mining men, we were

experienced in explosives, and because of this I found myself a day or two later on a special military mission. We were driving in a car, with a sapper major from GHQ as OC, followed by a lorry loaded with twenty-three tunnellers—and stalwart men they were, mostly miners from Durham and Yorkshire—a ton of gun cotton, an unnecessarily large amount of instant-detonating fuse, and about a mile of ordinary fuse. With all these explosives loaded on one vehicle and specially with highly sensitive and dangerous instant-detonating fuse, and no red flags showing, I felt a sense of outrage at such a breach of all normal regulations . . . In normal life I would, almost certainly, have been expunged from the register of our professional body, the Institution of Mining and Metallurgy, for such behaviour.

'We were bound for points south of Boulogne to blow up bridges in the face of the German advance. In fact, the Germans, as I now know, were already well beyond Hesdin, some thirty miles south-east of Boulogne, and still advancing. Our progress was slow. French Army personnel and civilians were streaming north with manifold vehicles, not excluding prams and wheelbarrows. We appeared to be the only people in northern France who were travelling southward. We were regarded with astonishment; some saluted, some raised a cheer at the mad Englishmen, while many rotated their right forefinger over their right ears in a Gallic indication of insanity.

'At one point a senior French officer waved us down and advised us that German tanks were not far ahead and we should retire at once. I fully agreed with this but our OC, who was straight from GHQ and therefore in touch with the situation, said . . . that the Germans were miles away. We pressed on. However, a rather sinister change soon came over the scene. There were no longer any refugees and we found ourselves travelling at speed through a deserted countryside with wide open fields on either hand. It was a lovely day. Spring was in the air and could be felt and seen all around us. I had that general feeling of expectancy which one has before the curtain rises . . .

'Bullets started coming through the windscreen. We had run into an ambush. We left the car and made for the ditch at the side of the road. "Thank God! It hasn't been raining," I thought as I dived in. "I won't get wet." Our lorry with its load of explosives and against which most of the firing was directed, also stopped and most of the men got off pretty smartly, fearing an explosion.

Bedtime reading. At a reunion of
Colditz prisoners in London in
1990 the Queen Mother was
presented with a copy of Jim
Rogers's book. Inset, the author

Some stayed on board, however. One of them started firing at the Germans with our machine-gun. Encouraged by this, I battled to get a shot off from the army rifle I was carrying, but I was completely untrained and had up till then never fired a shot, due to the shortage of ammunition for training purposes, [and] it took me some time before I loosed off a shot at a German tank advancing down the road towards us.

'It was my first and last shot of the war.

'The tank came right up to us; German troops appeared all round me; so with all the dignity I could muster I rose to my feet in the ditch, wondering if I might be blotted out at any moment.

'So I became a prisoner of war . . .'

And so also did his companions. For Jim Rogers it was the beginning of five years of incarceration in German prison camps. At Laufen he was concerned in digging one of the most ambitious escape tunnels ever driven in captivity—nearly 60 yards long. Just 15 feet from freedom the Germans discovered the tunnellers and Rogers was sent as one of the first of the British contingent to the most secure and most notorious prison of them all. Thus, as the title of his book indicates, he tunnelled his way *into* Colditz. There he and other determined escapers planned further dramatic escapades—to the increasing fury of their captors. Later, when transferred to Spangenberg, the plotting continued. Inch by inch Rogers tunnelled his way through solid rock until he was caught and returned to Colditz as an irrepressible 'bad boy' in the distinguished company of Douglas Bader, Mike and Pat Reid and many more.

*   *   *

The three other members of the quartet who had been among the first to join No. 170 Tunnelling Company, and were destined to become Presidents of the IMM, all had better luck than Jim Rogers. Brigadier Stokes, fighting in his third major war, was recalled from France early in 1940 to become chief engineer of the Allied expedition to drive the Germans out of Narvik and to retrieve some of Britain's lost prestige in Norway. Unfortunately, the operation was 'too little and too late', badly conceived and clumsily organized. But at least Stokes did not fall into the hands of the Germans and returned to apply his professional expertise to other theatres of war.

J.B. Simpson and Bill Williams were also back in England before the German breakthrough in France—Williams to supervise the formation of another Tunnelling Company, No. 80, and Simpson to do a spell at headquarters before being sent to Malta as commanding officer of No. 173 Company. Williams tackled his job at Chatham with skill and enthusiasm; he was appointed commander of the new Company and in October 1940 embarked with his men by sea for an unknown destination. For days their convoy dodged prowling U-boats and enemy aircraft before slipping safely into the harbour of Gibraltar.

For three centuries Gibraltar, in the shadow of the great limestone Rock that commands the entrance to the Mediterranean, had served the battleships of the British Fleet—ever since the days when Nelson used its dockyards before Trafalgar. Its strategic importance to the Allies in the Second World War was greater than at any time in its turbulent history, particularly in view of the ever-present possibility of a Nazi invasion of Spain from Occupied France, and it was vital that it should be defended at all costs.

The Rock, one of the Pillars of Hercules in the ancient world—the other was across the Straits near present-day Tangier—rises 1369 ft from a long and narrow sandy peninsula, only a few feet above sea-level, which connects it to the mainland. The British first occupied it in 1704 during the War of the Spanish Succession. For 20 or 30 years the Spanish showed little interest in its restitution, but in the last quarter of the eighteenth century agitation became intense. In June 1779 the Spanish and French besieged the garrison, which held out for nearly four years until it was relieved by Lord Howe on 11 October 1782. By the time that Spanish pressure for restitution boiled up again in the 1880s, the opening of the Suez Canal made any idea of the British parting with it quite unthinkable. And despite sporadic, and sometimes vigorous demands from the Spaniards, it remained firmly in British hands.

No one can tell when the Rock was first penetrated. During the great siege in the eighteenth century the British drove galleries to give their gunners a better sight of the enemy and to provide protection for themselves against cannon balls and primitive bombs. As well as these man-made excavations, the action of water percolating through the limestone for hundreds of thousands of years produced many caves and fissures, in some of which bone breccias, mixing with the debris, indicated the presence, at some time or other, of many species of mammals, including elephant, rhino and panther. Four levels of human occupation from Neanderthal to Roman times have also been identified. The Rock would have been a treasure house for that great scientist and tunneller of the First World War Edgeworth David (Chapter Six). Early in the present century the Rock was tunnelled to facilitate communication between its east and west sides and the excavated material was used to reclaim some 60 acres of land, on which Gibraltar's airfield was later built.

When Bill Williams and his Company arrived towards the end of 1940 they joined other units that had been working since the days of Dunkirk to strengthen the defences, hollowing out the Rock for gun emplacements, military headquarters, operations rooms and the storage of ammunition, food and water, always one of the colony's most precious commodities. Altogether, over the next four years, five Tunnelling Companies of the Royal Engineers were garrisoned at Gibraltar, together with units of the Canadian Royal Engineers, including a special detachment with diamond-drilling equipment.

The tunnellers worked round the clock; they seldom knew what a Saturday afternoon or Sunday meant; after an eight-hour shift they would spend two or three hours learning how to handle a Bren gun or mortar, for everyone was going to have to fight if the security of Gibraltar were threatened.

General Sir Noel Mason Macfarlane, who was Governor of Gibraltar in these critical days, told an IMM meeting after the war that one of the biggest difficulties had been to decide just where to start. 'It was', he said, 'a situation where a short-term policy had to be married to a long-term policy; and the short-term policy had to be very active. The overall objective was to make the Rock capable of standing up to a siege without relief for at least a year, which meant accommodation for many thousand people, with all the ammunition, rations, distilleries for water, etc., inside the Rock, as it was open to bombardment not only from the air, but from the ground from Spain'.

'The initial tunnelling served both purposes: it helped the short-term and it was the beginning of the long-term policy, and as time went on the whole vast network of tunnels as it is today finally emerged. By the time I left in January 1944, one million tons of rock had been removed and many more have been taken out since then.'

General Macfarlane recalled how he used to go round every Sunday afternoon with his senior engineers to inspect the week's work and to note the extraordinary advances made by each Company. The results became better and better as time went on. His own pet project had been to make a tunnel on the east side of the Rock, but there was a very bad corner and he could get nobody to build it. At last, in the construction of the airfield, a particularly big blast caused a landslide that covered the road and blocked the eastern access, so he was finally allowed to have his way.

'These were all first-class units and it was great to see the way they carried out their work,' said General Macfarlane. 'The organization was of immense interest but it was those behind the machine, officers and all other ranks, who counted in the end. I can honestly say that I have never seen a finer lot of men than those in the Tunnelling Companies in Gibraltar.'

Top-level tribute to the tunnellers came from Prime Minister Winston Churchill, who described the result of their work as looking like 'a giant Gruyère cheese'. The successful IMM fortification of the Rock was undoubtedly a key factor in keeping the Mediterranean open to Allied shipping and in helping to dissuade Hitler from attempting to seize it by an expedition through Spain. A memorial to Bill Williams's work is in a tunnel, still to be seen in the Rock, named after his initials 'Arow Way'. A second tunnel, 'Williams Way', was, as Bill was always quick to emphasize, quite unconnected with him; it was called after his successor, who, by coincidence, had the same name.

Early in 1943, Williams, by now Colonel in charge of all military tunnelling in Gibraltar, flew to Malta to see what could be done to help similar operations on the island, then being directed by Colonel Laurence Carr Hill. By this time Malta had been under intense air attack for nearly three years by German and Italian bombers and had earned itself a George Cross 'to bear witness to a heroism and devotion that will long be famous in history'. Not surprisingly, Williams's arrival coincided with an air raid and his RAF transport was turned back to Gibraltar, but a second attempt a few days later was successful.

Bill stayed in Malta a couple of weeks, enjoying his reunion

with Hill, and with J.B. Simpson, then OC No. 173 Company and
soon to take command of the 1st Tunnelling Group. Laurence Hill
remained in Malta until the end of 1944, when he was obliged to
resign his commission under age-limit regulations. But he was
determined to see the war through to the end—and did so as a
deck-hand in the Admiralty Runner Service aboard fleet tenders
and other small craft.

*   *   *

In all, some 400 members of the IMM served with the Forces in
the Second World War. Twenty-five became prisoners-of-war in
Western Europe. In the Far East names were received of close on
40 civil internees, caught up in the Japanese sweep through Asia.
A similar number were known to have been working in countries
overrun by the Japanese and many were still unaccounted for
when hostilities ended.

Not surprisingly, IMM men tended to choose a less traditional
way of assisting the war effort than those whose peacetime jobs
seldom took them abroad and whose daily routine was bounded
by catching the same train or bus from suburbia each morning
and returning at more or less the same time in the evening. If not
in the Tunnelling Companies of the Royal Engineers, IMM
members were more likely to be found in military intelligence
units, the SOE or other organizations whose operations were
cloaked under some odd-sounding titles in order to avoid the
glare of publicity.

One such body was the United Kingdom Commercial
Corporation (UKCC), formed in 1940 as a state-controlled
organization on company lines to limit the enemy's supplies from
neutral countries. British ships blockaded Nazi ports, but the
Royal Navy was stretched to its limits in convoy and anti-
submarine work and naturally had no control over the large
volume of goods reaching Germany overland from the 'neutrals'.
In these circumstances the most effective way of reducing the
intake was for Britain to act at source and secure all it could by
'pre-emptive' buying. The Government was prepared to spend
almost unlimited money to ensure the success of this operation,
which was put under the direction of Lord Swinton as 'chairman'
of the UKCC.

Swinton gathered around him some of the most experienced men in British commerce and industry, including Selection Trust's Alfred Chester Beatty, who at 65 was very much the 'elder statesman' but certainly not the least active of the team. When the Germans broke through in the West in May 1940, he foresaw the serious consequences of the loss of Britain's chief source of diamond dies, vital for the conversion of copper and other metals into fine wire essential to the working of the electrical equipment of a great range of armaments.

Before the war only three firms in the United Kingdom made diamond dies. The country's wire-making industry depended almost entirely on dies imported from France, Belgium and Holland, where they were made by a small number of craftsmen who jealously guarded the process and handed down their secrets from generation to generation in much the same way as the medieval mining and metal-working guilds of Agricola's days. Beatty voiced his fears to Lord Beaverbrook, who as Minister of Aircraft Production was closely concerned with anything that could affect the output of bombers and fighters for the RAF. Beatty provided a small party of volunteers from his own technical staff who were despatched by air to France in an attempt to save as many dies and die-makers as possible from the advancing Germans, and to capture a large consignment of industrial diamonds believed to have recently arrived in Bordeaux from the Congo.

The speed and power of the German advance made the attempt a 'mission impossible', and Beatty's men were lucky to escape, their aircraft hedge-hopping over France with Messerschmitts on their tail, to land safely in Jersey. When Beatty heard the news he insisted on Leslie Thompson, of the Directorate of Instrument Production, being sent to the United States with a million pounds in his pocket and the authority to buy every diamond die he could lay his hands on. Thompson was remarkably successful: he bought 32 000 dies, partly because the Americans were not yet fully alive to the problem, for they, like the British, relied mainly for their supplies on exports from France and the Low Countries. However, Beatty knew that Thompson's purchases were only a temporary solution and, in further talks with Lord Beaverbrook, he proposed the establishment of a Diamond Die Control within the Ministry of Supply to get things better organized. He also provided a

Controller in the person of Ronnie Prain, the man who ten years later was to succeed him as chairman of RST and play an outstanding part in the post-war development of the Northern Rhodesian Copperbelt. In the months that followed, the production of dies in Britain increased tenfold and an entirely new industry was created to manufacture diamond dies capable of drawing the finest wire.

Meanwhile, the Secret Service helped to make good the immediate shortfall by parachuting agents into Europe to snatch dies from under the noses of the occupying Germans and smuggle them back through Switzerland and Spain. The need of supplies from France diminished as British production developed; by the end of 1943 the country was 90 per cent self-sufficient, and totally so by the end of the war. Nevertheless, the dies obtained by British agents from France in the latter part of 1940 and throughout the following year were vital to armament production. Without them output of fighter aircraft could have been suspended for up to a year with consequences that might well have lost the war.

*   *   *

To Chester Beatty and his team of engineers at Selection Trust headquarters—almost without exception paid-up members of the IMM—belongs the credit for one of the UKCC's most spectacular operations—the purchase of large tonnages of wolfram from neutral Portugal in direct competition with the Germans.

Chief ore of the metal tungsten, wolfram was in great demand, primarily for the hardening of steel for armour plating, shells, bullets and other weapons and missiles. That the Germans were seriously worried about supplies was shown by the very high price that they were willing to pay for the ore. Any deposit, however small, was therefore worth exploiting: no quantity was too little to mine or buy to prevent it from falling into enemy hands.

Portugal's main source of ore was the Beralt mine at Panasqueira, in the foothills of the Serra da Estrêla range of mountains, which runs across the northern part of the country, 200 miles or more from Lisbon. Since 1934 the mine had been under the technical management of the British Metal Corporation, but at the beginning of the war the Portuguese Government took control of sales, with the consequent risk of much production finding its way to Germany. Ivan Sharp, member of a well-known mining engineering family and IMM member—his brother Fred, a Camborne man, was a contemporary of Jim Rogers at Trepca—was sent to Panasqueira to supervise production on behalf of the UKCC. In the first 12 months the mine produced 2400 tons of wolfram concentrates, but output fell when explosives and other production equipment became difficult to obtain.

Meanwhile, the price of wolfram on the Lisbon market rocketed to more than £6000 a ton—for a commodity that had been fetching no more than £150 on the world's markets just before the war. This was the signal for Portugal's great 'wolfram rush'. Everyone started a collection for sale: peasants, doctors, labourers, lawyers, old men, women and children—everyone streamed into the mountains to fill baskets, sacks and even tin cans with the black, lumpy material, and haul it home to sell to foreign agents ready and eager to buy with stacks of notes. Even little tobacco tins filled with wolfram fetched high prices.

To ensure that the UKCC got the lion's share, Beatty sent buyers to snap up every available pound of the ore. With them went many of his senior London staff, including Charles Forgan and Ernest Bunker, both recently escaped from the invading Germans in Yugoslavia, to supervise the work. Lisbon became a city of high intrigue and espionage. British and German agents rubbed shoulders in the market place and there was intense competition: raids were made on each other's dumps; armed guards patrolled the properties and there were countless acts of sabotage. The wolfram battle was a major victory for the Allies. The UKCC team knew at the time that they were achieving the high targets that they had set themselves, but it was not until enemy records became available after the war that it was realized just how badly munitions production in Germany had been affected.

The wolfram war was not without its casualties, among them Ivan Sharp, who was a fellow passenger with actor Leslie Howard in a civil airliner shot down between Lisbon and London. It was widely believed that the real target was Winston Churchill, who was returning home after a North African conference. German spies had seen a thickset figure smoking a cigar walk up to the aircraft in Lisbon. They signalled that the British leader was aboard; a German warplane was ordered out and the defenceless airliner was shot down into the Atlantic with the loss of all lives.

'The brutality of the Germans was only matched by the stupidity of their agents', wrote Churchill in his history of the Second World War. 'It is difficult to understand how anyone could imagine that, with all the resources of Great Britain at my disposal, I should have booked a passage in an unarmed and unescorted plane and flown home in broad daylight. We, of course, made a wide loop out by night from Gibraltar into the ocean, and arrived home without incident. It was a painful shock to me to learn what had happened to others in the inscrutable workings of Fate.'

As the war went on, the pattern of the work of the UKCC in Portugal was repeated in fifty or more other countries, big and small, with variations according to the strategic material that the people had to sell and the sort of goods that they required in return. Among the Corporation's responsibilities was to ensure that sufficient food to keep the civilian population alive and contented reached countries such as Egypt, Syria, Iraq, Persia and wherever else Allied forces were based. In many cases only such supplies prevented the outbreak of disturbances that could have hindered, if not wrecked military operations.

When Russia entered the war in June 1941, Churchill promised all the help that Britain could give and ordered the UKCC to provide and deliver to the new ally supplies of every kind other than armaments. The big problem was how to get them there. With the sea route to Murmansk infested with U-boats and within the range of German aircraft from Norway, it was decided that the best way to reach the heart of the Soviet Union was through Persia, linking up with the Trans-Caucasian and Turkestan transport systems. Nearly a thousand miles of bad roads, narrow, steeply cambered and often crossing rugged mountain country, separated the Persian Gulf from the zone that the Russians established on the shores of the Caspian Sea to receive the supplies and transship them to where they were most needed. At one time there were more than 8000 heavy lorries carrying aid to Russia over the route from the Persian Gulf and even more struggling their way through from India. George Sinclair, head of London Passenger Transport, who was brought in to help organize the 'hell run', used to joke that he had more lorries in Persia than he had buses and trains in London.

Despite the enormous amount of material handed over to the Russians, and the hazards of the journey, the Soviet military authorities did not show much gratitude, and at times were highly suspicious of British intentions. They wanted no foreign troops in their zone and British officers who crossed their lines were promptly arrested.

Once more, a mining man came to the rescue. H.E. ('Tod') Beecher had lived in Russia before and during the Revolution, and had worked for the Selection Trust mine at Tetiuhe in Siberia—and at Trepca in Yugoslavia, whence he had escaped with Charles Forgan, Clem Richardson and others a few hours before the Germans marched in. On Beecher's return to London, Chester Beatty had him switched to Persia as the UKCC's 'trouble-shooter'. With his deep understanding of the Russian mentality, his fluency in the language, his humour and adaptability, Beecher was immediately on good terms with the Soviet authorities and smoothed away many of the problems. As Sir Frank Nixon, one of the Corporation's directors, said after a visit to the Persian front: 'He [Beecher] was accepted without question and in certain circumstances his word was law. Others would have probably been shot dead for doing what he did. Securing his appointment was a touch of genius by Chester Beatty . . . but then I'm told he always had the knack of picking the right man for the job.'

Years later, someone close to Beatty told him that it had been suggested that this was probably the chief reason why he won the IMM's Gold Medal. The old man chuckled behind the thick cloak that he wore round his shoulders, summer and winter, and there was a hint of mischief in his twinkling eyes.

*   *   *

For every member of the IMM honoured for gallantry and distinguished service in the Second World War there were many others whose contributions to the national effort were no less valuable because they were not so spectacular. They were to be found not only in the Forces but in industry, in paramilitary organizations, in science laboratories, research teams, and in government departments where their expertise was applied in many ways.

Dr Edward George West, a Fellow both of the IMM and the Institution of Metallurgists, was typical of those who worked outside the glare of publicity. Having taken a First in metallurgy at Birmingham in 1930, he began a career in industry but left to set up a research team on the welding of non-ferrous metals under the joint sponsorship of the British Non-Ferrous Association and the then Welding Research Council.

In 1940 the leaders of the aluminium industry formed the Wrought Light Alloys Development Association and Ted West was chosen to be its manager. His task was to tackle the urgent need for technical information and advise on alloys, which were being used in many departments of war production for the first time. He also ensured that the association worked closely with the Government on the development of new alloys, notably for the aircraft industry. He became technical director when the association was absorbed into the Aluminium Development Association at the end of the war.

In 1963 West became director of the Copper Development Association, where he again built up a research team of engineers and metallurgists, doing, in fact, for copper what he had done for what was now its biggest competitor, aluminium.

Despite his significant contribution to the understanding of non-ferrous metals, Ted West will probably be remembered best for his leading role in furthering the metallurgical profession, working from within the IMM, the Institution of Metallurgists, the Welding Institute, the Institute of Sheet Metal Engineers and many other professional bodies. He devoted much of his energy and enthusiasm to encouraging young people to share his fascination for material science and engineering, and when he died in 1988 the profession lost one of its outstanding members.

CHAPTER ELEVEN

Winds of Change

As in the First World War, routine activities of the Institution of Mining and Metallurgy continued on a reduced scale between 1939 and 1945, except that this time the annual dinner was cancelled for the duration.

Charles McDermid having retired after serving as secretary throughout four decades, the task of keeping the administration going in the difficult war years passed to Bill Felton, well equipped for the job after seven years with the joint IMM/IME secretariat. For several months he presided over the small staff who remained in the offices that the two institutions shared at Salisbury House, in Finsbury Circus, relatively undisturbed by the momentous events that were unfolding in Western Europe other than by an occasional glimpse of the vapour trails left behind by Spitfire and Messerschmitt as they scribbled their quarrels across the sky. Then suddenly as the summer of 1940 began to fade, they found themselves in the front line when the Luftwaffe, defeated by the RAF's Few in daylight, began its blitz on London and provincial cities under cover of darkness.

Nights of terror were followed by days of resolution as the City counted its losses, shored up its buildings and waited for the sirens to wail again. Salisbury House was lucky to escape serious damage until May 1941, when it was rendered uninhabitable and the staff were evacuated. Consolidated Gold Fields, just round the corner in Moorgate, opened its doors to the homeless, and other London-based mining companies offered boardrooms for Council meetings and other deliberations. Later, the Royal School of Mines provided temporary accommodation in Kensington, and the joint library and institutional records were moved for safe keeping to an old mine office at Darley Dale in Derbyshire. By 1943 Salisbury House was sufficiently restored to enable staff to return, but to less commodious accommodation than before, and it was decided to leave the books and records at Darley Dale until the end of hostilities.

War or no war, the IMM celebrated its 50th anniversary with a luncheon at the Savoy on 13 January 1942—a time when Britain's War Cabinet had been thrown into confusion by the news that Singapore had been left without landward defences against the advancing Japapese. A month later the 'impregnable fortress' fell and Winston Churchill went on the air to call for 'a display of that calm poise, combined with grim determination which not so long ago brought us out of the very jaws of death'. The indefatigable British responded by taking fewer baths and using only five inches of water when they did so; women defied a cosmetics famine by substituting beetroot juice for lipstick and soot for eye shadow; and, with razor blades in short supply, men were encouraged to sharpen their old blades by running them round the inside of glass tumblers—also hard to come by in those difficult times.

At the Savoy the IMM heard its praises sung by Sir William Bragg, one of the most eminent scientists of the day, who doubted if it was fully realized how much depended on the work of mining engineers and metallurgists. 'The war in the air', he told them, 'could not be maintained without a plentiful supply of aluminium and magnesium and other light metals. Nor could ships and guns be made effective without the rarer metals, tungsten, vanadium and the rest. Nevertheless, recognition grows under the stress of war, and many now understand how much cause the nation has to be grateful to you for all the work that you have done.'

With the future of the free world so perilously in the balance, it was hardly an occasion to look backwards, but those with time and inclination to do so were able to identify some significant changes in the pattern of the metal-mining industry over the past half-century, and to acknowledge those whose professional skills and expertise had helped to shape its progress.

Perhaps the most interesting change that had taken place was in the anatomy of the IMM itself. Of those who gathered at

Winchester House for the inaugural meeting in 1892, most were London-based consultants in mining engineering and metallurgy, senior partners and members of staff of firms that had already won worldwide reputation; the balance was made up largely by academics who were generally uninterested in the profit motive. The geographical pattern of membership had also changed. There was still a big majority of members overseas, but whereas 50 years ago there were substantial numbers in such countries as Russia, Siberia, Korea and China, relatively few now remained behind the 'iron curtain'. Losses in Communist countries had, however, been more than offset by strength gained in happier lands, particularly in the African continent, Australia and Canada, where vast areas were still open for further mineral exploration.

The introduction of machine drilling and other labour-saving equipment around the turn of the century had provided a new impetus to the industry that found its most noticeable expression in the establishment of some very big mining operations. Although smaller mines continued to be numerous for the next 30 years or so and looked mainly to the consultancies for technical assistance and advice, the larger mining companies soon found it more economic—and in many cases more efficient—to employ top-level professional staff of their own. Moreover, as time went on, owners of mineral rights tended to take their prospects to the big mining houses for investigation rather than to the consultancies, whose business thereby started to decline. It will be remembered, for example, that when Radomir Pašić decided to test the potential of his father's mineral rights in Yugoslavia, his agent went to an experienced mining group, using a local consultant merely as intermediary. Nevertheless, the older-established consultancies continued to do quite well, not so much from giving advice on operations but as middlemen in the promotion of new projects that were outside the orbit of the big mining groups.

The impact of these changes on the IMM was to be found in its current list of members: mine superintendents, ventilation officers, underground managers, geologists, smelter and refinery superintendents, and men in other operational categories now outnumbered the consultants and educationalists who had dominated the register 50 years earlier. However, the aims and objects of the Institution remained basically unchanged.

Throughout the half-century the IMM had maintained and strengthened its role as chief collector of technical information about the metal-mining industry, disseminating the knowledge and experience of its contributors to every country where mining men were to be found, and ensuring an ever-increasing status for the profession that it represented in a swiftly changing world. Indeed, it could be claimed that the Institution's most outstanding achievement in its first 50 years was to bring respectability to the organized search for, and the development of the world's mineral resources, undertakings that had bred so many devious characters and unscrupulous companies in the second half of the nineteenth century.

*   *   *

The peace that followed the defeat of Germany in 1945 and the dramatic end to the war with Japan after atomic bombs had obliterated the cities of Hiroshima and Nagasaki was marked by changes that were to have a great impact on the international mining industry and, in consequence, on its professional institutions.

Of these developments, perhaps the most significant were: first, the remarkable progress in aviation and other means of transport and communication; secondly, the decline of the British Empire as it had existed since mid-Victorian times and the emergence of the new-styled Commonwealth—a title bestowed upon it by South Africa's General Smuts; and, thirdly, the determination of many mining countries to bring their natural resource industries under state control. In many, but by no means all, cases the two last-named developments were interrelated.

It seemed unbelievable that in the space of two generations, and within the working life of one IMM member, the world could have shrunk so small as to bring its continents and principal countries to within a few hours' flying time of each other. In his retirement, Gold Medallist Chester Beatty would entertain his friends by telling them of a lunch that he had in New York in 1904 with the American entrepreneur Charles R. Flint. Over coffee, Flint excused himself to read a telegram from Wilbur Wright reporting that he and his brother had that day flown at

Kitty Hawk, North Carolina, in a heavier-than-air machine, built in their bicycle shed. Flint—who was later to compete unsuccessfully with Beatty in securing a contract for mineral development in the Congo from King Leopold of the Belgians—had been one of the few who believed in the brothers' project; he backed them financially, held options on their patents and, accordingly, was one of the first to be told of their success. 'I believe', said Wilbur Wright's cable, 'that we have solved the mystery of the air.'

Within the next ten years the airplane developed sufficiently to become a potent weapon in the latter part of the Great War, thereby providing a touch of high adventure to an otherwise horrific struggle. The years that followed to 1939 saw the beginnings of modern civil aviation, based primarily on services that the British, Dutch, Belgians and French introduced to their colonial possessions in Africa and the Far East. Such services were made possible only by the availability of intermediate landing grounds for refuelling along the routes and, in the case of Britain's Imperial Airways, of moorings for its famous flying boat service to the Sudan, Rhodesia and South Africa, with which numerous IMM members were familiar.

It was the expertise of airline operators and crews, coupled with the work of the designers of Second World War military aircraft as they competed to extend range and loading capacity to enable their creations to carry the frightfulness of air bombardment to the most remote targets, that provided the impetus for post-war civil aviation development on an enormous scale. During the war commercial aviation had come to a virtual standstill, but the aircraft and the airlines' personnel were pressed into military service to provide an air transport network that covered every major theatre of war. Regular flights were launched across the North Atlantic, throughout the Pacific, over the 'hump' of the Himalayas from Burma into China, into the Arctic regions, across Africa and into Latin America. Efficiency of performance, never before attained, kept these long-range flights transporting troops and materials to tight schedules, and it also familiarized thousands of servicemen with the advantages of air travel.

Within less than twelve months of the ending of hostilities four-engined airliners were introduced commercially, some with pressurized cabins and navigational facilities that made all-weather flying a reality. By the early 1950s civil aviation had developed into one of the world's most significant industries accepted as a common form of intercontinental passenger transport and already beginning to challenge the hitherto unassailable position of the steamship companies.

The effect of these developments on the mining industry, and hence on IMM members working as expatriates in distant lands often for a London-based company or consultancy, was very sharp indeed. As the world contracted under the influence of the fast aeroplane, so the way in which overseas mining companies and international groups were run also changed. No longer was it necessary for a board of directors to wait weeks for the return of a specialist geologist or engineer to hear and debate his personal report on the viability of a new project, or the expansion of an existing undertaking. A London-based consultant could now fly out to the furthest parts of the earth and return within a few days with his recommendations. Meetings of multinational executives could be set up at a moment's notice in almost any one of the world's capitals with the confidence that everyone would be able to attend and contribute his views and experience. A great variety of machinery and spare parts could be flown to mines in remote places to obviate long production delays through mechanical failure. Mining men, and in particular those in the professional classes whose interests were catered for by the IMM, were soon to become among the most regular users of the airlines, and the companies they served benefited immeasurably from their mobility.

If, as Sir William Bragg had told the IMM at its 50th anniversary luncheon, the aeroplane depended on the mining industry to keep it flying in wartime, so now the international mining community was coming to rely in no small measure on the aeroplane to help it remain competitive in world industry.

Out in the field, the airplane was also beginning to play an important part in geological survey. Among its enthusiasts was a young Royal School of Mines geologist and IMM member named Tony Barringer, who joined a Canadian company's prospecting team in the early 1950s and spent much of his time putting together airborne electronic equipment designed to detect geological anomalies over vast areas. He eventually came up with what was known as 'Input', a system that was closely analogous to radar in that it depended on the generation of high-powered electromagnetic pulses that were returned as an echo when striking certain objects—in this case minerals within the range of the transmitter. It was a development of 'Input' that pointed the way to the discovery of the South Bay copper mine on Uchi Lake, after 15 years of unrewarding surface exploration in the area. Barringer later formed his own aerial prospecting company and won worldwide recognition as a pioneer of a technique of mine-finding that was in sharp contrast to the painstaking methods of the old-timers who plodded the trails with their picks and pack-mules—and their unbounded optimism that one day they would find their fortune.

Meanwhile, mining companies all over the world were beginning to buy aircraft of their own and to employ professional pilots for the rapid transportation of personnel and equipment within the territories in which they operated. Oil companies and public utilities also became big users of aircraft, and 'flying doctor' services brought swift medical aid to those working in remote mines and cattle stations in the Australian and African bush, in the mid-western United States and in Canada. By the mid-1960s one big mining group in Zambia started its own airline company, operating five Hercules transports to fly copper 1000 miles north to the Tanzanian port of Dar es Salaam for shipment to overseas markets when rail routes to the south were closed for political reasons. The air bridge continued for three years on a round-the-clock schedule that hauled 150 000 tons of freight, more than half of it copper for export, and the remainder much-needed fuel and lubricants for an industry that would otherwise have remained cut off from the outside world.

The ripple effect of quick and easy air transportation went far beyond its direct impact on mining operations. In many cases it helped to change the very social pattern of thousands of people working for the industry all over the world. In its early days mining, and particularly prospecting, had been very much an adventure for a man with no family ties. The pioneer miner in Africa, North America, Australia and many places elsewhere had usually worked alone—partly for preference, and partly because he feared that if ever he struck it rich an unscrupulous partner would beat him to the claims office.

This trend continued in the early years of the twentieth century. Between the wars wives began to join husbands in some of the bigger overseas mining 'camps', but it was not until after the Second World War that a European-style family life developed in communities that had grown up in hitherto remote and unhealthy localities. This is not to suggest that wives waited for the development of air travel before joining their husbands abroad: in Northern Rhodesia, for example, there was a strong family community among the expatriates as early as the 1930s. Twenty-five years later families were still going out in the traditional way by steamship, but as communities expanded there were increasing demands for modern facilities—paved roads, fast motor cars, good shops, hospitals, schools and sports grounds. A regular air service did much to speed such developments; it also provided an opportunity for employees to enjoy a full quota of home leave without time-wasting travel and the chance to have children educated in the country of their birth—and be 'home' for the holidays. Naturally, the quality of local facilities was a factor that new graduates from the mining schools and other potential employees took into consideration when deciding where to apply for jobs, and companies soon found themselves competing to provide the best on offer.

Inevitably, the development of civil aviation was not without its setbacks and casualties. The dawn of the jet age accelerated growth to a significant degree. Britain led the way with the Comet, which went into service on BOAC routes in 1952, but two serious accidents, accompanied by heavy loss of life, resulted in the model being grounded in 1954. It was nearly five years before a modified version was back in public service, by which time the Americans, the French and the Russians were producing jet-powered machines for their own airlines.

There were casualties, too, among IMM members. Two of Chester Beatty's American engineers, Arthur Storke and Russell Parker, who had made outstanding contributions to the development of the African Copperbelt, decided to return to the States in the middle of the war. On his way back through London Parker spent some time at IMM headquarters and accepted an invitation from Council to act as liaison between the Institution and its members in North America. After the war, Storke was appointed president of Kennecott Copper Corporation and recruited Parker to assist him. While they waited to take up their new posts they were killed when an aircraft in which they were flying over Canada was blown up by a bomb, smuggled into the cabin before take-off. Everyone on board, including the outgoing president of Kennecott, E.T. Stannard, lost their lives. It was the first known case of mass murder in the air, planned with the object of claiming an insurance taken out on the life of one of the passengers.

*   *   *

Within a few weeks of the beginning of 1947 two events occurred that were to have heavy and widespread repercussions on the mining industry at home and abroad.

As the new year dawned, flags were hoisted at Britain's 1500 collieries, marking the first step in a massive programme of public ownership and social reform, pledged by the Labour Government when it swept to power at the end of the war. The flags were still fluttering when Westminster announced the appointment of Lord Louis Mountbatten as Viceroy of India to preside over the transfer of government to the Indian people after 163 years of British rule, and to endeavour to solve the deep-rooted differences between Moslem and Hindu by the partition of the sub-continent into two independent states.

The Victorians had boasted that the sun never set on the British Empire. Now the shadows were lengthening and people began to wonder where and when the next breakaway would occur—and what the effect would be on the industries and enterprises built up by generations of British expatriates.

Naturally, the nationalization of British coal was a matter of much deeper concern to the IME—still cohabiting with the IMM at Salisbury House—than it was to an institution concerned almost wholly with metalliferous mining, and whose members worked mostly abroad. The IME had always opposed nationalization; the IMM gave its sister institution moral support, though it was careful not to become too heavily involved as, certainly in the eyes of the public, the matter was a humanitarian one and hence highly emotive. Curiously enough, after years of struggling for better working conditions and higher pay, union leaders of the coalface workers were not overjoyed with the change. True, the hated capitalist pit-owners had been bought out, but miners were suspicious of the National Coal Board, which now not only controlled their working lives but was also the landlord of their villages.

Even the Cabinet did not appear to be over-confident. Clem Attlee, the cricket-loving Prime Minister, commented wryly that the NCB was 'going in to bat on a distinctly sticky wicket', and 'Manny' Shinwell, now Minister of Fuel, warned: 'The five-day week for miners is difficult . . . coal exports are down to vanishing point'. As he spoke, reports were coming in of massive absenteeism from the pits; a major fuel crisis loomed and in the coal fields there was more lingering resentment than rejoicing. As one miners' leader reflected: 'The New Jerusalem for British mining may still be some time coming . . .'.

Concerned that the new pattern of things should not result in any deterioration of its work, or lack of support from the industry itself, the IME busied itself with measures to protect its position and eventually came through the changes virtually intact and more determined than ever to assert its professionalism. For the IMM and the metal-mining industry generally, perhaps the most significant consequence lay in the fact that for years to come the governments of many countries, bent on nationalizing their natural resource industries, were able to point to Britain as having led the way to state ownership; moreover, supporters of nationalization were not slow to point out that the home government had for years exercised a controlling interest in British Petroleum's operations in Persia, and in more recent times in the development of North Sea oil.

In retrospect, it is surprising that a dozen or more years were to elapse after the Union Jack was hauled down in India before the winds of political and economic change began to stir in colonial territories, many of them long accepted as British 'possessions'. Suddenly, expatriate mining companies found themselves under siege from the political leaders not only of independent countries whose peoples were imbued with a new sense of nationalism, but in some cases from older established Western democracies. For a hundred years or more most mineral-rich countries had been content to see their extractive industries develop and expand according to their own disciplines; governments were more than anxious to encourage the importation of the best technology, professional skills and management, and to allow finished products to be traded in overseas markets, most of which had a complexity and sophistication that was hardly understood outside the world's capitals. Generally speaking, as long as an expatriate mining company abided by the laws of the land, paid its taxes and royalties, and made any other appropriate contribution directly or indirectly to the state—or its ministers—then everybody was happy.

The 1960s brought a dramatic change to this situation. Perhaps the best example of the revolution in ownership is to be found in the copper-mining industry, though the experience of many producers of other base metals followed a similar pattern. At the beginning of the decade copper production in which government had any sort of interest did not amount to more than 100 000 tons a year, or 2.5 per cent of capacity in the so-called 'free world'. By 1970 this total had risen to some 2.25 million tons, or about 43 per cent of capacity. More than a quarter of the world's copper was now being produced by mines that were totally state-owned, 12 per cent by companies in which government had a majority interest, and 5 per cent by companies in which the state had minority interests.

The first major change in the old pattern had come in Zaïre, the former Belgian Congo, where Sir Robert Williams had pioneered the industry half a century earlier, and it followed swiftly the tragic events that occurred after the end of colonial rule in 1960. Nationalization of the big mines owned by Union Minière du Haut Katanga was inevitable after independence, but no one imagined how long and painful the process would be, strung out against a background of insurrection, destruction and bloodshed.

Chile was next to nationalize its mineral wealth. For some time its government had controlled the sale of all minerals produced in the country through a state corporation, and had taken a majority interest in most of the smaller mines. But at the end of the decade legislation was passed to nationalize, first, the big Chuquicamata and El Salvador copper mines belonging to Anaconda, one of the two major United States groups operating in the country; and then the El Teniente mine, owned by the other American group, Kennecott Corporation.

For the next big takeover it was back to Africa in 1969 when the Zambian Government 'invited' the companies that had discovered and developed the world's most concentrated deposits of copper to sell 51 per cent of their shares to the state—the first step in what was to become total nationalization. The Copperbelt at that time was running neck and neck with Chile as the world's second biggest producer after the United States, with an annual production of three quarters of a million tons.

In Peru the position was different from that in any of the emerging African nations, whose main concern was to get rid of colonial rule. Nearly 150 years had passed since Simón Bolívar had broken Spanish power and won the Peruvians their political independence. The problem here was how to achieve *economic* independence without damaging foreign investment on which the country so heavily depended.

Peru had always been a mining country. Its gold and silver were the chief attractions for the Spaniards to invade in the sixteenth century; they conquered the Incas, seized their mineral wealth and turned their land into the most important colony in the Spanish Empire. In more recent times—since the latter part of the nineteenth century—copper, lead and zinc overshadowed precious metals in economic importance, together with considerable quantities of tungsten, iron ore, vanadium and bismuth.

After the end of the Second World War Peru struggled through a series of political crises that climaxed in 1962 when a military junta seized power. However, a succession of beribboned generals found the Presidential chair too hot for comfort and, in 1968, scandals and delays in settling the rights of foreign countries to exploit Peruvian resources—oil as well as metals—led to the overthrow of the Cabinet, and General Velasco Alvarado assumed command.

Whatever faults may be found with the manner in which the Revolutionary Government of Peru implemented its nationalistic and socialistic policies in the early 1970s, its attitude to the mining and metals industry revealed a degree of realism that had been sadly lacking in those ex-colonial territories of Africa and elsewhere which had been so concerned with winning political independence that the economic consequences of their action was overlooked. Indeed, when the euphoria of political 'freedom' began to wear off, it was often replaced with a childlike surprise when it was discovered that although international investors had been happy to put money into private enterprise owned and managed by those who knew their business, they were reluctant to finance a state-owned project controlled by people who, as yet, had little idea how a modern industry should be run.

The effect on the professional engineers and skilled artisans employed by mines that fell under state control was in many cases dramatic. In Zaïre there was a mass exodus of staff—not, it must be emphasized, simply because of nationalization but on account of the violence that accompanied the political changes that brought it about. In Chile the expatriate technicians, skilled workers and administrators—in this case mostly Americans—were not retained and their departure at one time threatened to bring the industry to a standstill.

In Zambia the transition was peaceful, but the pious hopes of the African government that expatriates would all be willing to stay until the process of 'Zambianization' of jobs was complete was not fulfilled. Standards of production, operational efficiency and safety fell to a low level, and the situation was worsened by a slump in the metal market—a near disaster for a country with a mono-economy. The mining companies' professionals began to trickle away to new jobs in more politically stable parts of the world and business became noticeably more brisk among home-based consultancies whose specialists were not required to spend too long in the countries that engaged them.

Today, more than 30 years after the nationalization of mining companies first made headline news in the world Press, the problems that it created have still not been completely resolved. Third World countries remain in a dilemma. On the one hand is their passionate desire to have full charge of their own natural resources—not only for reasons of political nationalism but because by doing so they believe they are grasping the only means available to them of bridging the gap between their poverty and the affluence of the developed world and raising the living standards of their people. On the other hand, they have become conscious of the necessity of continuing foreign investment and of the high standards of technical and managerial assistance that only professionals and members of such institutions as the IMM can provide.

To reconcile this situation would be a major contribution to the peaceful progress of the world into the twenty-first century, for it is abundantly clear that if the gap is not reduced, the community of nations will become even more dangerously fragmented into the privileged and the deprived, the self-satisfied and the frustrated, the complacent and the bitter, and the ultimate result could be disastrous for all.

*   *   *

Alive to the challenges of the post-war era after five years in which so many of its members had been diverted from their normal activities, the IMM took stock of its position and began to plan for the future.

Its first task was obviously to put its membership in healthy order. The register showed total numbers of around 2200, of whom some 650 were full members, 1150 were associates, and 400 were student members. Sixty per cent of all members lived and worked abroad—roughly the same proportion as before the war—and of these about half were employed in the larger mining fields, such as South Africa's Rand, the Kolar gold fields of India and the Copperbelt of Northern Rhodesia, the other half being scattered among smaller mines in sixty or seventy countries.

For many of its members the Institution was thus a distant and impersonal organization—a fact emphasized by Sydney Taylor, great-grandson of the pioneer John Taylor and a partner in the family firm, when he became President in 1948. 'There is', he warned, 'always a danger of the Institution tending to serve the interests of its home members more than its members abroad . . . there is little actual mining going on in this country, other than coal mining, so many of our full Members [50 per cent] are in England and more particularly in London [24 per cent].

'I hesitate to generalize but these facts are suggestive that perhaps too high a proportion of our full Members have reached retiring age. I do not wish to infer that these elder statesmen are not wanted—on the contrary, their experience and wisdom are quite invaluable. What I am suggesting is that the Institution would be enriched in every way if our roll of full Members included more mine managers abroad who are the active leaders of our profession in the field.'

Taylor then went on to stress the importance of preserving high standards of individual membership and appealed to sponsors to give the fullest possible information about candidates whom they recommended to enable Council to make a fair decision as to whether or not to admit them. This was particularly important in the changing pattern of things. As the President explained: 'Until recent years the British mining and metallurgical engineers had wide opportunities provided by British companies operating in all parts of the world. There is now a universal trend on the part of governments towards a greater measure of control of the development of their own natural resources. There is no reason to think that this trend will affect the demand for mining engineers and metallurgists but, unless I am mistaken, the British engineer will no longer be able to look to British companies for his main field of employment, but will have to compete on an equal footing with engineers of all nationalities. It therefore behoves him and his Institution to see to it that he is in the first flight of mining engineers and metallurgists. This may involve greater attention to education and upbringing, for character and culture are just as important as technical knowledge and practical experience . . .

'All this is ample justification for raising the standard of qualification for membership and for renewing our efforts to equip British mining engineers and metallurgists in the best way possible. I want to see this Institution retaining its high place and leading the profession and I want our members to be universally accepted as the best mining engineers and metallurgists throughout the world.'

It was with such objectives in mind that Council, and perhaps more especially secretary Bill Felton, had worked for twelve months or more on a revision of the Institution's by-laws to tighten up the qualifications for membership and to increase numbers both at home and abroad. The new by-laws were adopted at a special meeting just before Christmas 1948, and were hailed the following year by the incoming President, William Newman, as 'a milestone', the annual report of the Council referring to the revision as 'an important stage in the history of the Institution . . . a foundation for future growth . . . in numbers and prestige'.

After the passage of so many years this may well be seen as attaching rather more importance to the event than it deserved. Strangely, no record of the memorandum adopted at the special December 1948 meeting seems to have survived among the otherwise carefully preserved archives of the Institution, and today anyone who wishes to know the precise nature of the amendments will have his curiosity satisfied only by courtesy of the Privy Council Office, whose seal of approval is—and always has been—required for any amendments to a Royal Charter and whose filing system seems to be of an unusually high standard.

Briefly, the amendments were twofold. First, it was decreed that admission to corporate membership (full members and associates) would be by examination at the associateship stage 'unless exemption is approved by Council'. The introduction of a written examination was justified by the contention that 'an institution which lays down a clearly defined minimum standard of general and technical education, tested or confirmed when necessary by examination, enjoys a more widely recognized professional status than that of bodies which do not limit their membership'. Full-time attendance at a university or school of mines would continue to be the normal requirement for the acceptance of students, but 'for those who for special reasons have been unable to qualify for an approved degree or diploma, the Institution's examination will be available'.

The amendment appeared to be little more than the introduction of a sledgehammer to crack a nut, and if its provisions were to be taken literally—which obviously they never were—Council would have spent a great deal of time making the required 'exemptions', as the number of cases in which written examinations have been demanded is extremely small.

The second amendment made much more sense. It provided for the establishment of a new class of member, to be called 'affiliate', to fill a gap between students and associates and to meet a wish to have within the Institution a cadre of people from other engineering disciplines and sciences associated with, but not an integral part of the metals industry. As time went on the scope was widened to include a big variety of professions: doctors, lawyers, architects—even journalists and authors, provided, of course, that they were closely concerned with the natural resource industries and could be relied on to pay their dues!

The response was not very good, initially at any rate, despite some judicious lobbying at the annual dinners at which a wide cross-section of eligible applicants was available. Fewer than 100 were recruited into the new class during the next eight years—a period in which overall membership increased by 550 to 2750, the biggest gains being made by students (268) and associates (135).

*   *   *

The problem of headquarters accommodation was now high on the list of Council's priorities. With the coming of peace it was obvious that the space provided by Salisbury House was neither sufficient nor suitable for two institutions of the size and standing of the IMM and IME, and house-hunting had to start all over again.

The blitz having taken a heavy toll of the City's buildings, the task was a thankless one and, with the passage of time, the situation seemed to worsen rather than improve. It was in some desperation, therefore, that in 1950 Council bought a building in Great Winchester Street, a block or two away from Finsbury Circus, off the eastern end of London Wall. The premises were already let under various leases that were not due to expire until 1958 or later, and it was accepted that the purchase was no more than a long-stop to prevent the staff being forced into the streets in eight years' time.

The situation became even more acute in 1954 when Salisbury House passed to new owners, who made it quite clear that they were unwilling to extend the existing lease, which was due to end in September 1955. The search for new headquarters was intensified and, although no building suitable to accommodate both institutions could be found, there were several on the market that appeared satisfactory for separate occupation. For its part, the IME favoured a building in Belgravia, partly because it was near the headquarters of the National Coal Board. The IMM Council was attracted by a four-storey terraced house in one of London's more elegant avenues, linking Regent Street and the hub of West End shopping at Oxford Circus with the wide expanse of gardens and the zoo in Regent's Park.

When first inspected, No. 44 Portland Place was in a very dilapidated condition, but it was obvious that after repair and reconstruction it could provide precisely the facilities that the Institution needed: a ground-floor library with basement storage; above it, a spacious members' lounge with Adam ceiling and fireplace, and an adjoining Council room; secretarial offices on the second floor; editorial and other rooms on the third. The building was offered on a 999-year lease. Council lost no time in snapping it up, and later managed to sell the property in Great Winchester Street at a reasonable profit.

There were naturally some regrets at moving out of the City, where for more than half a century the Institution had lived in London's 'mining camp', close to the headquarters of some of the world's big mining houses, the offices of the principal consultancies, the technical and trade periodicals—and the Mining Club, which occupied the lower ground floor of London Wall Buildings and was the first call of scores of IMM members on leave from overseas.

There were also regrets at parting from the IME, with whom the Institution had lived harmoniously for 35 years. For Professor John Ritson the moment was especially poignant as he was in the unique position of having been President of both the IMM and the IME and, as he told those at the annual IMM dinner, 'I am very sorry indeed that this severance should come about during my occupancy of the chair of this Institution'.

Professor Ritson had indeed enjoyed a high place in the esteem of both institutions. A product of Uppingham and Durham University, he had earned his colliery manager's certificate before the First World War, in which he won the DSO and Bar, the MC and was four times mentioned in despatches. In 1923 he was appointed to the Chair of Mining at Leeds University and 12 years later became Professor of Mining at the RSM. In between times he also found time to play a lot of rugby and must be among the very few members of either institution to be capped for his country.

To Brigadier Ralph Stokes, who followed Ritson as President in 1955, fell the task of steering the IMM through the physical problems of the move to Portland Place. Like everything else that he did, he took the job in his stride. He also had plenty of stories to tell the newest honorary member, the Duke of Edinburgh, who sat at his right hand at the annual dinner and proposed the traditional toast of 'The Institution'. With a frankness that charmed his audience, Prince Philip confessed that he did not know much about metals but was glad to have had a good dinner in the company of those who did.

Replying, Stokes, who had weathered more changes than most in his adventurous life, drew attention to the fact that recent innovations enabled geologists to estimate 'the age of our great ore deposits with meticulous accuracy—sometimes to the nearest 30 million years'. With a quick glance round the hall, he added: 'I can't say I like this new habit. They will soon be trying to determine the ages of our senior Members of Council.'

Stokes himself was then 73. He continued to give the IMM the benefit of his vast experience for at least a dozen more years, and was still writing about controversial aspects of the 1940 Narvik campaign, in which he took a prominent part, when he died in 1979, aged 96.

CHAPTER TWELVE

In Conference

On 15 April 1947—at a time when the Royal Family were touring South Africa to an enthusiastic welcome from the country's many races—the Institution of Mining and Metallurgy held its first Sir Julius Wernher Memorial Lecture at the Royal Institution in London.

There was a popular view in London society around the turn of the century—and to some extent it persists today—that those who made huge fortunes from mining in South Africa were flamboyant characters who spent most of their time drinking champagne, gambling in shares and watching their racehorses win the world's classic events.

Swiftly, dramatically after the Boer War, the Witwatersrand became a great 'gold factory', processing its product like any other industry. With the Transvaal now part of the British Empire, the investing public saw the prospects of big profits continuing for years and they rushed to buy shares. Those who did best in the boom were those who had pioneered the larger companies, men such as J.B. Robinson, Alfred Beit, Julius Wernher, Barney and Harry Barnato, Solly Joel and Lionel Phillips. Most of them were Jews and many were of German origin. The Rand millionaires had palatial residences in Johannesburg and were big landowners in the Cape. But these were just *pieds-à-terre*. Town houses in London and estates in the English countryside and Scotland were necessary to qualify for membership of this exclusive 'club', as were yachts, grouse moors and racing stables. Robinson bought

Dudley House, one of London's historic homes, and filled its beautiful gallery with a collection of world-famous pictures. Alfred Beit had a house in Park Lane and an estate in Hertfordshire. His friend Julius Wernher—they had gone out to Kimberley together as clerks for Jules Porges and Co., diamond buyers of Paris—bought Bath House in Piccadilly and Luton Hoo in Bedfordshire, where he lived in Edwardian splendour.

Wernher's fortune was the biggest of them all. When he died in 1912 he left £11.5 million, four times as much as poor Beit, his partner in the Central Mining and Investment Corporation and Rand Mines Limited, the famous 'Corner House' group. And this was odd because Julius was a cautious, retiring man, so overshadowed by Beit that many thought that the 'Wernher' of Wernher, Beit and Company was Beit's first name and clients would arrive at the Johannesburg office asking for 'Mr Wernher Beit'. Cecil Rhodes used to say that as fast as Beit bought interests in speculative ventures in South Africa, Wernher sold them before they reached London, and perhaps that was the secret of his fortune.

Of course, there was 'wheeling and dealing' on a gigantic scale, but the Johannesburg mining millionaires were not just the carefree and amusing playboys that London society took them to be. The outstanding characteristic of most of them was their generosity: they accepted the responsibilities of their wealth as seriously as they undertook their company and public duties, and present generations should not forget the debt that is owed to the endowment of education and technical training by Rhodes and his henchmen, and at a later date by men such as Sir Abe Bailey and Sir Ernest Oppenheimer.

Of particular concern to the IMM was the lifelong interest of Julius Wernher in science and art. As has been seen, he was a member of Lord Haldane's Committee that led to the formation of Imperial College. The RSM building in South Kensington owes its existence largely to the munificence of Wernher and Beit. Wernher made handsome gifts to other educational and research bodies; he was awarded the IMM Gold Medal for his personal services to the advancement of technological education, and when he died he bequeathed the Institution £5000, to which a like sum was added by his widow, who later provided another £10 000 towards the purchase of the 'House of the Institution' in Finsbury Circus just before the First World War (Chapter Four).

Sir Julius Wernher, most wealthy of the early Rand millionaires and generous benefactor of the IMM

The IMM had long wished to honour Wernher's memory and eventually, 35 years after his death, established a series of lectures in his name with the object of bringing to public attention matters of importance to the mining industry. In selecting silicosis as the subject of the first lecture, Council recognized the high importance of the dust hazard in mining and the responsibility of the profession to take a lead in combating its effects and solving its problems.

Moreover, this was a malaise that was by no means confined to mining. As chairman Sydney Taylor told those who gathered at the Royal Institution, by focussing 'public attention on the problems of silicosis [we] hope that new recruits may be induced to join the ranks of those who are trying to combat this disease and that the team of scientists who are engaged in the struggle may be encouraged to redouble their efforts'.

Council had good reason to congratulate themselves on securing as lecturer Dr A.J. Orenstein, the leading authority on industrial hygiene in South Africa, where methods of dealing with silicosis were the most advanced in the world. It was also a happy coincidence that for more than 30 years Dr Orenstein had worked for the Corner House group and had become chief medical officer to the mining house that Sir Julius Wernher had played such a major part in creating.

The Wernher lectures have continued into modern times. They are significant not only for their practical value but because they can perhaps be seen as an early stage in the widening of the status and function of the IMM from a professional institution to one of the Commonwealth's learned societies.

*   *   *

In the world at large, post-war reconstruction and an accelerated rate of industrial expansion generally led to rapid growth in the demand for minerals—so much so that twenty years after the end of hostilities there was concern in many quarters that resources could soon become seriously limited. That this demand was largely satisfied was due not only to new and evolving technology in mining and minerals processing but to the great advances, dictated by the war, in transport, communications and materials handling, and the ever-growing use of computerization in the industry.

Moreover, the new technologies themselves generated demands for the less common elements—uranium, thorium, zirconium and beryllium—and even for hitherto unwanted impurities, such as antimony and arsenic. They also sparked an explosion in research and marketing as the commercial end of the industry sought outlets for the new products.

This growth, comparable in many ways to the Industrial Revolution that burst upon Britain, and later Europe, two centuries earlier, created a new demand for information from suppliers and users of mineral products. It also stimulated a resurgence of activity in the IMM.

From its foundation, the Institution accepted that one of its major functions was to collect and disseminate information about developments in the minerals industry to its members wherever they were to be found throughout the world. Its main vehicle had always been the *Transactions*, and later also the *Bulletin*, which, between them, carried comprehensive reports of technical and scientific papers presented to the general meetings, and of the discussions that followed. Naturally, these publications were generally confined to members, who paid for them as part of their annual subscription.

Now the number of information seekers had become much greater. The 'mini-revolution' brought a host of new specialists—electronic engineers, systems analysts, chemical engineers, applied chemists, geobotanists, microbiologists, marine biologists, environmental technologists and many others—into direct contact with the minerals industry. Some of these were already 'affiliates' of the IMM by virtue of the new class of membership introduced in 1948; to them, the Institution had a direct responsibility, and it was in the interests of everyone that the net should be cast as widely as possible.

The IMM met its new challenge in two ways. First, it increased its production of books, most of them technical, but with a widening general appeal; and, secondly, it began to step up the number and broaden the scope of conferences and symposia held under its auspices.

In the first half of the century IMM conferences were relatively rare events, triggered every seven years or so by demands for higher standards and safety codes. The 1950s showed no dramatic change as far as numbers were concerned, but two events in particular reflected a growing initiative by the Institution in sponsoring action on matters of importance to the long-term interests of the industry.

The first was in 1952 when a symposium on mineral dressing saw the birth of a series of international congresses that has grown in strength and influence over the years and is today acknowledged as the most significant in its field. The second followed two years later, a conference on research and industrial productivity providing the blueprint for the establishment of the Warren Spring Laboratory in Hertfordshire.

As the French consulting engineer Jacques Astier reminded the sixteenth Mineral Processing Congress in Stockholm in 1988, processing is necessary because ores, as they are extracted, are not suitable for use in metallurgical plants or for industrial applications. The big demand for metals in the early and middle years of the present century naturally led to an increased rate of production, which, in turn, resulted in the depletion of the richer reserves and the mining of lower grades, thus intensifying the need for development of new and improved methods of mineral concentration.

In the years following the Second World War this trend began to reach serious proportions and a group of international scientists, headed by Dr Marston Fleming, then a senior lecturer at Imperial College, put the idea of a symposium to the IMM, which readily accepted sponsorship. By 1952 the Royal School of Mines had opened new mineral processing laboratories and started Britain's first degree course in this subject, and it was thus anxious to play host to the conference. In the event the organizing committee boasted three RSM professors, the head of the Mineral Processing Department, and 10 Imperial College graduates out of a total of 13!

Not only was the symposium an outstanding success but in behind-the-scenes meetings it was agreed to hold follow-up conferences in France and Sweden. The driving force of this venture was provided by Dr Fleming, Dr E.J. Pryor, Professor P.G. Kihlstedt (Sweden), Dr J.C. Nixon (Australia), L.E. Djingheuzian (Canada), Professor Rush Spedden and Professor N. Arbiter (USA), together with the IMM's secretary Bill Felton. The project also had the backing of many past and future IMM Presidents, including Professor C.W. Dannatt, who introduced the proceedings of the first conference, Dr Joe Watson and John Denyer.

By 1973, when the tenth congress was held at Imperial College (for the third time), similar events had taken place in France (twice), Germany, Sweden, the United States, the USSR and Czechoslovakia. The tenth congress attracted more than 700 delegates, the largest contingent being from the USSR, and simultaneous translation into Russian, German, French and English made it possible for visitors from these and 40 other countries to take an active part in the proceedings. Christopher Chataway, Minister for Industrial Development, opened the proceedings and the meetings, each attended by never fewer than 450–500 people, were followed appropriately by the tenth Sir Julius Wernher Memorial Lecture. Professor Fleming, by now Head of the Department of Mining and Mineral Technology at Imperial College, chaired the organizing committee, which had begun its work three years earlier.

Since 1952 continuity of the congresses has been the responsibility of an International Scientific Committee, but the job of organization lies with the national sponsoring institution. For 40 years the meetings have been the chief international forum for scientists and engineers concerned with this important technology. Moreover, they have created friendship and mutual understanding between delegates stretching far beyond national frontiers, and publication of the proceedings has provided a continuing record of development that has proved invaluable to the industry and to those who direct its affairs.

$$* \quad * \quad *$$

Towards the end of 1954 many members of the IMM attended the conference in London on research and industrial productivity, and some took part in discussions on the various papers, including one entitled 'Mineral resources strategy' by D. A. Oliver, Director of Research of the BSA Group of Companies. Discussion had, however, to be curtailed and the IMM was subsequently asked by the Department of Scientific and Industrial Research (DSIR) to arrange a debate on Mr Oliver's paper so that Government might be fully informed of the views of its members. Thus, in the following year the IMM organized a symposium at the Royal Society of Arts at which Mr Oliver amplified his original address and five other papers were presented, including one by

Marston Fleming on a proposal for the establishment of a central ore treatment laboratory.

Nearly half the 130 or so who attended spoke in the debate or made written contributions. After examining them all, Council told the DSIR that the consensus of opinion was in favour of the provision of adequate facilities for ore testing and mineral processing, and the setting up of an advisory committee to give guidance to the Government on both short- and long-term policy on mineral development and use.

Surprisingly quickly, both these recommendations were implemented. The new laboratory was established at Stevenage in Hertfordshire, its name, Warren Spring, deriving from its location and deliberately chosen to avoid association with any particular science or engineering discipline. Quintin Hogg, newly appointed Minister of Science and Technology (which he later combined with being Minister of Sport before becoming, as Lord Hailsham, Lord High Chancellor of Great Britain), opened the building in 1959, and in his usual forthright manner made it clear that the Laboratory was an experiment in itself and if it was not successful it would be closed. Its purpose was to work in those industrial research fields not adequately covered by industry or other Government laboratories and organizations. Its management was given an almost unheard-of degree of freedom to diversify and change its research programme—but not its budget, which was at first set at around a quarter of a million pounds.

Initially, industrial process technology and control of environmental pollution were high on the Laboratory's programme. Today industrial process technology is no longer part of the work programme and the Laboratory is now the Environmental Agency for the Department of Trade and Industry. With the withdrawal of DTI support for industry funding and the switch into wholly environmental based activities, mostly for Government, it was decided to close the Minerals and Metals Division in September 1990, thus ending more than 30 years of innovative research and support for industry in the minerals and metals field. The central ore processing facilities, pyrometallurgy and hydrometallurgy pilot plants, amongst the finest in Europe, remain available for industrial contract in the meantime.

*   *   *

In view of the success of the two major conferences in the 1950s and the important developments that they promoted, it is surprising that the frequency was not increased by the next decade. By the 1970s, however, the average had gone up to more than two conferences a year, and the first of two long-running series, 'Advances in extractive metallurgy' and 'Tunnelling', had both got off to a good start.

The Institution's decision to play a more active part in the conference business was undoubtedly influenced to some extent by the consideration that not only were these meetings well patronized by members but they were also beginning to add substantially to revenue; in fact, by the end of the 1970s, conferences and publications combined were accounting for a very large part of total income.

The IMM was also spurred in its endeavours by growing competition from other sources, notably international technical and metal marketing journals, and later from certain universities. It is impossible to pinpoint precisely when the publishers got themselves into this business, but the idea was most likely to have been the brainchild of a member of the third generation of a remarkable family that for close on 80 years owned and ran the New York daily *American Metal Market*. When Archer Trench took over in the late 1930s he brought a combination of the 'Harvard touch' and the bustling enterprise of an outgoing activist to what had always been an exceptional publication. His career was interrupted by the World War II, in which he served with the US Naval Reserve, commanding British corvettes in both the Atlantic and Pacific. Patrolling in Far Eastern waters soon after the end of hostilities, his ship picked up 40 survivors from a floundering Japanese fishing junk and brought them safely to shore.

Twenty years later the Japanese Government thanked Commander Trench with the Order of the Rising Sun and, when in Tokyo to collect his award, he took the opportunity to sponsor a 'briefing breakfast' for American top-executives attending a meeting of the International Iron and Steel Institute. The venture was a great success and was repeated in Toronto and Paris. Soon afterwards Trench introduced *American Metal Market*'s well-known Forums with the object of bringing together those concerned with the production, processing and marketing of metals for free exchange of opinion and ideas. They quickly spread from coast to coast in the United States and to a number of overseas countries, eventually invading the sanctity of the London Metal Exchange annual dinner 'week', attended by upwards of 2000 of the industry's personalities, many of whom made a point of attending the Forum for as long as it was run by *American Metal Market* and its talented and attractive editor, Patricia Walker.

Meanwhile, New York's *Engineering and Mining Journal* and London's *Metal Bulletin* extended their own programmes of conferences at home and abroad to a point if not of saturation then certainly to one at which busy professional men were obliged to become very selective when examining the countless prospectuses that thumped through the letterbox. By the beginning of the present decade *Metal Bulletin* was budgeting a turnover of £1 million a year and planning two dozen conferences annually.

Traditionally for many years, the IMM confined its activities to the United Kingdom, but in the early 1970s the idea was conceived of a conference on prospecting in glacial areas and, in the belief that such a subject could be more appropriately discussed at a location where the problem was of prime importance, it was decided to seek the cooperation of associates in Norway and the first event was held there in 1973. Since then there have been similar symposia every two or three years in Finland, Scotland, Ireland and Canada.

In the 1980s the frequency of IMM-sponsored conferences rose steadily to peak in the middle of the decade when six were held in 12 months. The practice of taking conferences to countries where the problems discussed are of particular local concern has resulted in the series of 'Asian Mining' events, held so far in Singapore, Manila and Kuala Lumpur, and due in India in 1992–93; in South America there have been meetings in Chile and Mexico; and Zimbabwe has had the two 'African Mining' conferences that have taken place to date, the organizers' task being eased by the cooperation of a strong and enthusiastic local IMM section.

Until recent times most conferences have been at least three-day events with time allowed for visits to local plants, informal discussions and other social activities. Between 1978 and 1986 the Institution ran more than twenty major conferences and technical tours in as many different countries.

Today, with the increasing pressure on members' time, the

IMM is running more one-day events, which are generally cost-effective and simpler from the point of view of logistics. At the same time, the subject matter is becoming more specialized, providing a forum for people in smaller and more highly technical sectors of the industry, leaving wider issues to be debated by the four-yearly congresses of the Council of Mining and Metallurgical Institutions, the present-day successor of the old Empire Congress, which started life in Wembley Stadium in 1924.

*   *   *

For nearly twenty years after the third Empire Council congress was held in South Africa in 1930 no further events took place, initially because of the slump in global economic conditions, and later because of the advent of World War II.

However, a core organization was kept going in London and in June 1943 a meeting was held, attended among others by E.D. McDermott, a stalwart of the IMM for many years, Bill Felton, later to become honorary secretary, and Dr J.G. Lawn, representing the South African Institution of Engineers. John Allen Howe, the current IMM President, was appointed chairman of the Council. The books showed a membership of ten, comprising the Australasian, Canadian, South African and Indian institutions, together with the home-based IMM, IME, the Iron and Steel Institute, the Institute of Metals and the Institute of Petroleum.

The meeting was well timed as at long last the tide of war was starting to turn in favour of the Allies. In North Africa all organized resistance had ceased and, with the release of large numbers of escort ships and aircraft carriers, the battle against the U-boats in the Atlantic was beginning to be won. Wing Commander Guy Gibson had become a national hero overnight for leading the RAF's dam-busting raid on the Ruhr, and Prime Minister Churchill bubbled with confidence and high spirits when he delivered another historic speech to the United States Congress in Washington. As he spoke the bells of St Paul's pealed in London as King George VI led a day of national thanksgiving.

Encouraged by these momentous events, the Empire Council meeting decided to prepare for another congress in Britain as soon as possible after the end of the war. Unfortunately, three more years were to elapse before Council was able to get down to business and set its sights on 1949 for the fourth congress. By this time Allen Howe had resigned and Clive Baillieu was invited to accept the office of chairman.

It was fortunate that he did so as the future Lord Baillieu was able to bring both prestige and a flair for organization to the Council's affairs. He was then President of the Federation of British Industries, having previously represented the United Kingdom Government on a whole string of matters connected with the supply of raw materials. Moreover, the family had already a long association with the mining industry, William—Clive's father—having been awarded the IMM's Gold Medal in 1928 for his work in the development of the Empire's mineral resources, especially in lead and zinc in Australia.

Up at Oxford, Clive, who was born in Australia, won a rowing blue, studied law and was called to the Inner Temple before the Great War, in which he fought, initially, with the Imperial Australian Forces and later with the Flying Corps. It was due very largely to Clive Baillieu and his happy knack of raising considerable sums of money from some of the world's leading mining and metallurgical companies that the fourth congress was such a success, heralding a new era of international conferences.

A fifth conference was held in Australia in 1953 and a sixth in Canada four years later, but between the two it was considered expedient to drop the word 'Empire' from the Council's title, which thus became the Commonwealth Council of Mining and Metallurgical Institutions. Soon after the Canadian event Clive Baillieu asked Sir Ronald Prain, chairman and chief executive of the African-based RST Group of Companies, to succeed him as chairman. Though not then even a member of Council, it was appropriate for Sir Ronald to accept as his appointment was due to become effective immediately after the seventh congress, which was to be held in South Africa and the two Rhodesias in 1961. The congress lasted some six weeks, of which four were spent in South Africa and one each in Northern and Southern Rhodesia. It was the first of the 'big jamboree' congresses, attracting close on 1000 people; apart from a full programme of meetings and discussions, visits were arranged to some of the most interesting mining and metallurgical plants in Southern Africa; there were scores of social occasions, ranging from informal 'sundowner' parties to a grand banquet in Salisbury, which brought proceedings to a close.

Ten days after the delegates had gone home, South Africa left the Commonwealth and became an independent republic. Ronnie Prain assumed his chairman's office on the very day this was announced. It was a tricky situation; as Sir Ronald put it: 'South Africa was one of the most important members of the mining scene and we were naturally anxious to retain its institutions on the Council without having to open membership to other non-Commonwealth countries'. Delicate negotiations followed in London and Johannesburg and the matter was eventually resolved when the South Africans accepted a new class of membership that did not carry quite the same voting rights as the other participants. It was a sort of apartheid in reverse, which soon disappeared when the hue and cry died down.

In the 13 years in which Sir Ronald Prain was chairman of the Council three other congresses were held—in Australia in 1965; in London in 1969; and in Canada in 1974. During that period there was another change of name—to the Council of Commonwealth Mining and Metallurgical Institutions (CCMMI) and it is significant that at the 1969 congress there were delegates from 14 Commonwealth nations as against 20 non-Commonwealth countries, of which 13 were European. This was a very different picture from the cosy Empire 'club' that pioneered the conferences after the First World War. But, as Sir Ronald pointed out at the plenary session in London, although the right of attendance had been extended to people of any nationality or race, and subject only to professional qualifications, the objectives of the Council had remained basically unchanged for 45 years.

And, at the congress dinner, where Princess Alexandra was guest of honour, Sir Ronald, with the deftness of a magician, identified a living link with the past. Pointing to a man only a month or two short of his 85th birthday, he declared: 'I am particularly pleased to welcome one who, as Parliamentary Secretary for Mines, attended our first congress at Wembley in 1924. Ladies and gentlemen, Mr Emanuel Shinwell. . . .'

A few months later, 'Manny' became Baron Shinwell of Easington, Durham, and in 1984 he celebrated his 100th birthday in the House of Lords.

*   *   *

Sir Ronald Prain retired from the chairmanship of the Council after the Canadian congress in 1974 and was succeeded by Sir Val Duncan of RTZ, IMM Gold Medallist, who served only one year before he died, leaving the mining world to mourn one of its great leaders and most pleasant personalities. By this time the Congress had become a grand event, more important to those engaged in metalliferous operations than the World Mining Congress, which it pre-dated and which, in its early days at any rate, was primarily concerned with coal. More than 1500 people had gathered for the United Kingdom congress in 1969 and attendance at overseas congresses was running, on average, between 700 and 800.

Val Duncan's untimely death in 1975—at the opera at Covent Garden after flying home from New York—thus presented the Council with a problem, which was compounded by the death soon afterwards of Bernard Kerrigan, who for more than 20 years had looked after the Council's administrative work as well as being secretary of the IMM. Professor Marston Fleming agreed to become President and Michael Jones, IMM's publications editor, was appointed secretary of the Institution and, in accordance with tradition, assumed a similar role with the CCMMI.

It was soon apparent that the new team was not going to have an easy time. Some 15 years earlier the Mining, Geological and Metallurgical Institute of India had been invited to host a congress, but had declined as it was felt beyond its financial means. In 1974 the invitation was renewed and it was suggested to the Indians that they might like to have the 1978 congress in their country. The Institute welcomed the idea and preparations went ahead, despite some nervousness that the Indian Government might have some reservations about playing host to South African delegates, with whose government relations were becoming increasingly strained.

Matters came to a head in September 1976 when a letter from the Institute confirmed that 'the Government of India has given its consent, in principle, to the holding of the proposed eleventh congress [in India] subject to the condition that the Mining, Geological and Metallurgical Institute of India shall not invite any South African nationals, whether as nominees of the South African Geological Society or the South African IMM, or as individuals'.

Council acted quickly and decisively, informing the Indian

Institute that it could not accept such a condition and speedily made arrangements for the eleventh congress to be held in Hong Kong, at the same time noting an offer from the South African bodies to have the twelfth congress in their country in 1982. This was a bitter blow to the Indians, whose plans for a congress based on Calcutta were well advanced; but, although they had no part in the restrictions that their government sought to impose, they accepted Council's decision with understanding.

The Hong Kong congress went off without any hitch; at its conclusion Council confirmed its acceptance of the South African offer to host the next, and issued a Press notice to this effect—under a CCMMI heading. This brought a sharp reaction from the Secretary-General of the Commonwealth Secretariat, Sir Shridath ('Sony') Ramphal, who objected to the congress being held under a Commonwealth flag and declared that if it did so the Secretariat would encourage members of the Commonwealth, and more particularly the neighbouring African states, not to attend.

While Council did not like being threatened in this way, it had to concede that its title was something of a misnomer in current circumstances when the majority of countries likely to be represented at the congress were certainly not Commonwealth members. Accordingly, the organization was renamed simply the Council of Mining and Metallurgical Institutions (CMMI), as it continues to be known today. Honour was thereby satisfied and the South African congress went happily ahead.

But sensitivities over South Africa remained brittle in many parts of the world. Australia was scheduled to host the congress in 1986, the thirteenth, and it certainly proved unlucky. Feelings on racial issues between the governments of the two countries—neither of which could boast very good records in this respect—were becoming intense and the Australian Federal Government indicated quite strongly that South Africans might not be admitted.

The Australasian IMM was divided in its view: some of its members considered that it should go ahead and risk the consequences; others were more cautious. In an attempt to resolve the dilemma Michael Jones flew out to Australia for a one-day meeting. He arrived in Brisbane at 11 a.m., spent the afternoon conferring with Sir James Foots and his colleagues of the Australasian IMM, continued those discussions over dinner and left for London at nine o'clock the next morning. He wrote his report in the aircraft, regretfully recording that it would be expedient for the venue to be switched to Singapore.

Back in London Michael had one day for discussions with members of the Council and to bring participating countries up to date with the situation. Next day he went on holiday.

Today the CMMI comprises 11 institutions in various countries, including two in the United States and one in Japan. The most recent congress, the fourteenth, in Edinburgh in 1990, was undoubtedly a success but, in tune with the Scottish character, certainly more restrained than some of the grand occasions of the past.

*   *   *

The IMM's busy programme of conferences, combined with the international congresses of the CMMI and its predecessors—of which the IMM can legitimately claim to be the father—have now been an outstanding feature of the world mining scene for more than 30 years. They have also contributed substantially to the fulfilment of the Institution's declared objective to maintain an uninterrupted flow of technical knowledge to its members and thereby to the industry at large.

The regular assembly in all five continents of the world's leading figures in mining and its associated sciences, the high standard of papers and debate, and the skills with which the complicated logistics of organization have been solved to bring the delegates together have combined to produce a series of events that not only advanced awareness of the industry's developing technology but has done much to improve the public image of mining internationally. Moreover, in a world that is not yet entirely free of prejudice, the Institution has chosen its venues and arranged its programmes uninfluenced by political or racial pressures. Where difficulties have occurred it has dealt with them with dignity and understanding, its overriding consideration being to provide an unfettered exchange of views that will encourage the further development of the world's natural resources in a manner that will be of benefit to all.

CHAPTER THIRTEEN

Looking after the Shop

Because of excessive and often indiscriminate use, the word 'devotion' has become devalued in modern times and is sometimes even regarded with cynicism and suspicion. When reflecting on the records of those who have served the IMM, either voluntarily or as salaried staff, it is difficult to think other than in terms of dedicated loyalty to describe the manner in which they have discharged their duties.

It must surely be more than coincidental that, as the Institution approaches its centenary it has had but five full-time secretaries—four if one discounts the first, whose service was the shortest and whose conduct was unbecoming of his trust. One member of staff served for a record 51 years, another for 39 years. Terms of 20 years have been almost commonplace, and one lady who officially retired in 1976 stayed on 'for a short while' to familiarize her successor with the work—and at the time of writing is still there with 40 years' total service.

Of the honorary appointments, the present treasurer is only the sixth in the line, and the Benevolent Fund, which was formed in 1924, has required few volunteers to direct its affairs; in fact, it used to be said around the office that any member who wanted to live for ever should get himself onto the committee of the Benevolent Fund—or, better still, become its secretary!

After the embarrassing experience with its first salaried secretary at the end of the last century, the Institution was indeed fortunate in its second choice. It must have taken much to woo Charles McDermid from his job at the well-established Iron and Steel Institute; in fact, it has been said that he accepted the position only after insisting on an assurance from the IMM Council that its members would make good the defalcation of his predecessor. He was wise to be cautious: he was then aged 30, six months married, and keen to raise a family.

Charles himself was the youngest of a large family in Darlington in the county of Durham. His father Daniel, a Quaker, was an engineer and inventor, as well as a gifted amateur cabinet-maker. Among his inventions were a ceiling- and wall-papering machine, and a self-feathering paddle-wheel for steamers. Daniel had seen how much power was wasted by ships' paddle-wheels and his invention was based on the attachment of an endless chain of buckets which overturned and emptied the water after they had done their work. His invention was put to test when paddle tugs challenged him to a tug-of-war on the river Tees. With son Charles on board he pulled over two tugs downstream and then one upstream, but when two tugs upstream were set against him they tore the engine out of his boat and it sank. Charles and his father were both rescued, but Daniel had a stroke from which he never recovered.

Charles was educated privately, helped by an older brother who was a master at Newcastle Grammar School. He then got a job with Sir David Dale, well known in the iron and steel industry, and soon became his private secretary. When Sir David was elected President of the Iron and Steel Institute in London, he installed Charles as its assistant secretary.

In the years before World War I Charles travelled widely on IMM business, including to the United States and Canada. He also undertook the job as honorary treasurer of a fund set up to establish the Bessemer Memorial Metallurgical Laboratory at the Royal School of Mines, and persuaded Charles M. Schwab, President of Bethlehem Steel Corporation, to part with a cheque for £10 000, which gave the project a good start. Returning from a trip to Canada shortly before the war, he had a lucky escape when he missed the *Empress of Ireland*, for which he had a booking: the ship sank with heavy loss of life in a collision in fog in the St Lawrence river.

McDermid's work for the IMM during the Great War, and more especially his collaboration with the brilliant but eccentric John Norton-Griffiths in providing officer-recruits for the Tunnelling

Charles McDermid, Secretary of the IMM and its main prop for nearly 40 years. Like the Eddystone Lighthouse, he stood 'through all weathers and vicissitudes of fortune, above the ebb and flow, as a familiar and trusted symbol of integrity and a tower of strength'

Companies, has already been told (Chapter Five), as has his part in the formation and administration of the Empire Council of Mining and Metallurgical Institutions. It was also his hand that steered the IMM into closer association with the IME in the early 1920s and, as joint secretary, he held a delicate balance between the two institutions for the first half of their 32 years of cohabitation.

A multitude of other concerns, all closely related to the interests of the IMM, included membership of the governing body of Imperial College, and he was largely instrumental in bringing together the secretaries of a wide range of scientific bodies in an unofficial organization that, in a quiet way, did much to develop a second line in the administration of systematic technological research.

At the IMM, McDermid served 35 Presidents and enjoyed especially close friendship with Frank Merricks (1920–21) and Robert Palmer (1927–28). His powers of concentration were phenomenal, and he drafted long memoranda and letters very quickly. He never used a fountain pen, always an old fashioned holder with a 'J' nib; if a typed letter had a mistake, he scored it through and had it retyped, though that did not happen often as his staff knew that only the best was acceptable. In politics he was originally a Liberal, a great admirer of Gladstone and strongly in favour of Home Rule for Ireland, but after the war he left the Party, disgusted by the sale of honours by Lloyd George. Joining the Conservatives, he became chairman of the Sevenoaks Division of the Association, in which he lived not far from Chartwell, Winston Churchill's newly acquired home at Westerham.

McDermid was a very humane man. In his youth he saw misery and near-starvation in northeastern England during the long strike in the iron and steel industry. Years later he was distressed when the short-lived General Strike of 1926 collapsed and miners were forced back to work at lower wages and longer hours. He deplored the attitudes of both sides of this dispute, which caused suffering to more than one million miners and their families, but his position as joint secretary of the two mining institutions obliged him to keep his views to himself.

When Charles McDermid joined the IMM in 1900 it was in an indifferent position with fewer than 700 members. When he retired in 1939 it had achieved high professional standing, was financially sound and its members numbered over 2200. His knowledge and experience, his organizing skill and energy, coupled with patience and good temper, had provided the mainspring for the development of the Institution into a finely balanced and smooth-running organization. His departure was marked by the granting of honorary membership of both institutions and the traditional gold watch, presented by the reigning IMM President, Dr Charles Kingston. For his retirement Charles chose the seaside town of Bexhill in Sussex, where he died in 1952 at the age of 83. The family association with the IME continued with the appointment of his younger son John as secretary of that institution on his return from the war, and he remained in office until 1967.

*   *   *

When Bill Felton moved into the secretary's chair in 1939 he had been well groomed for the job by McDermid, under whom he had worked for six or seven years. It was a particularly happy choice for if the appointment had gone to an 'outsider', yet to acquire a sense of belonging and loyalty, it is difficult to imagine how the IMM would have carried on as it did through the Second World War. Blasted by German bombs, for long periods homeless and always in the firing line, it eventually emerged to grapple with the problems of peace, thanks largely to its secretary and the few headquarters staff who remained to support him.

A graduate of the London School of Economics, Felton joined the IMM staff after being personal assistant to two successive Directors of Geological Survey on the Gold Coast, Sir Arthur Kitson and Dr N.R. Junner, both of whom had been closely concerned with the discovery of diamonds in West Africa. Norman Junner, in fact, was leader of a small expedition that found gemstones while panning in the Kono district of Sierra Leone in January 1930. Their discovery passed almost unnoticed; it was not until Junner was posted to the Gold Coast a year later that a casual remark to a mining engineer sparked a major exploration that subsequently led to Sierra Leone becoming an important source of the world's diamond supply.

Both Kitson and Junner were members of the IMM and it is likely that it was through them that Felton was introduced to the staff after six years in West Africa. His term of office was perhaps the most difficult in the Institution's history, the war being followed by rapidly changing conditions in the international mining industry with which it was vital to keep abreast.

At first, the pressures did not appear to trouble him; he was relaxed and cheerful, giving, as one who worked with him has said, an impression more of a good public relations officer than of a good secretary, stamped with the traditional hallmarks of 'tireless energy and great efficiency'. In fact, bad health began quite early to take toll of his energy; he struggled against it for many months before he went into hospital in 1955—a time of great upheaval for the IMM when the offices were being moved from Salisbury House to Portland Place. Though still a sick man, Felton returned to his desk in the autumn and continued to work in spite of much physical pain and mental anxiety until a few days before his death in the following February. He was only 52.

*   *   *

Scholar, lawyer, academician, Bernard Kerrigan, who succeeded Bill Felton, was the very model of a 'proper' institutional secretary. Like McDermid, he came originally from County Durham, and was educated at Ushaw College and at Oxford, where he took honours in 'Greats'.

He began his career as a teacher in 1936 and when war broke out joined the RAF, spending a couple of years at the Marconi Company's Research Station in Essex before being commissioned in the Education Branch. When peace came he decided to study law and joined the Middle Temple, taking his final Bar examinations in 1949. Meanwhile he got himself a job with the British Committee of International Student Service, and in 1947 joined the registrar's staff of Imperial College, becoming deputy registrar three years later. Seconded to the College planning office as chief assistant to the Director of Building Works, he was responsible for much of the administration of the big expansion programme going on at the time.

On paper, therefore, Kerrigan's record matched the IMM's requirements almost exactly and he very quickly became one of the family, enthusiastically applying his experience to all its interests, particularly in promoting its membership—which almost doubled to more than 4700 during his tenure of office—and in the dissemination of its published papers and debates to the furthest corners of the earth where mining men were to be found. Like his two predecessors, he was honorary secretary of the Empire (by now Commonwealth) Council of Mining and Metallurgical Institutions and was responsible for the detailed organization of the ninth congress in London in 1969. He was also secretary of the Mineral Industry Research Organisation (MIRO).

As secretary of the IMM he was closely concerned with the founding in 1962 of the Engineering Institutions Joint Council (renamed the Council of Engineering Institutions (CEI) in 1965) and served on its board from its inception. As each President of the Institution came in turn to grapple with the complexities of the CEI, he relied on the experience and advice of Bernard Kerrigan. Indeed, this was the general pattern in Institution affairs—every President and Council member leaned heavily on Bernard's patient and understanding support.

Unlike Felton, who could be something of an extrovert, Kerrigan had no wish to occupy the centre of the stage. Rather, he was to be found modestly in the wings, watching what was going on and ready to step in when necessary with help and a friendly word. It came as a shock, not only to the IMM but to the mining industry at large, when he died suddenly in March 1975, at the age of 60. Ken Heath—an honorary fellow and Gold Medallist, who died in April 1990—was then President and recalls that on the previous day he and Kerrigan lunched with the President of the Australasian Institute of Mining and Metallurgy. 'That same evening', says Ken, 'he and his wife dined at home with some old friends. It was hard to believe the unhappy news the following day.

'All over the world there are people who may never have met Bernard Kerrigan but who will remember the kindly help and encouragement that they received from him through the post. Those who knew him best will miss him most, but the number that will mourn him is very great among the members of the profession and industry to which he gave so much.'

*   *   *

The man who served longest on the staff of the IMM—for more than half of its first 100 years—is perhaps the least remembered. His name appears only twice in the annals of the Institution: when he retired and when he died.

Herbert Rose was not the sort of man to attract attention to himself. He was a 'backroom boy' who for 51 years kept a meticulous record of the Institution's membership. He took charge of the register three years before Charles McDermid became secretary in 1900 and was designated 'chief clerk', probably in anticipation of a rapid expansion of the Institution's activities; in fact, he was the only one on the clerical side and remained so for many years to come. It is said that his memory was phenomenal and, even when membership came to be measured in thousands rather than hundreds, he could still recite the personal details of most of his charges, past and present.

His son Bill, who joined Selection Trust in the 1930s and later became senior accountant on RST's head office staff in Rhodesia, remembers his father in army uniform in 1916. When Bert decided to do his bit in the Kaiser's war he had already become involved in the comings and goings of John Norton-Griffiths and it was therefore natural that he should join the Royal Engineers and be posted to one of the Tunnelling Companies on the Western Front. He had never before been underground, but he survived the horror of the trenches and when it was all over he returned quietly to the IMM and got on with his job.

'In my early days at Selection Trust's office in Mason's Avenue my father used often to take me to lunch at the Mining Club, only a short distance along London Wall from Salisbury House', says Bill. 'I was then in the Territorials, but Dad said I wouldn't be needed, there would never be another war . . . I remember him taking me to Westerham to spend a day with Charles McDermid, and I also met McDermid's son John, but my recollections of the IMM in those days are only fragmentary. My father retired in 1948 and died at a ripe old age in 1961.'

*   *   *

Another quiet man behind the scenes was Frank Higham, who for more than 20 years combined his job as editor of *Mining Magazine*, the London creation of T.A. Rickard, with that of technical editor of the IMM, and made a major and lasting contribution to the high quality of the Institution's publications.

One of the most kindly personalities in the mining world, Frank had no early ambitions towards journalism—rather was it thrust upon him by the vicissitudes of a life in which he had more than his share of misfortunes, but for which he could well have become an outstanding figure in the field of economic geology.

He began as an articled pupil to an analytical chemist but, because of a laboratory accident that cost him the loss of an eye, he turned to geology and graduated at the Royal School of Mines in 1923. His first and only appointment as a geologist was with the Nile–Congo Divide Syndicate in the Sudan and Uganda. He had hardly got to grips with his job when he was gored by a buffalo and invalided home. During his convalescence he joined the RSM staff as a demonstrator in the Department of Geology, where he remained until his appointment to *Mining Magazine* as assistant editor in 1929, and to full editorial control ten years later.

Frank never looked on this change of direction in his career as easy—and that is probably why he made it such a success. Since the days of the 'Three Rs'—Raymond, Rothwell and Rickard—there had been something of a recession in mining journalism: the early part of the present century was not notable for those who could demonstrate a successful combination of mining and editing. Rickard himself had always been the first to admit the considerable difference between being an occasional contributor of technical articles and the complexities of editing a quality publication with a closely defined deadline.

Whilst the engineer-turned-editor was—and still is—usually the best judge of what will appeal to most of his colleagues in the industry, he is often not so well equipped to put his decisions into effect, with the result that many publications fall short of acceptable levels of writing and presentation.

Higham realized that journalism was not 'just something to be picked up'; it had to be learned in the framework of its own professional codes of practice, ethics and disciplines. Having graduated in the hard school of experience, he set about lifting *Mining Magazine* out of the mediocrity into which it had slumped after Rickard's return to the United States in the middle of World

War I. It took a dozen years or more before he felt that it had reached a level at which he could take on another job simultaneously and in 1943 he accepted an appointment as IMM's technical editor.

Traditionally, the Institution's secretary has, nominally at any rate, also been editor of its *Transactions*. Except for the early days, he has been relieved of much of this burden by a small department, today headed by Simon Dunton, and as publications have grown in numbers and frequency, the editorial staff has increased to deal with them. For several years before the Second World War, Denis Soubry was assistant editor and, when he was killed in action while serving with the RAF, his widow Gladys carried on the work. She continued for 20 years until retirement in 1964, when she was succeeded by Michael Jones, the Institution's present secretary, who had previously worked with her.

Frank Higham's contribution was of special importance to the IMM in the field of high technology. Besides editing the *Transactions*, he was chiefly concerned with the production of accounts of the proceedings of various symposia and conferences. Not only did he speak and write with authority on a wide range of technical subjects but he did so with charm and friendliness while adhering to the strict standards that he set himself and never hesitating to be firm and forthright when necessary.

He was 67 when he died in April 1966 after being in poor health for some time. He left the IMM a legacy of professional excellence in the best traditions of the founder of *Mining Magazine*, who had always been his hero.

In the year of Frank Higham's death the *Transactions*, hitherto produced in one volume, were split into three separate quarterly publications dealing with mining, geology and mineral processing and extractive metallurgy, respectively. From earliest times the handling of the manuscripts followed a well-defined pattern. After being received and logged, the papers were passed to two or more referees, selected for their familiarity with the subject being dealt with, together with a questionnaire, the answers to which indicated either a recommendation to publish, possibly after modification, or a rejection.

By dividing the subjects into the three disciplines and appointing specialist editorial boards to provide or recommend referees, the task was made easier for everyone and a wider authorship for, and readership of individual papers was ensured.

*   *   *

Second only to Herbert Rose in length of service, Regina (Ina) Oblatt has worked at IMM headquarters since 1950 and is well known to hundreds of members at home and overseas.

Ina studied medicine in Vienna, the city of her birth, and managed to get away to Britain just before the Nazis occupied Austria in 1938. She spent the early part of the war nursing, joined the Land Army at the time of Dunkirk, and later worked in the instruments department of the Royal Ordnance factory. After the war she took a secretarial job in Cheltenham and in 1950 joined the IMM at Salisbury House to assist librarian Bill Watts.

'At first I did not do much library work', recalls Ina. 'There had been a big international conference, the office was snowed under with papers and reports in several languages, so with my German, French and English, and a smattering of other languages, I spent most of my time translating.

'About this time I had to apply for British citizenship and Mr Felton, the secretary, kindly sponsored my application. A week or two later I had a visit from two MI5 officials who suggested that it would be better if I found another sponsor. I asked them why on earth I should do that, and they discreetly replied that my present sponsor was not acceptable: he had a prison record! I told them that I just couldn't believe it. How could he? He had just been awarded the MBE! They went away and returned a day or two later, full of apologies. It was a case of mistaken identity. So I got my citizenship without anyone else having to back me.'

When IMM moved its headquarters to Portland Place in 1955 completion of the library was held up because of a delay in the delivery of some special shelving. Ina waged a long campaign against the suppliers, who sought to reinforce their excuses by quoting edicts from 'our Major', the head of their firm. This annoyed Ina: 'Eventually, I had to tell them that their Major cut no ice with us, our boss (Ralph Stokes was then President) was a Brigadier and outranked him. The funny thing was that it turned out that "their Major" had, in fact, served under Brigadier Stokes in the late war. So they got together and had a good laugh. And we got our shelves.'

Ina officially retired in 1976 after being librarian for 20 years, but agreed to stay on for two or three weeks while her successor, Jennifer Edkins, settled in. It was then apparent that there was a multitude of other jobs to be done around the office, especially on the editorial side, so Ina stayed on as a member of the 'temporary staff' and in 1990 she completed a total of 40 years' service.

*   *   *

Michael Jones, who succeeded Bernard Kerrigan as secretary in 1975, had been editor of the Institution's publications for more than ten years and was previously concerned in scientific and technical editing, partly for the IMM and partly for a commercial publisher.

Born in 1938, he was at Monmouth School and the University of London, where he read Spanish and Portuguese. As well as his editorial duties he had become increasingly involved in the general organization of meetings and symposia, during which he travelled abroad and represented the Institution at several overseas conferences. His already wide knowledge of the workings of the IMM, coupled with the personal links that he established overseas, made him a natural choice for the job.

In terms of service he is, of course, still only a 'youngster', barely 30 years on the staff and only half that time as secretary! But he has already shepherded the IMM through a significant period of its history, an era in which its status as a well-run professional institution has widened to that of one of the Commonwealth's learned societies.

This development has been neither swift nor dramatic; at times it has been almost imperceptible. As has already been suggested, the Julius Wernher lectures, followed by others covering a wide range of topics and delivered by eminent specialists in their various fields, may well have given the process an early start. Other observers point to the high scholarship of many of the Institution's Presidents and members of Council over the past two or three decades, men such as Marston Fleming, Kingsley Dunham, Joe Watson, Robert MacWilliam, Gerald Mortimer, Robert Lethbridge, Denys Richardson and Alan Robinson. The movement has also been

much advanced by the development of the library and information services and by the very big increase in the number
of quality books published by the Institution over the past 15
or 20 years

But the biggest influence has undoubtedly been the sharp
increase in the frequency and scope of the national and
international conferences held during Michael Jones's tenure of
office. The enormous post-war development of air travel and other
means of communication enabled such events to become almost
commonplace, but there were still many problems to be
overcome. Hitherto IMM-sponsored conferences had normally
attracted only modest numbers: now the organizers had to think
in terms of travel and accommodation bookings for several
hundreds of delegates—and often also for wives, for whom special
programmes had to be arranged.

Up to the second half of the 1970s it had been possible to cope
with conference arrangements by inspanning members of existing
headquarters staff. 'But', says Michael Jones, 'after the eleventh
CCMMI congress in Hong Kong in 1978, it was apparent that if
we were to expand in this field we just could not go on working in
this way and it was decided to set up a small department to
handle all such arrangements.'

Today, this is one of the IMM's busiest offices. Planning for any
single conference begins about 18 months before the event and
the department handles all the complicated logistics necessary for
its success, including advertising and the production of
handbooks and guides for people attending conferences and
tours, often in parts of the world that they would otherwise never
visit.

*   *   *

The long service of IMM secretaries and others on the salaried
staff has been matched by several members who have undertaken
honorary positions, more especially the important one of looking
after the Institution's finances. All six treasurers to date have also
been President of the Institution—some before, others after their
appointment to the top office, and in two cases the jobs have been
undertaken concurrently.

In the early days the work was not too arduous as there was

seldom very much money to handle. Arthur Claudet, the first incumbent, who had been among those at the inaugural meeting in 1892, held the post for 21 years. After his father's death in 1906, he ran the family firm of assayers and metallurgists in Coleman Street in the City of London, its clients including the Bank of England and the Royal Mint. He was the IMM's twelfth President and at various times served on the Council of the Institute of Chemistry, of which he was a Fellow, the Faraday Society and a host of other scientific bodies. Two of his sons followed him into the business and both were IMM members.

*   *   *

Edgar Taylor, who took over the job when Claudet died in 1913, was the youngest of four brothers, grandsons of the pioneer John Taylor, who all became partners in the family business, much of whose work was centred on the Kolar gold fields in India. Like Claudet, he was a founder member of the Institution and for more than 40 years he was never out of office. He held a unique record as President, with two terms, each of more than the usual one year's duration, and was treasurer for more than a quarter of a century—longer than anyone else. When at last he gave up in 1939 he was awarded honorary membership, having become a Gold Medallist 17 years earlier.

*   *   *

Dr James Lawn, or 'the Professor', as he was popularly known, especially to those who studied under him, was treasurer for only a relatively short period (1939–46), but he brought to the office a wealth of experience and prestige. Before beginning his studies at the Royal School of Mines in 1888 he had already spent six years mining and surveying under the tutelage of his father, who was manager of the Barrow Haematite Steel Company. At the RSM he won both the Murchison Prize and the De La Beche Medal, and after another spell of practical work he returned to the School to become assistant to Sir Clement Le Neve Foster.

But it is for his long and intimate association with the South African gold fields that Dr Lawn will always be best remembered.

In 1896 he went out to Kimberley to organize the South African School of Mines, later to evolve into the University of Witwatersrand, and was principal for seven years, serving with the Kimberley Town Guard in the Boer War. He was lured back to England to become head of mining at Camborne, but the call of Africa was too strong and he was soon there again, first as Professor of Mining at 'Wits' and, later, as consulting engineer to Johannesburg Consolidated, for which he worked for many years.

Dr Lawn was President of the IMM in 1930, and his award of the Gold Medal came appropriately five years later when the Witwatersrand gold-mining industry was celebrating its jubilee. He went back to South Africa to enjoy his retirement and to continue to enrich those who kept in contact with him. A man of wide learning, clarity of thought and faultless memory, he had a happy knack of imparting his knowledge to others in an entertaining way. His chief hobby was botany and it was said that to accompany him on a country walk was a delight and liberal education in itself.

*   *   *

Like Dr Lawn, whom he succeeded as treasurer in 1946, Robert Annan made his name in South Africa, but years before he arrived there he had experienced the rough and tumble of the raw mining camps of the American Wild West. His father John, an English engineer, was a contemporary of such men as John Hays Hammond, T.A. Rickard and Alfred Chester Beatty—in fact, Beatty hired the young Robert soon after he graduated from Columbia University to help open up the Ray copper deposits in Arizona. Annan re-joined Beatty when he formed Selection Trust in London, but in 1930 he left for Johannesburg to be resident engineer for Consolidated Gold Fields, the company founded by Cecil Rhodes and John Rudd, becoming managing director in 1940 and chairman four years later.

As a leading figure in international mining finance, Annan's expertise was invaluable to the IMM, which accorded him every major honour it could bestow, including the Presidency in 1936–37 and a Gold Medal in 1949. He was treasurer for more than 20 years, continuing for several years after his retirement from the chairmanship of Gold Fields. Deeply interested in early mining literature, he presented his collection, probably the most valuable in private hands, to the Royal School of Mines before he died in 1981, aged 96.

*   *   *

It would be difficult to name one who contributed more to IMM affairs in its second half-century than Robert Herman MacWilliam. He was its treasurer from 1968 until his death 16 years later, but his work for the Institution knew few boundaries and, in addition to the high honours which it conferred upon him, he was one of the few to receive the OBE for his services to the industry and the Institution from the hands of the Queen.

Bob MacWilliam was a graduate of the University of Witwatersrand, the foundation of which, as has been seen, owed much to Dr Lawn, who was the IMM's third treasurer; MacWilliam was its fifth; only Robert Annan separated them on the rota.

As soon as he took his degree in mining engineering, Bob went straight to Union Corporation and stayed with the group for the whole of his career. He trained under the famous H.R. Hill and developed an early knack for laying out new gold mines on the East Rand, among them those of St Helena, of which company he was general manager until 1953, when he switched to the Corporation's headquarters in Johannesburg as consulting engineer. Four years later he was manager of the Corporation's London office, becoming chairman and managing director in 1967.

Johannesburg's loss was London's gain, and the IMM's exceedingly good fortune. First elected to Council a couple of years after his arrival in London, he gave much time and energy to the Institution's affairs. As an ex-officio member of all standing committees, his contributions were invariably of exceptional value and his advice was widely sought. In later years he paid particular attention to international conferences, serving as chairman of the organizing committee of the eleventh CCMMI congress in Hong Kong in 1978, and of an IMM-organized conference in Bangkok in 1983 that exhaustively debated the controversial subject of the role of government in mineral resources development. For his Presidential address in 1966 he reviewed in masterly manner the changing patterns of mining finance, a topic on which he had few equals.

MacWilliam gave much assistance and encouragement to the development of mining education in Britain; he was Chairman of Governors of Camborne School of Mines and worked on the mining scholarships committee of Imperial College. He was a leading figure of the Mining Association of Great Britain and of the Mineral Industry Manpower and Careers Unit. A member of the Fellowship of Engineering, he was also Middle Warden of the newly established Worshipful Company of Engineers. There seemed no end to his appointments to further the interests of the industry and he gave each his fullest attention.

Perhaps more than most holders of honorary office, he identified closely with the IMM staff. The interests and well-being of those with whom he had regular contact at Portland Place were of much concern to him, and he was always available for counsel and encouragement. He was a friendly and unpretentious man whose presence had an enlivening effect on those in his company. All who knew him were saddened by his death in April 1984 at the age of 71. His life was laced with humour, hospitality and good fellowship; he consorted freely with great men, for he was truly of their number.

*   *   *

MacWilliam having died shortly before the IMM's 1984 annual general meeting, Michael West of the *Mining Journal* took temporary charge of the Institution's finances until K.B. (Barry) Smale-Adams, the outgoing President, was appointed treasurer in July. Born in Zambia, educated in Johannesburg and at Camborne, Barry joined the Anglo American corps of graduate trainees in South Africa, becoming underground manager, first of Western Holdings and then of Free State Geduld. In 1960 he went to Malaysia, where he worked with Associated Mines (Malaysia), followed by a shorter period with Powell Duffryn as adviser to the Hellenic Industrial Development Bank in Athens. In 1967 he joined the RTZ group as executive director of Conzinc Riotinto Malaysia and Riotinto Bethlehem Indonesia, with responsibility for exploration and mining development in both countries. Five years later he was transferred to London, where he worked at RTZ headquarters for a dozen years until joining the Robertson

group of natural resource consultants. He succeeded Bob
MacWilliam as chairman of Camborne's governing body and was
awarded an OBE for that work in 1991.

From the small amounts handled by Arthur Claudet nearly a
century earlier, Barry Smale-Adams has had to deal with six
figure accounts and an investment portfolio in excess of half a
million pounds—still very small compared with his
responsibilities at RTZ and Robertson, but highly significant in
the context of IMM development.

Smale-Adams relinquished the post of treasurer in May 1991
and was succeeded by Dr Barry Scott, who presided over the
Institution's affairs for the session 1990–91.

*   *   *

When the IMM Benevolent Fund was inaugurated in 1924 it had
only £2500 in the bank, £2000 of which had come from Edward
Riley's generous legacy (Chapter Seven). In recent years the book
value of the Fund's investments has exceeded a quarter of a
million pounds, and annual contributions from an average of 300
members have been running at more than £5000, thus enabling
some substantial grants to be made.

Harry Sargent, the Fund's first honorary secretary, became a
member of the Institution in the year of its foundation and had,
in fact, retired from active mining practice when he took on the
job. Articled to C. Algernon Moreing in 1885, he accompanied his
chief on a visit to the Transvaal, liked what he saw and remained
in Africa for several years, becoming Bewick Moreing's resident
engineer at Umtali, in present-day Zimbabwe. Later, his company
moved him to New Zealand and then to Australia, where he was
working at Coolgardie and Kalgoorlie when the bearded Herbert
Hoover arrived, pretending to be much older than he was. In 1905
he joined the consultant W.R. Feldtmann and for the next six
years travelled with him to Canada, the United States and
Siberia, eventually taking a partnership in his firm.

Sargent remained secretary of the Benevolent Fund until 1945,
when Dr Sydney Smith, who had been a member of its
management committee—and chairman in 1938–39—took over
and continued to run its affairs until 1961. An eminent
metallurgist, Smith joined the staff of the Royal Mint in 1902 and

remained there until his retirement in 1938, being chief assayer for the last 12 years of his service. He was IMM President in 1932–33 and for his many public services he was awarded the CBE.

Dr Joe Watson, Smith's friend and colleague at the Royal Mint, has described him as 'a strong traditionalist who would scrutinize all innovations with a sternly critical eye, but was never reluctant to admit them on their merits'. Of his work for the Benevolent Fund, Dr Watson says: 'He coupled an encyclopaedic knowledge of the petitioners and their resources with a deep humanitarian reaction to their needs and desires . . . nothing was too much trouble for him, and he carried out this principle in his relations with all those who came his way and sought his help.'

John Bell Simpson, who had served on the committee since 1950—for five years as chairman—succeeded Sydney Smith as secretary and continued to hold the post for the next 16 years, completing his last twelve months under the chairmanship of his old comrade of the Tunnelling Companies, A.R.O. Williams. Ken Heath took over for a year or two when Simpson retired, followed by Tony Schnellmann, another Tunneller, Bob Hood, and then the present incumbent, Ted Bailey.

To date, 50 members have served the Benevolent Fund in one capacity or another, including some of the best known names in IMM's history. Edward Riley would have been well satisfied with the way they have handled the venture which was begun with his legacy and has benefited so many deserving causes.

CHAPTER FOURTEEN

Ex Libris

If you are looking for a book for bedtime, you are unlikely to find it in the library of the Institution of Mining and Metallurgy. This is no storehouse of popular literature, fiction or non-fiction; nor does it pretend to be.

· Time was when a library was a place where a lover of books browsed quietly in search of knowledge or mental refreshment. He fingered the volumes lovingly, admired the tooled leather of the binding and the presentation of illustrations before plunging into the text, savouring the carefully chosen words, attentive to the message that they conveyed.

To the modern scientific researcher or student, a well-run technical library is a gem to be treasured. To one more used to reading for the love of books it is an abattoir—a place where periodicals, treatises, monographs and reports of scientific lectures and debates are systematically scanned and dissected and the pieces stuffed into a machine that gobbles them up and stores them in its ever-expanding stomach ready to regurgitate them at the touch of a key onto a screen or a gigantic toilet roll, there to be photographed and despatched to provide an answer for someone with an eye on a Ph.D. or help in the solution of some abstruse problem.

It is a miracle of our age. Or is it? Like a ministerial Press officer, the machine tells us only what it wants us to know and expects us to believe what it says without question. Perhaps we delude ourselves as we become increasingly the servant of the computer instead of its master.

The IMM library occupies the ground floor and most of the basement of 44 Portland Place. The main collection of contemporary books and publications is at ground level. Here, literature is at once recognized as being more of a science than an art. To anyone brought up among the classics it is a strange place: there is no Chaucer or Milton, Voltaire or Molière, Homer or Pindar, Kipling or Shaw—not even a Shakespeare with whom a mining man can chat on production rates . . . *Well said, old mole, canst work i' the earth so fast?*

The books are full of statistical tables, engineering and chemical equations, and spidery graphs. They even smell differently from other books . . . the essence of the laboratory, the acrid smell that follows blasting in a stope deep underground. The odour is tinged with a whiff of cigarette smoke, which drifts in from the 'machine room' next door where a row of moon-faced computers stands grimly aloof. Here the weed is permissible for one needs to be slightly drugged to work in the presence of Big Brother.

Along the corridor towards the men's cloakroom, an occasionally convenient storeroom for publications awaiting despatch, turn right before you reach it, descend the stairs and you are in the basement. This is where the older books and records are kept—*Transactions* and transcripts not only of deliberations of the IMM but of scores of other institutions and societies, some now no longer with us; reports of long-forgotten symposia; bound volumes of scientific journals and newsletters; house magazines and other publications of mining companies all over the world, going back deep in time.

Here, the books have a different smell from those on the floor above, a musty odour of age and decay. Handle them gently lest the crisp brown pages shatter to dust. No thief will ever attempt to steal them . . . a trail of cornflakes would lead quickly to his capture.

For an ageing writer on mining affairs descent to the 24-ft level can be a sentimental journey. Or it can be a terrible shock. Now and then he may stumble upon something that he wrote 40 or more years ago, compelling him to take a peep into his own grave.

If there is a ghost in 44 Portland Place—and there are some who are convinced that there is—then this is where it must surely walk. Tier after tier of metal shelving hold the books and records in place. They move easily to the touch and you can imagine being trapped as they are pushed together by some unseen hand. At once you are in a James Bond film . . . the tiers close relentlessly inwards and you have not the ingenuity of 007 to save yourself. In the moment before you are crushed to death you hear the cackle of laughter as the villain—or the ghost—flees up the stairs.

In the secretary's office on the second floor there is another category of books. With these the non-technical visitor may feel more at home. But he will probably have no chance to find out. Mercifully, they have been untouched by the scalpel of the abstractor; they have not even been properly catalogued. There are two or three hundred of them, but they are not for the likes of the 'gentle reader'. They are secured behind locked glass doors, a museum piece that is to be looked upon and admired, but not to be touched, let alone to be read.

Who knows what the case contains? Press your nose against the glass, contort yourself to catch the reflected image, and what do you see? An Agricola of uncertain vintage, but certainly old enough to carry the woodcut illustrations of medieval mining practices that have enthralled historians for five centuries. Perhaps there are other treasures—a Sebastian Münster, or a Vanoccio Biringuccio, a Lazarus Ercher or a Sambuci? Maybe even a work of Albertus Magnus, or of Marbus, Bishop of Rennes, collector of strange rocks, which he claimed would cure blindness—and drunkenness.

But this is all conjecture. Perhaps one day there will be a catalogue and the doors of the glass prison will be flung open in a gesture reminiscent of the release of Nelson Mandela, or pulling down the Berlin Wall.

*   *   *

Someone once described the IMM library as 'the powerhouse of the Institution'. Accepting that a modern generating station, however great its output of energy, seldom reflects its strength to the casual visitor, the analogy is not entirely inappropriate. Without its library and the information services that go with it, the IMM would be a very different body from what it is today. Its status would sink to that of an exclusive West End club, its members snoozing in leather chairs behind copies of *The Times*; it would lose at a stroke the means of achieving the objectives that the founding fathers set for it a hundred years ago.

All engineers are confronted daily with far more printed material than they can digest, even if they manage to scan most of it. For them the dilemma is how to find the time to attend all the conferences and meetings at which learned papers are delivered and discussed, and how to visit operations to see the practical effects of new developments.

The IMM set itself the task of easing this problem for its members early in its history. By 1894 the nucleus of a small library or, more properly, a 'collection of books', had been established, and shortly afterwards the detailed indexing of articles from periodicals, reports, proceedings of conferences and other events was begun. Announcements of items indexed started to be published in the *Bulletin* around the turn of the century and abstracts were included from the end of World War I, more than 30 years before the first edition of *IMM Abstracts* appeared as a separate publication in 1951.

In those early days it was quite unusual for professional institutions in Britain to have such a sophisticated system; certainly, many of them possessed libraries, but most were content simply to collect literature in their respective fields and made no attempt at detailed indexing. For the IMM the difficulties of such a task were compounded by the fact that two-thirds of its members lived abroad and worked in all sectors of the minerals industry: mining companies, consultancies, universities, geological surveys, metallurgical plants, research establishments and so on. Thus, very quickly in its development the Institution assumed the role of an international information exchange and for close on a hundred years has maintained and improved upon its service.

Today the IMM library is at the centre of a complex network of information sources and has contacts with hundreds of organizations worldwide, some operating directly in the minerals industry, others involved in peripheral activities. Among its closest links are those with its 'sister' institutions, members of the CMMI and other 'unaligned' societies, few of which have comprehensive library services of their own.

While books provide valuable information, particularly for those looking for general background reading, the main source of data lies in what is known as 'serial titles', regularly produced publications on a wide variety of subjects, but principally on the Institution's core interests of mining, mineral processing, economic geology and non-ferrous extractive metallurgy.

To have to pay for all these publications would cost a fortune; they are acquired, therefore, chiefly by the exchange of IMM publications with those of other organizations. Currently, the IMM has such arrangements with 200 bodies in 50 or more countries, and its database has expanded to 400 000 cards relating to nearly 100 000 items indexed, half of which have found their way into the system since the Second World War. The publication of abstracts is complemented by a service that provides photocopies of articles in response to requests anywhere in the world: it is a well-used facility and returns a nice little profit.

There have been five full-time IMM librarians over the past sixty years: Bill Watts, whose service was interrupted by war, Lindsay Corbett, Ina Oblatt, Jennifer Edkins, and the present incumbent Mike McGarr, who has been in charge of the team since 1980.

A Scot and geology graduate of Edinburgh University, McGarr will quickly convince any visitor—even a Sassenach—that there is more to running a technical library than arranging books in neat rows on the shelves. He admits not knowing how many books he has in his care. 'The numbers are not important', he says. 'It is what we do with them that counts.'

In fact, on average, 500 books are received into the library each year, together with 1200 serial titles. Counting everything, the library probably now contains something like 50 000 volumes. By and large, professionals in the mining industry do not produce many books as such, and this is probably true of other industries. Most contributions, certainly in the non-technical field, come from those outside looking in. After all, Agricola, the greatest mining writer of all time, was a medical man, not an engineer.

Library searches to provide the sort of abstracts that are useful and durable are time-consuming and therefore costly. To keep pace with the volume and range of published information and the industry's needs of flexibility, speed and ease of access, the IMM decided in 1981 to embark on the development of a computerized bibliographical database. Such an innovation had often been

In the Library. Top,
Valerie Wicks sel-
ects index terms for
an abstract; above,
Astrid Cimals keeps
up to date with
developments in
library technology;
above right, Mike
McGarr, in charge
of the library team
since 1980; right,
Samantha Duerden
scans a journal

discussed since the 1960s, but each time it was shelved, largely because it was considered prudent to await further technological developments.

By the late 1970s it had become more and more apparent that a change was needed. The card indexes were beginning to show signs of being unable to cope with the ever-increasing volume of material. Moreover, it was questioned whether the level or use of the existing system justified the high cost of maintaining it.

Early in the planning stage it was realized that the costs involved in any computerized project would be beyond IMM's resources. Informal approaches to several mining companies for financial support met with encouraging response and four of the bigger groups agreed to share in the development costs—Selection Trust (later BP Minerals), RTZ, Charter Consolidated/Anglo American and Consolidated Gold Fields. The Department of Trade and Industry also joined the sponsors, each of which contributed £10 000 a year for three years.

The outcome was IMMAGE (Information on Mining, Metallurgy and Geological Exploration), which was born in 1984 after a gestation period in which records were keyed into its computers at the rate of 4000 a year to provide a coverage starting with publications that appeared in 1979.

In its early stages of development IMMAGE had critics who questioned the value of a database with such a limited number of retrospective years. Time has since taken the sting out of such an argument and, with the advent of the 1990s, IMMAGE had not only proved its usefulness but it was earning its keep. Its popularity among individual IMM members paying their own fees for such a service is, naturally, very small. Standard charges start at £975 for 15 hours' usage a year, and rise to £6250 for 130 hours, with discounts for a 'subscription service' The service is also available on a 'pay-as-you-go' basis at £80 per hour. Unlimited access can also be had for £8000 a year—a rate unlikely to promote much singing in the valleys.

Not surprisingly, the biggest users are to be found among mining economists working for the big companies and consultancies, many of them London-based, who need quick answers to specific questions. In 1990 a new service was introduced to provide universities (for £300 a year) and industry (at £500 a year) with records added to IMMAGE during the previous twelve months.

For those who still need to look to the years before 1979, the old card index system continues to provide good service at a price that most people can afford, and it is well to keep a balanced perspective on this matter of computerization in the information business. Barry Smale-Adams summed it up well in his Presidential address on the eve of the IMMAGE launch in 1984.

'Much has been made', he remarked, 'of the need for the "transfer of technology". What we should really be concerned with is "the transfer of appropriate technology", but here again is a dilemma: who decides what is appropriate—the transferor or the transferee? Some would consider the ability to manufacture a water wheel as useful to a potential cottage industry in a remote hill tribe area, but is that what the hill tribe wants? It may well want, or think that it wants, a nuclear power station with downstream manufacturing industry.

'Another converse but simple example: computers are being used in the West to cope with the information explosion . . . In a Third World country an expensive computer that never works because of an erratic electric current, or too high a level of humidity, or whatever, may not be appropriate. Rejected in the West because of its requirement for expensive manpower, an old-fashioned card-index might well be appropriate in a country in which, *inter alia*, manpower is cheaper.

'These are human problems that no computer or other new technologies can solve. The fundamental need is for mutual understanding, which necessitates the ability to communicate on a personal level, and for compromise where compromise can be accommodated.'

It would be well not to forget these words, for they are the very essence of good communications.

CHAPTER FIFTEEN

Storm in a Teacup—Sections at Home and Overseas

At the annual general meeting of the IMM on 25 May 1989 the President, Dr H.R. Bichan, announced that the Gold Medal of the Institution was to be awarded to the Zimbabwe local section in recognition of its long and distinguished service to the development of the minerals industry in that country and to the Institution.

It was an historic moment: the first occasion that the IMM had so honoured one of its sections, and the first time the medal had been awarded other than to an individual. That the honour was fully deserved was beyond question, not only for the value and continuity of service given for nearly 60 years but because the section's record had been attained against a background of almost continual political unrest, racial tension and economic difficulties.

Zimbabwe, or Rhodesia as it was until 1980, is one of Africa's loveliest countries, a land of plains and mountains, inhabited by warm-hearted people and with a near-perfect climate. But it has seldom been without its troubles. Tribal warfare, usually between the Ndebele in the west and the Shona in the east, had been going on for many years before the Pioneer Column, sent from Bechuanaland by Cecil Rhodes's British South Africa Company, reached the site of the future capital of Salisbury (Harare) on 12 September 1890—just two years before the formation of the IMM in London. The main objectives of the expedition were to colonize the territory and secure all mineral rights from the

Limpopo to the Zambezi in return for guarantees of protection and security to the local chiefs.

The Ndebele resented the invasion; they took up arms and were defeated only after months of bitter fighting. Their chief, Lobengula, fled and the BSA Company took control of Matabeleland. In 1896 the Ndebele rose again and the Shona, who had at first accepted the Europeans, also became rebellious and the country was not pacified until the end of the century. By this time many future members of the IMM had begun to prospect the country's rock formations, which are among the most ancient in the world, and found veins and lodes of gold, silver and many other minerals.

The BSA Company continued to administer the territory for the next quarter of a century, but the task, for which it was never suited, became increasingly difficult, and the company increasingly poorer. In 1923 it gave up the struggle, leaving the country's 35 000 Europeans to decide whether to accept an offer from South African Prime Minister General Smuts to be the Union's fifth province or to become a self-governing British colony. They chose the latter—but not by such an overwhelming majority as had been expected.

The period between the two world wars saw the development of a reasonably prosperous economy, depending largely on agriculture—maize, tobacco and cattle—and mining, which in course of time embraced more than 30 minerals, of which the most important were gold, chrome, copper, asbestos, iron ore and coal.

It was in this period that a local association was formed for IMM members in both Southern and Northern Rhodesia. The inaugural meeting was held in the Board of Executors' building in Salisbury on 11 August 1931, under the chairmanship of Mr D.V. (later Sir Digby) Burnett—he continued to hold the office until 1955, when he was over 80—and a constitution was approved. The whole process did not take more than 40 minutes.

Hardly had the association got into its stride when the country's economy was hit by global depression, and a few years later the Second World War robbed it of some of its most active members. Meanwhile, racial and economic problems intensified. Between 1953 and 1963 political federation with Northern Rhodesia and Nyasaland offered an opportunity for development and racial conciliation, based on a partnership between Black and White, but the European population as a whole had difficulty in accepting its social and economic implications. First Nyasaland and then Northern Rhodesia seceded and became independent African states. The ruling White government in Rhodesia responded by making a unilateral declaration of independence, thereby virtually isolating itself from the rest of the world except South Africa.

Black activists stepped up their struggle and 15 years of guerrilla warfare followed in which many were killed on both sides, including one of IMM's leading members, Arthur Bensusan, and his old friend of RSM days, Peter Gray, who were among 59 passengers of an Air Rhodesia Viscount shot down in a missile attack by the nationalists. The eventual outcome of the conflict was inevitable: on 18 April 1980 Britain's last African colony saw the Union Jack lowered and the flag of Zimbabwe raised as Prince Charles handed the instrument of sovereignty to the leaders of a Black majority government.

In all these years of violence and uncertainty the IMM's local association strove to 'enhance the eminence and status of the Institution by ensuring a high standard of professional conduct and integrity', applying itself to the task with a full programme of meetings, conferences, technical papers and social events, and by studying each other's production processes and operations. With such a wealth of mining projects in the country, ranging from the very small to the large, field visits have always been among the highlights of its activities. Within a few months of inauguration there was a trip to the Cam and Motor mine, during which the chairman reported a membership of 60 and Major Ewan Tulloch was elected first member of Council overseas. Other field events in the 1930s included excursions to such famous old mines as the Bushtick, the Wanderer, Globe and Phoenix, and Rezende, but, unhappily, they had to be discontinued when war broke out.

In 1950, with a greatly increased number of members working in the Copperbelt, a Northern Rhodesian local section was formed, but another 11 years were to pass before the Southern Rhodesian association attained a similar status. The reason was a delicate one, the only time that members found themselves seriously divided. To become an authorized section of the IMM required acceptance of the parent body's constitution, which laid down that all local sections should conform to the same set of rules. Those rules made no provision for a colour bar or any other form of discrimination.

While few members of the Rhodesian association had strong feelings about the admission of non-Whites or visiting delegates of different colours to their conferences, some worried about possible embarrassment, particularly on field days. It had long been the custom on such occasions for members' ladies to serve refreshments to all those present; some complained that they could hardly expect their wives to hand round cups of tea to Blacks, whether they qualified for IMM membership or not.

In today's circumstances it seems incredible that this should have been a major issue, threatening the whole relationship between the Institution in London and in Salisbury, but it did reflect the feelings of many of the Rhodesian 'settler' population at the time. For the next ten years tea-time continued to be sacrosanct for the Rhodesian Whites and it was not until A.R.O. Williams, no stranger to Africa, became President of the IMM in 1961 and had meetings in Salisbury with the local executive that a more realistic attitude prevailed. Later that year a postal vote among Rhodesian members overwhelmingly confirmed agreement of a new constitution in line with the Institution's requirements for a local section.

Gala visits to Wankie colliery marked both the 25th and 50th anniversaries and another milestone was reached with the seventh CCMMI congress in Southern Africa, when Rhodesia arranged tours and hosted 400 delegates from all parts of the world. Since then the section has been responsible with the parent body for the organization of two 'African Mining' conferences in Harare and other symposia of national and international concern. During its 60 years it has met at more than 40 different mines and increased its membership to close on 150.

The records show that fewer than a dozen IMM members attended the inaugural meeting of the Rhodesia section in 1931. Among them was a man who had already devoted 30 years of his life to mineral exploration in this part of Africa.

Frederic Philip Mennell was born on 1 January 1880 in Australia. His father, a well-known mining engineer in Victoria, sent him to England to study geology under Professor John Wesley Judd at the Royal College of Science. Judd, who was to succeed Huxley as Dean of the Royal School of Mines and Royal College of Science, recommended Mennell as first curator of the

Bulawayo Museum after Cecil Rhodes had stipulated that the job should go to a geologist so that early miners and prospectors in the territory should have competent advice in the identification of its minerals.

Mennell arrived in Bulawayo in 1901 and made it his home until he died 65 years later. He ran the museum for eight years, during which he was the first to identify several minerals that later became economically important, including diamond, chromite and chrysotile asbestos. He also represented Sir Abe Bailey's mining interests in Rhodesia.

After World War I he spent a year or two at Broken Hill in Northern Rhodesia and had much to do with putting the mine on a sound footing. He then began a series of remarkable journeys on foot, examining mineral occurrences in Tanganyika, Northern Rhodesia and Portuguese East Africa. It is thought that between 1920 and 1939 he walked about 30 000 miles, acting chiefly as consulting geologist to Inyaminga Petroleum Company in Mozambique. He also investigated iron ores in the Sabi Valley in Rhodesia and discovered the alkali ring complexes of Shawa and Dorowa that led to the production of phosphate rock for the manufacture of fertilizer. He was probably the first to suggest that platinum should be present in certain horizons of the Great Dyke; this proved to be true, but the problems of its economic recovery were not so easy to solve.

Mennell's influence on mining in Central Africa was therefore considerable, and his books, *The Rhodesian Miner's Handbook* (1908), *A Guide to Mining in Rhodesia* (1909) and *Hints on Prospecting for Gold* (1934) must have helped many prospectors to work more systematically. He became a member of the IMM in 1914 and for more than 60 years was a Fellow of the Geological Society—a record that is probably unique.

Frederic Mennell's name was surprisingly not recalled when Dr Bichan presented the Gold Medal to the Zimbabwe section in 1989. Those he did mention as having served with distinction over the years included J.C. Ferguson, A.L. Gilmour, R.B. Anderson, C.H. Chandler, Bernard Davey, Alan Marsh, Professor K.A. Viewing—the section's Honorary Fellow—T.C.A. Wadeson and the then chairman, Dr J.D.G. Groom. To those must be added many committee members and others who, as enthusiastically in modern times as in 1931, have contributed much to the well-being of both the Institution and the industry in this mineral-rich country of southern Africa.

*   *   *

With the rapid increase in production and importance of the Copperbelt mines after the Second World War it was inevitable that Northern Rhodesian members of the IMM should want a section of their own. Most of the territory's mining had become concentrated in a strip of land no more than 70 miles long fringing the border of the then Belgian Congo. Although communications with the south were fast improving, it was quicker to reach the great mines of Katanga than to drive on dirt and 'strip' roads to Southern Rhodesia.

The main post-war impetus to the prosperity of the Copperbelt derived more from an event in the world money market than from technical development, though that in itself was considerable. Throughout the war the British Ministry of Supply remained the sole buyer of Northern Rhodesian copper, dictating its own terms but, with the coming of peace, pricing reverted to the 'open market'. However, as the Government would not yet permit the reopening of the London Metal Exchange, the traditional barometer of market prices, another basis had to be found. It was eventually decided to adopt what was known as the *E&MJ* price—a quotation in American dollars published by the New York *Engineering and Mining Journal*. Although quotations began to rise internationally with the end of hostilities, there was little or no immediate prosperity for the Northern Rhodesian mines, producing as they then were at only half-capacity, and much better prices were necessary to produce anything like a fair return on investment, or in some cases even an adequate cash flow.

Then suddenly in September 1949 sterling was devalued against the dollar by no less than 44 per cent. Such a sharp fall changed the fortunes of the mining companies in a dramatic way, laying the foundations for their subsequent prosperity and compensating for 20 or more lean years. The Copperbelt was at once transformed into an economic asset that merited substantial expansion and paved the way for the development of two new mines, Chibuluma by the RST group and Bancroft (Konkola) by Anglo American. Later, Chambishi, the development of which had been shelved in favour of Mufulira, was brought into life; Mufulira itself was greatly expanded; and, in the other group, Nchanga grew to become one of the world's biggest and most profitable copper mines.

Not only did the companies enjoy the benefits of devaluation but the *E&MJ* price continued to rise, and so did the payments received from the Ministry of Supply, which was still contracted to buy the whole of the mines' output. It was not until 1953 that the Government reopened the London Metal Exchange and its quotations once again became the basis on which the companies' contracts were written.

With both production and development moving into top gear, professional expertise was in big demand: engineers, metallurgists, geologists and other highly skilled personnel flooded into Northern Rhodesia from all parts of the old Empire, more particularly from Britain and South Africa. New graduates from the mining schools and universities were especially drawn to the Copperbelt because of the experience that it offered to begin their careers in some of the world's best-run and best-equipped mines—and because the local salary structure included a built-in bonus, linked to the copper price, which showed every promise of continuing to rise. At one time during the Korean War, which gave another fillip to world demand for copper—and cobalt, which was also beginning to be produced locally—staff found that their monthly 'copper bonus' was often bigger than their basic salary.

In these circumstances the formation of a section of the IMM with headquarters in Kitwe, the 'capital' of the Copperbelt, could not have been other than a great success. A camaraderie, rivalled by few other mining 'camps' in the world, quickly sprang up among men who were not so inhibited with the problems of cohabitation with the Africans as their colleagues in Southern Rhodesia. This was undoubtedly due, in part, to the fact that they seldom became too closely identified with the country in which they worked: they were expatriates, there to enjoy the benefits of high salaries, good housing, superb sports facilities and generous holidays for as long as it suited their convenience. To the Whites in the south, with two or three generations of settlement behind them, Rhodesia was as much their country as it was the Africans': the pity of it was that there were too many who believed that it was more so.

As has been shown (Chapter Eight), the IMM Section not only provided a link between mining men in this part of Africa and 44 Portland Place but, more importantly, it formed a bridge between the two big mining groups operating there—the British-orientated RST and the South African Anglo American. On one of his early visits to the Copperbelt after becoming RST's managing director, Sir Ronald Prain had the unusual experience at a sundowner party of introducing a departmental head of one of the group's mines to his opposite number of one of the Anglo American properties. The establishment of the IMM section ensured that such a situation never arose again. The two groups, bound by the common interests of their professional staffs, worked together, played together and sat round the table to tackle the problems of the day.

The section's first chairman was H.L. Talbot, Anglo's consulting metallurgist, with A.A. (Jerry) Haynes, Mufulira's smelter super-intendent, vice-chairman. Haynes, once a leading figure in the Scouting world, was later responsible for the local arrangements for the seventh CCMMI congress in 1961. Jim Ainsworth, who arrived at Mufulira as a learner mine official in the early 1950s and was eventually to sink his not inconsiderable bulk into the general manager's chair, was the section's chairman for four years, and others who occupied the same position or who served on the committee included O.B. Bennett, Ken Mackay and Mike Stephenson on the Anglo American side, and W.A. (Bill) Garlick, Dave Young and P.J. (Taffy) Hansen in the RST camp.

Bill Garlick, then RST's consulting geologist, was one of the leading authorities on the mineralogy of southern Africa. A dedicated supporter of the syngenetic theory for the zonal arrangement of the Copperbelt's sulphide minerals, he wrote and spoke extensively on the subject. Taffy Hansen remembers in particular one talk he gave to the IMM section at the Kitwe Club. 'The evening began at 8.30, broke for refreshments at 10.30 and then continued until well after midnight. It speaks very highly of Bill's competence and his ability to hold an audience that no one walked out before he had finished.'

Though he had relatively little to do with the IMM locally during his African service, Ken Heath was concerned with both the beginning and end of the Northern Rhodesian Section. 'I was at the first annual dinner and, in fact, made the speech welcoming the guests', he recalls. 'I believe I was asked to undertake this through a misunderstanding of my importance in the Institution since I had been in the Copperbelt for only a month and nobody knew me. However, before I left London I had been nominated for election to Council, not with any hope of being voted in—I wasn't—but just to fill up the list. The only other dinner I attended was just after Zambian independence in 1964. When the chairman proposed the Loyal Toast I was just about to respond with "The Queen", but was saved embarrassment when everyone else said "President Kaunda".'

It was in Ken Heath's Presidential year (March 1975) that the section was disbanded. In retrospect it is surprising that it survived for so long. Independence was followed quickly by nationalization of the mining companies and Zambianization of the workforce. European staff saw their benefits fast diminishing and African politics became increasingly unacceptable: a big trek out of Zambia began as they sought more stable countries in which to practise their expertise. Membership of the IMM section dwindled and was eventually replaced by a division of the Engineering Institution of Zambia, which attracted little support from what remained of the old expatriates.

*   *   *

On the West Coast of Africa, IMM sections flourished in the 1950s and 1960s in Nigeria and Ghana, but, like the Rhodesias, these countries went through traumatic times after the break-up of colonialism and the atmosphere has not since been conducive to any significant revival.

Although European mining began in Nigeria in the early years of the present century, recent archaeological discoveries indicate that tin was being smelted in primitive kilns and other metals, including bronze, were produced in small quantities at least 400 years earlier. The Benin and Ife Bronze Arts date to the fifteenth century and the metal from which recovered relics were forged derives from native mining and metallurgical industries. In Eastern Nigeria, Awka people were famous smiths who forged weapons and ornaments of iron; pre-colonial mining of lead and zinc has also been established, and galena was recognized as an important ingredient for a particular cosmetic used by African women on their eyes to give them definition and character.

For four centuries Portuguese, British, Danish and Dutch entrepreneurs traded along the coastline of the great bulge of Africa for gold and slaves. But they did not venture far into the interior, for it was a land of steamy forests, malaria-ridden swamps and violent storms. Instead, they strung out fortresses along the shoreline to protect themselves from hostile tribes—and from each other—and waited for the treasures of the hinterland to be brought to them by local merchants.

Nigeria, biggest of these coastal countries and four times the size of Britain, was somewhat different from the rest, though even in 1900, when it was added to the Dependencies of the Empire, it was regarded at home with indifference and suspicion—'an unlucky pestilential spot out of which no good can ever come'.

The judgement was hasty and premature, made at a time when knowledge of the country was restricted largely to the Niger Delta, about which there were few differences of opinion: 'a land of swamps and impenetrable forests, intersected by a vast network of streams and creeks, and inhabited by numerous pagan tribes addicted to every species of vile custom, including cannibalism and human sacrifice'.

But, as explorers became bolder, they found that beyond the pagan lands, north of the confluence of the great rivers Niger and Benue, there was a marked change in both the country and the people: swampy wastes gave place to rocky hills and far extending plains, and Mohammedan influence began to show itself in the villages. As the ground rose four or five thousand feet, it opened out onto a plateau where the grass was green and the air was sweet in contrast to the oppressive humidity of the river valleys. With its equable climate and gentle vegetation, the plateau, extending for miles in all directions from the urban centre of Jos, was for the venturing Europeans a veritable paradise. What was more, it was a treasure house of minerals.

First hint that Nigeria might be a rich source of minerals reached the outside world when the British explorer, Captain Clapperton, noticed metallic tin in the market at Kano, already a town of some size and importance in the northern territory. Some 70 years later an African walked into the Royal Niger Company's trading post at Loko, on the Benue river, and offered to sell a small quantity of metal in the form of 'straw tin' which, he said, had been produced in the north.

In 1902 a party led by George Nicolaus—years later to become a key figure in Selection Trust's African explorations—found deposits of cassiterite on the banks of the Delimi river on the Jos Plateau. In the following year a second expedition arrived on the Plateau, headed by Colonel H.W. Laws, newly appointed chief engineer of the Niger Company. Both explorers reported that extensive deposits of cassiterite were being worked—and had been worked for a very long period—by Africans in the headwaters of numerous rivers and streams draining north to Lake Chad, and south to become tributaries of the Niger and Benue.

It is to these two men, Laws and Nicolaus, classmates at Camborne School of Mines and both members of the IMM, that twentieth century mining in Nigeria owes its origins. What they reported attracted much attention in the world's metal markets, though it was a few years before any of the big mining companies decided to risk capital investment. But by the outbreak of war in 1914, 120 companies were operating on the Jos Plateau. Although 500 miles from the nearest port, and communications only partly developed, production costs were relatively low, thanks to the availability and willingness of thousands of Africans to work for the White man. Even so, many of the bigger expatriate companies were soon bringing in draglines and power-driven excavators to transform primitive workings into a more sophisticated operation. By 1921 Nigeria could claim to be the fifth largest tin-producer in the world—a fact perhaps not so impressive as it might sound since it contributed no more than 5 per cent of the global total.

As in Northern Rhodesia, Britain's Ministry of Supply became the sole buyer of Nigeria's output in World War II and encouraged maximum production. In some respects this was a good thing for producers, as the Ministry met the cost of mining low-grade deposits that otherwise might never have been exploited. But 'maximum production' also meant 'picking the eyes' out of a deposit at the expense of its future life, and Nigeria was to suffer from the effects of this policy in post-war years. And, despite the introduction of mechanization by the bigger companies, ten years after the contracts with the British Government expired at least 40 per cent of ground moved in mining operations on the Jos Plateau was carried away by calabash or head-pan in much the same way as it had been for centuries.

George Nicolaus did not stay long in Nigeria: he moved on

quickly to mine for gold in South Africa and Australia and to prospect in Russia, China and South America before Chester Beatty appointed him to take charge of his group's diamond-mining operations in present-day Ghana.

Laws remained with the Niger Company as general manager until 1926, except for the war years when he served with the Tunnelling Companies of the Royal Engineers in France, Belgium and Gallipoli, collecting a DSO and CMG. In 1954 his arrival on the Plateau half a century earlier was remembered in a ceremony at Bukuru organized by the Nigerian Chamber of Mines and tribute was paid to him, not only for his pioneer work but also for his success in pacifying and uniting the indigenous tribes. He served on the IMM Council for two periods in the 1920s and died, aged 78, in Canada, where he had become a director of the Mining Association of British Columbia.

Appropriately, the 50th anniversary of Colonel Laws's arrival on the Plateau saw the foundation of the Nigerian Section of the IMM. Major J. (Jessie) West was its first chairman with Major J.L. (Jack) Farrington vice-chairman and T.W. Bennetts honorary secretary. Committee members were W. P. Gaskell, D. (Tubby) Hinton, R.H. Punnett, D.W. Watson, H.E. Wilson and David Dent-Young, whose father John, also an IMM member, began his mining career in Nigeria in 1912 and served there for 38 years. Farrington, Hinton and Bennetts all subsequently became chairmen and others who took turns in the top job over the next 15 years included W.E. Sevier, G. Griffin, Tom Penhale, G. Hawkins, A.J. Thomson, G. Strong, Frank Williams and W.S. (Steve) Baker.

Between them, Tom Penhale and David Dent-Young recall a busy programme of talks and excursions, including visits by Dr Judith Kinnaird and Dr Peter Bowden from St Andrew's University and by Dr Gloria Borley from London University; trips to the Shell installation at Bonny and an offshore drill rig; outings to some of the numerous operations of Amalgamated Tin Mines of Nigeria; and to the Nigerian Electricity Supply Corporation's hydroelectric scheme at Jekko Falls.

Meanwhile, since the end of the Second World War a number of important changes had been made in Nigeria's constitution, culminating in Federation between its various regions in 1954 and a declaration by the British Government in 1960 that it was ready to give the country its independence. Three years later

Nigeria became a republic, but in 1966 an army mutiny, led by Ibo officers, overthrew the civil government and tribal tension, ever-present on the Plateau between Ibos and the warrior Hausa, exploded into extreme violence and thousands of Ibos were slaughtered.

The troubles were compounded when the Eastern Region seceded from the Federation and set up the Biafra Republic, which was the signal for a bitter civil war.

To add to the difficulties of the European population, the Nigerian Immigration Department introduced swingeing cuts in the expatriate quota—a hard blow for the mining companies, which had recruited heavily since 1966 in an attempt to stabilize the situation. Curfews, road blocks and trigger-happy troops had a dampening effect on IMM activities, especially as most of its meetings had to be held after dark. Despite attempts by the Organization of African Unity and others to reconcile the combatants, fighting continued until January 1970 by which time Biafra, its population already starving, had reached a point of collapse. By the end of the month it ceased to exist.

And so, for the time being at any rate, did the Nigerian section of the IMM.

*   *   *

One of the most important lessons to come out of Africa over the past 30 years is that, however bitterly political and racial battles are fought, they can only end with compromise when the two sides are brought together round the negotiating table. The South Africans have learned the lesson—and so have the British, except perhaps within the boundaries of the United Kingdom, where, for some extraordinary reason, it is generally assumed that different rules must apply.

When in November 1989 the first free elections were held in Namibia, which for three-quarters of a century had lived under South African administration, a local section of the IMM had been operating for six years and several of its members had experienced at least some of the consequences of the 23-year conflict between South African forces and local guerrilla fighters and Cuban-backed Angolan troops. The last of the South African soldiers disappeared almost before the polling

booths were closed, leaving behind an enemy that had lost
virtually every battle but had won the war. The once outlawed
South West Africa People's Organization (SWAPO), led by Sam
Nujoma, captured 57.3 per cent of the popular vote in elections
that were potentially the most accident-prone phase in the
implementation of the United Nations' plan for the territory's
independence.

Bigger than Texas and four times the size of the United
Kingdom, Namibia has fewer than 1.5 million inhabitants of a
dozen different population groups. It stretches from the Angolan
border southward to the Orange river, from the Atlantic Ocean in
the west to where the Kalahari Desert straddles the border with
Botswana in the east. Geographical wonders abound and many
are unique. The Namib, with its extraordinary life-supporting
properties, is probably the oldest desert in the world and has land
formations ranging from the tallest sand dunes to spectacular
steeply eroded canyons second only to those of the American
West.

The country is rich in minerals. Spreading north from
Oranjemund are the fields of the De Beers-owned Consolidated
Diamond Mines with their wealth of gemstones. In the far north is
Tsumeb, the only known mine to contain more than 100 different
minerals. Between them, on the coast some 50 miles from
Swakopmund, is Rössing, which since 1976 has mined a huge
low-grade uranium body and contributed many millions of
pounds to RTZ's mammoth profits. Rössing in particular has
welcomed Namibian independence, removing as it does the
political obstacle of selling South African uranium in the 'free'
world market and which, on current reserves, it should easily be
able to maintain until well into the next century.

If the German Chancellor Bismarck had been aware of South
West Africa's great mineral potential he would not have been so
hesitant in giving a Bremen merchant named Lüderitz permission
to secure from a Hottentot chief a piece of land on the coast
between the mouth of the Orange river and Walvis Bay, land
which would later bear the merchant's name. The purchase
developed into German annexation of the whole territory—an act
regarded by the British in Cape Town as decidedly unfriendly.

As George Seymour proclaimed the formation of the IMM in
London in 1892, the first German farmers were on their way to
settle around Windhoek. By the outbreak of World War I the

European population had risen to nearly 15 000, attracted more by the discovery of diamonds near Lüderitz Bay than by the territory's farming potential. When war was declared South Africa sent an expedition to attack the German garrison, which surrendered in 1915; its troops were repatriated, but German civilians were allowed to remain and life continued very much as usual.

Under the Treaty of Versailles, Germany ceded its colonies to the Allies, and South Africa was mandated to administer the land as part of the Union. Until the coming of Hitler the Germans were reasonably cooperative, but in 1939 most of them were in the grip of the Nazis, and when the Second World War broke out the South Africans had once more to move in and deal with the enemy. When peace returned wrangles about trusteeship of the territory dragged on for 25 years before agreement was reached in 1972 whereby South Africa would 'assist' United Nations' efforts to resolve the issue of self-determination for Namibia—and it took another 18 years for independence to become a reality.

Between the wars the mineral potential of the country increased dramatically. In the early 1920s the German-born Ernest Oppenheimer, now a fervent British patriot, won control of extensive diamond discoveries along the coastal belt north of the Orange river, laying the foundation for later monopoly by De Beers, which he also controlled. South of Alexander Bay the desolate wastes of Namaqualand had never been properly explored. Then, in 1925, gemstones were found in gravels near Port Nolloth and prospectors began to move in from the Cape in large numbers.

Among those attracted by the new discoveries was Chester Beatty's man, George Nicolaus, who 20 years earlier had been a pioneer of the tin mines of Nigeria and later managed Selection Trust's diamond production on the Gold Coast. Outward bound from Southampton in 1926 for a visit to the copper projects in Northern Rhodesia, Nicolaus fell in with a small party of entrepreneurs who had a stake in a diamond prospect at Kleinzee, a few miles south of Port Nolloth, and were looking for technical expertise to develop the property. Nicolaus could not at that stage personally oblige, but when the ship arrived in Table Bay he cabled Beatty who immediately arranged for African-based engineers to converge on Cape Town and travel with the partners 300 miles up the coast to Kleinzee. And there they found diamonds galore!

Nicolaus, accompanied by his wife, did, in fact, look in at Kleinzee on his way home from Northern Rhodesia, by which time several hundred shallow pits had been dug along the coastline. His report makes interesting reading: 'There were so many diamonds that we hardly knew what to do with them. They were gems of great value. You would have thought Aladdin's Cave had been robbed and all the loot dumped in this desolate spot on the South Atlantic coast. The diamonds were kept in tin canisters, bottles, jam jars, wooden boxes, just anything we could lay our hands on. It was hot, and one day my wife went in for a swim. She took off her cloak on the beach and to prevent it blowing away she weighed it down—with diamonds.'

Satisfied that his engineers were on to a good thing, Beatty authorized a deal that gave Selection Trust control of the project and by 1928 claims had been pegged along more than 100 miles of the coastline. Meanwhile, in Alexander Bay the German–South African geologist Hans Merensky had discovered his famous 'oyster line'—diamonds carried to the sea by rivers rising in mountains hundreds of miles away and then washed around the mouth of the Orange river by the strong inshore current of the Atlantic.

News of the Namaqualand finds, coupled with simultaneous development of the rich diamond fields at Lichtenburg in Western Transvaal, threw the diamond moguls into panic. They knew that unregulated production and further deliveries to an already overcrowded market could end in the complete collapse of the diamond world. Ernest Oppenheimer decided that the only way to secure the orderly exploitation of all these deposits was by an amalgamation of interests. In the process Chester Beatty lost control of Kleinzee, and Oppenheimer went on to become the undisputed master of the diamond business—the 'King of Diamonds', as the newspapers called him. And Kleinzee fulfilled its early promise: more than 60 years after its discovery, it was still contributing substantially to De Beers' production.

Today, much of the romance has gone out of mining in Namibia and in the diamond fields that stretch south into Namaqualand. The huge opencast pit at Rössing is impressive, but it can hardly be expected to generate the same excitement as comes from seeing the sparkle of diamonds on the seashore, or being able to identify the 99th mineral at the old German mine of

Tsumeb, close to the game-packed Etosha National Park in the far north. Tsumeb remained desolate and flooded throughout World War II, after which it was handed over to the Custodian of Enemy Property in South Africa, who sought a buyer. It was eventually picked up by a consortium, headed by America's AMAX, for £1 million, which was quickly recovered by the sale of metal in dumps scattered around the property.

Birthplace of the IMM's local section in 1984 can be said to be Rössing Uranium, though the first moves to establish it began some twelve months earlier. The main driving force was Gordon Freeman, then the company's general manager, who saw the need for a technical and professional organization in which the various disciplines could be represented.

Because of the widely spread mining operations it has been virtually impossible to bring all members together at any one time. Sub-sections have therefore been formed in Swakopmund and Windhoek, followed by efforts to establish a third at Tsumeb. These sub-sections organize technical presentations and visits, often supported by various other bodies. Biggest attendances are usually at the annual general meeting and the annual dinner, to which some members have to travel very long distances.

The section has developed good relationship with the Engineering Council in Namibia and with the Engineering Professions Association, an umbrella body that includes engineers of almost every discipline. Although no formal arrangement exists, the IMM's local section is accepted as the voice of mining industry professionals in the country.

In an independent Namibia the acquisition of technical skills by local people is obviously a high priority of Government; the IMM section quickly recognized this and a working group was set up to identify the particular needs of the mining and mineral processing industry and to examine means of providing the necessary training. No one believes that the way ahead will be easy, but it offers a challenge that the IMM local section has not hesitated to accept.

*   *   *

The Malaysian section of the IMM was formed in 1961—a year in which John Kennedy became the youngest President of the United States, the Soviet Union put the first man into space, the Berlin Wall was built to provide an iron curtain between East and West, and a man named Nelson Mandela leapt into the headlines when he was 'not at home' to South African Police carrying out mass arrests of black activists to head off a nationwide strike.

It was a relatively peaceful year in the turbulent history of what the old atlases referred to as the Malay Peninsula. Politically, the greater part of this spur of land thrusting between the Strait of Malacca and the South China Sea had been the Federation of Malaya since Britain gave up the last of its major Asian colonies in 1957 after 170 years of rule.

Towards the end of 1960 J.H. Polglase, then the IMM's Overseas Member of Council for Malaya, was invited by President David Williams to consider the formation of a local section. The proposition was circulated to 86 members of all classes known to be living in Malaya; most of them voted in favour and in May 1961, the first annual general meeting was held at the Ipoh Club.

Hardly had the section become established when it had to change its name in line with a new national constitution after the independent Malay states joined with self-governing Singapore and the former British colonies of Sarawak and Sabah (North Borneo) to become Malaysia. The change was met with great hostility from Indonesia and disapproval from the Philippines, which had laid claim to Sabah. Singapore also found it expedient to withdraw after only two years of membership, its two million Chinese claiming that the Malay population had been given preferential treatment.

In 1966 a new Societies Act required the IMM section to apply for registration, from which it had been exempt under the old constitution. The process proved to be more complicated than at first expected and ten years were to pass before a revised set of rules, acceptable to both the Registrar and the IMM Council in London, was approved. Fortunately the section—Institiut Perlombongan dan Kajilogam, Cawangan Malaysia—did not suffer any undue frustration as a temporary permit enabled it to pursue its activities without restraint.

For the mining man Malaysia is synonymous with tin, of which it has always been among the world's biggest producers. The country owes its rich mineral endowment to the mountain range that bisects the peninsula from north to south with peaks up to

7000 feet high. The tin-bearing granites of this range are the source of deposits washed down into the valleys, principally on the western side but with one large lode and numerous small workings on the eastern flank of the mountains.

Because of its strategic position Malaya frequently found itself involved in European expansion in the Far East. When the Portuguese conquered Malacca in the sixteenth century tin was being used in local currency. One hundred and thirty years later the Dutch drove out the Portuguese and established stations to control the tin trade on the Perak river and at Kuala Selangor.

When Penang was ceded to Britain in 1786, 300 tons of tin a year were being exported from the Perak State; fifty years later output had doubled, the metal being produced mainly by Malays, but already several hundred Chinese were working in the mines. The discovery of further deposits brought the Chinese flooding in and by 1870 no fewer than 40 000 were working in Perak State alone. Quarrels between members of two powerful Chinese secret societies resulted in much bloodshed and, with a running civil war between rival Malay chiefs, the country did not offer many attractions for European settlement.

In the 1870s the world's largest single tin producer was still the United Kingdom, but with the decline of the Cornish industry the picture changed completely in the next twenty years and Southeast Asian countries became dominant, Malaya alone producing over half the global total.

The closing of the Cornish mines provided a boost to Malayan mining, not only because it removed the most powerful competitor from the world market but because it led to a flow of British capital and Cornish expertise into the Peninsula. The link between Cornish and Malayan interests was further strengthened through the Camborne School of Mines, whose graduates had increasingly to look overseas for their careers.

Several of the mines visited by the IMM section, such as Gopeng Consolidated and Tronoh Mines, with its innovative hydraulic drive dredge, had their roots in Cornwall. Gopeng was the first British company, floated with Cornish capital and know-how, to become established in Malaya in 1902 and it survives still today. Another well-known mine visited was the 500 ft deep Sungei Besi opencast, which began operations in 1906 and gained recognition by *The Guinness Book of Records* as the deepest opencast mine in the world. Twice in the 1970s visits were made to Pahang Consolidated's mine on the eastern side of the peninsula—the only underground tin mine in Southeast Asia. The company was founded in 1877 and after more than a century of operations was forced to close after the 'tin crisis' in 1985.

In 1976 Malaysia Mining Corporation (MMC) was formed following the acquisition of London Tin Corporation by the Malaysian Government-controlled Pernas Group and the injection of Charter Consolidated's Malaysian tin-mining interests—principally the Tronoh Group—into the new company. The scheme brought together 16 major mining companies, eleven in Malaysia, two in Thailand and one in both countries, together with several exploration and mining interests in Nigeria and Australia, making it the world's largest tin-producing conglomerate with gross assets of 600 million dollars. This big advance in the commercial acquisition of natural resource-based companies domiciled outside the country was presented to IMM members in a talk by Haji Mokti bin Mahmood, executive chairman of Pernas Charter Management, the mining and general management arm of MMC.

Visits to metallurgical works employing a number of IMM members have been made, including Malaysia's two tin-smelting plants: the Eastern Smelting Company, which was restructured in 1975 to form the present Datuk Keramat Smelting Berhad, and the plant belonging to the Straits Trading Company, which since 1982 has become the Malaysian Smelting Corporation. Malayawata Steel Berhad, visited in 1975, was the first integrated steel mill in Southeast Asia, incorporated in 1961 with expertise from Nippon Steel of Japan.

The section has been active in supporting the Institution's 'Asian Mining' series of conferences and played a major part in the 1988 event in Kuala Lumpur. A Malaysian tour was also arranged for those attending the eleventh CCMMI congress in Hong Kong. Members' contributions to technical papers read at conferences have not been limited to IMM events and have included international gatherings such as the World Tin Conferences and seminars organized by the Southeast Asia Tin Research and Development Centre.

To date more than 50 discussion meetings have been held by the section. Topics have ranged widely, mineral dressing and exploration being among the most popular. Representatives of both local and overseas manufacturing companies have also contributed to the programme.

The talk that attracted the biggest audience was given in 1972 by R.T. Adnan, the Buffer Stock manager of the International Tin Council, supported by the governments of 22 leading tin-producing countries. Few who attended could have foreseen the dramatic events of 1985 when what had been described as 'the only example in the field of commodity control of a successful working agreement' suddenly collapsed because of the failure of its members to fulfil their obligations, leaving astronomical debts with serious repercussions on the international tin industry that are still being felt in the 1990s.

*   *   *

'Things in Hong Kong are seldom what they at first seem', observed P.A. Roberts, of the local IMM section and its Overseas Member of Council, writing in *Minerals Industry International*, the restyled *IMM Bulletin* in 1989. They are likely to be very different again in 1997 when, under the terms of an agreement in 1985, Britain will hand over the colony to the People's Republic of China.

When IMM members meet in plush surroundings in the heart of Hong Kong's financial district it is not easy to identify any mining engineers or metallurgists among them. Since its formation in 1984 the section has consisted almost entirely of geotechnical engineers and geologists. By the end of the decade membership had climbed to more than 40 and a census of members at that time revealed interests ranging from engineering geology through rock mechanics, tunnelling, terrain evaluation, mining and drilling equipment, to placer geology, mineral exploration—and, of course, cricket.

All this is understandable in Hong Kong, where the pace of urban growth and infrastructure development has been frenetic by any standard. Ground engineering is challenging and the colony can claim perhaps the greatest concentration of geotechnical expertise anywhere in the world.

'Such are the expertise and wide experience of our members and guests that the topics presented seldom fail to stimulate and animate the audience', says Roberts. 'We have an increasing number of young local Chinese members and are looking forward to the planned arrangements for the validation of prospective members by local professional interviewers. Despite the much publicized "brain drain" in Hong Kong due to 1997 jitters, many young local professional engineers are entering the stage in their career at which they can justifiably apply for corporate membership of the IMM. We welcome them and wish them the best of luck in the world.'

Prominent in the activities of the section from its formation until his death in November 1989, was Dr Stephen Sze-Fun Hui, Honorary Fellow—a keen supporter and benefactor of the Institution since the eleventh CMMI congress was held in Hong Kong in 1978.

Roberts was the first chairman of the Hong Kong section and Peter Whiteside the second, after serving as secretary, and Jeff Hewitt is the present incumbent. Alex Carbray, treasurer and later secretary, left the colony in 1988; and Norman Woods, Paul Strange, Clive Franks and Trefor Williams have served in various capacities in this unique non-mining IMM section.

*   *   *

The success of the IMM local sections overseas encouraged the formation of similar bodies in the United Kingdom, and in the space of four years in the 1980s sections were established in the North of England (1983), the Midlands (1985) and Scotland and Ireland (1987).

The North of England section had its inaugural meeting in the Department of Mining and Mineral Engineering at Leeds University after some 50 potential members had listened to a lecture by Professor Bernard Jennings on the history of mining in the Pennines. Annual programmes have since included at least six technical and general interest lectures, which have attracted attendances of up to 120 members and guests, and one field trip. Joint meetings have also been held with, among others, the Yorkshire branch of the Institution of Geologists (now merged with the Geological Society), the Midlands branch of the IME, and the Metallurgical Society. In 1989 the section, together with its parent body, organized a conference in Leeds on mineral processing in the United Kingdom and ran a similar joint event in 1990 to discuss industrial minerals and the environment.

Annual dinners are held at Bodington Hall, which was also the venue for the IMM's annual dinner in 1988—the first time that it had been held outside London.

Since the inception of the section the posts of chairman, secretary and treasurer have been occupied by Peter Halsall, Dr P.A. Dowd and Dr A.G. Neill, respectively.

An East Midlands section, centred on Nottingham in the mid-1980s, quickly expanded to include more western counties and today, as the Midland section, it stretches from north Staffordshire to south Herefordshire, and from north Lincolnshire to south Northamptonshire. Unlike other home-based sections, membership is automatic for all IMM members living in the area, thus ensuring that more than 300 people receive details of all activities.

Up to six events take place each year—more visits than talks as the former have proved much more popular. Meetings are often joint affairs with sections of the Institution of Geologists, the IME, the Institute of Quarrying and the Younger Members Committee of the IMM. Professor Tom Atkinson, Professor Noel Warner, Dr Barry Scott and Dr W.L. (Bill) Barrett were chairmen in the 1980s; Dennis Ostle, the first secretary, was succeeded by Dr Stephen Cribb, who recently handed over that post to Dr Malcolm Brown.

The Scottish section derived from modest beginnings when a note in the *IMM Bulletin* invited prospective supporters to make themselves known to J.S. Hawkins, the hopeful convener in Glasgow. There were seven replies, spread along a thin line from Thurso in the far north to Helensburgh on the Clyde. However, a circular to all 190 IMM members in Scotland resulted in some 70 attending a meeting at Strathclyde University, hosted by Professor George Maxwell and the Department of Mining and Petroleum Engineering. The inaugural meeting confirmed the committee, adopted the constitution and listened to IMM President Gavin Moncrieff give a synopsis of his presidential address, appropriately entitled 'The Law of the Sea', and took part in a discussion on its salient points.

Levels of support were not, however, maintained and as time went on initial fears that IMM membership in Scotland was too thinly spread and its interests too diverse to sustain an organization began to recur. However, enthusiasts were hoping that the CMMI conference in Edinburgh in July 1990 might give the section a new lease of life.

The idea of a local section in Ireland was first mooted in the late 1950s, but the number of IMM members at that time was deemed to be too small. In 1961, when Professor David Williams raised the matter again, the prevailing view was that too few IMM men would be interested in an Irish branch. In the mid-1980s, however, Past-Presidents Alan Robinson and Bill Yuill took up the subject once more, Sean Finlay, Overseas Member of Council for Ireland, undertaking to assess its feasibility.

Views were sought from some 70 members (including seven in Northern Ireland)—not without some trepidation as Ireland was already well served with a number of resource industry representative groups, notably the Irish Mining and Quarrying Society (IMQS, founded in 1959) and the Irish Association of Economic Geologists (IAEG, founded in 1973). IMM members were, and still are, commonly members of these two groups. Nevertheless, a substantial majority supported the project on the understanding that its functions should in no way compete with the existing organizations but, rather, cooperate with them. It was also felt that the section should also have a strong social dimension. A preliminary meeting was held in Dublin in late 1986 and a constitution formally adopted the following spring.

Since then, the section has had two or more meetings a year and an annual field trip, some of which have been jointly organized with the IAEG. Topics covered by meetings have been gold exploration, reporting standards by resource companies, sea-water magnesia extraction by Premier Periclase, Ltd., near Drogheda, and gold extraction at the old Avoca copper mines by Connary Minerals, Ltd. Other activities have included making representations to Government and media participation on mining and environmental matters.

The section has also been active with the IAEG in proposing improved definitions for ore and reserves for Stock Exchange purposes and played a prominent part in the field visits to Ireland during the 1990 CMMI conference.

Various members in Ireland contribute to the Institution's affairs in a substantial way: John Clifford, John Ashton and Peader McArdle serve on the editorial board, while they and others, including Colin Andrew, Colin Woodham and Richard Fry, have published extensively in the *Transactions*. In 1988 Murrough V. OBrien was awarded honorary fellowship and in

1989 Conor Haughey was nominated by the local section as Ireland's representative on the World Mining Congress. Among others, Cyril Williams, Frederick Westlake, Redmond Morley, John Hamilton, Colin Burton, Ron Holman, Sean Finlay and Christian Schaffalitzky, Sean's successor as Overseas Member of Council, have been prominent in their support of the Institution.

In a few short years the Ireland section has thus become well established and continues to meet its stated objectives. Inevitably, it will increasingly be drawn into the often heated debate on possible gold-mining developments in Ireland and recognizes that a measured and fair response to the public concern in this matter is required.

CHAPTER SIXTEEN

Like Father, Like Son

I know not anything about which a man of sense ought to feel more anxious than how his son may become the very best of men.—Plato

Next to agriculture, mining is the world's largest industry, but it is by no means the oldest. Man came to it a mere eight or ten thousand years ago after countless millenniums in which he was content to make do with those materials that lay more easily to hand about him—wood, stone, bone, clay and shells. Then, whether by accident or design, he discovered how to smelt the green-stained copper-bearing rocks that he found among the hillsides and beneath the surface of the earth to produce a metal, strong but malleable enough to shape into hammers and knives, spears and arrowheads. Later, he came across iron, lead and tin, and used his new-found technology to release them from their host rocks.

In taking these first steps from the Stone Age into the Age of Metals, man set himself firmly on the road to civilization. In the process he found that gold and other precious metals and stones were not just pretty baubles: they could be traded to finance his metal-working and enable him to make more and better implements with which to cultivate the land, better weapons with which to fight his enemies and better utensils for his household. With the passing of the centuries the landscape of history changed as the world's population came to rely on metal to provide the food, shelter, energy, transport and industrial products that make life comfortable.

In *De Re Metallica* Agricola reminds us that Priam, King of Troy, had gold mines round Abydos; that the fabulous King Midas drew much of his riches from sources in Mount Bermius; that Croesus, King of Lydia, had mining properties in Asia Minor. The Athenians' silver–lead mines at Laurium were a main provider of the republic's revenue and financed the building of the fleet that vanquished the Persians at Salamis in 480 BC. Phoenicians, who founded the city state of Carthage on the North African coast in the eighth century BC, traded silver from the rich mines in Spain, later a prize of the Roman conquest. Spain also became a major source of copper for the Roman Empire, and the recent discovery of stone mining tools among the millions of tons of ancient slag at Rio Tinto has established an almost unbroken sequence of operations in the Huelva province stretching from the third millennium BC to the present day. No other working mine in the world has such a record of longevity.

As has been seen (Chapter Two), the Saxon miners of Agricola's time were a closely knit society—even more so when they worked as expatriates in a foreign land, as in Serbia—and guarded their expertise jealously, handing down their skills from father to son. The miner stood high in Agricola's esteem: 'Trained to vigilance and work by night and day, he has great powers of endurance when occasion demands, and eagerly sustains the fatigues and duties of a soldier, for he is accustomed to keep long vigils at night, to wield iron tools, to dig trenches, to drive tunnels, to make machines, and to carry burdens.'

This reputation has echoed down the centuries, shared by mining men who have worked in many lands. The Cornish miner, for example, has shown similar characteristics to his Saxon counterpart. A family man for whom mining was a way of life, he had little need to encourage his sons to follow in his footsteps, for often there were few alternatives. When the home industry finally collapsed the Cousin Jacks took their skills to America, Australia, Africa and to the furthest corners of the earth, there to establish communities with the same spirit and loyalties as those they left behind among the smokeless chimney-stacks and crumbling pump-houses of their native land.

*   *   *

It is little wonder that so many of those who have won success in the industry over the past hundred years and have occupied high position in its professional institution have sired sons who have carried on the family tradition. A considerable number have come from Cornwall, where John Taylor played such an outstanding part in laying the foundations of British mining education and transforming industrial practices into a scientific discipline.

The record of the Taylor family is unique in the history of metal mining. When the IMM was founded in 1892 the Taylors had already been mining in the Westcountry and elsewhere for nearly a century. Between 1798, when the 19 year-old John took over the Wheal Friendship copper property on the edge of Dartmoor, and his arrival in London in 1812 to set up a national headquarters for his firm, his interests had expanded to chemical manufacture and the promotion of technical societies as well as mine management. In 1815, the year in which Wellington defeated Napoleon at Waterloo, he was granted a patent for producing 'inflammable air or olefiant gas applicable to the process of giving light' from fat, bitumen or resin, and he installed a plant to illuminate Covent Garden Opera House—60 years before gas was in general use for London's street lighting.

In 1824 John Taylor formed a company to work silver mines in Mexico and was thus one of the first to direct an overseas mining enterprise from a London office. About this time there was much speculation in joint stock ventures, particularly in foreign mining, and Taylor's comment on the situation was apposite, not only to the time it was made, but for many years to come. 'Mining', he declared, 'is neither, as the public seem to think, a certain source of immeasurable wealth to be obtained by everyone lucky enough to get a share in any mine . . . nor, as now seems the fashion to designate it, is it all bubble, cheat and delusion. I maintain that British capital may be applied with fair chance of competent profit, if the means properly adapted to the end be used and steadily continued.'

In all, John Taylor had the control and management of 92 mines, at home and overseas, and was in the forefront of the rapid technical and scientific progress that underpinned the supremacy of Victorian England in the latter part of the Industrial Revolution. He played as big a part in bringing modernization to metal mining as Josiah Wedgwood, Richard Arkwright and Matthew Boulton achieved in various sectors of the manufacturing industry and as Robert Bakewell, Thomas Coke

John Taylor, 'father of British mining' and the first of five generations of
mining men. The picture is of an engraving from a portrait, since
destroyed by fire, by Sir Thomas Lawrence

and others produced in agriculture. Like most of those great figures, Taylor's most important contribution was not as an inventor but as an innovator, improver, manager and publicist, and within such fields he had no serious rival. But, as his biographer Roger Burt points out, his record was not unblemished by some errors of judgement and even monumental failures, as in Mexico, where he was caught in a fever of speculation and trapped in a situation where his reputation and the trust of his supporters depended on his continuing to pour money into a bottomless pit of disappointment.

Long before he died in 1863 his two sons, John and Richard, joined him in the business, having been sent to Germany to study the latest mining and metallurgical practices. During the next hundred years, eleven other members of the family, extending over five generations, became partners in the firm, which was not wound up until the 1960s.

For the latter part of its existence the partnership was primarily concerned with managing mines of the Kolar gold field in southern India, the first of which in 1880 were the vanguard of a great new era of gold discovery and production that began when world output was declining as the alluvial areas, particularly in California and eastern Australia, were becoming exhausted and lode mining had yet to take their place.

The development of the Kolar field was a romance of nineteenth century mining; it succeeded after so many of the original companies concerned had either been wound up or were about to pull out. It was John Taylor III, born in 1841 and an early graduate of the Royal School of Mines, who persuaded disheartened shareholders of the Mysore company to let his firm make one last effort to bring the mine into payable production. Twenty years later when he retired he was presented by grateful shareholders with a cup made of 50 oz of Mysore gold with an inscription commemorating his 'indomitable pluck in advocating, against strong opposition at the memorable meeting on October 5, 1883, the continuance of operations . . . had the mine then been abandoned the Kolar field, instead of becoming one of the world's great gold producers, would in all probability have been numbered among its failures'.

It would, of course, have been inconceivable to attempt to launch the IMM without the support of at least one member of the Taylor family. Edgar, a grandson of the first John, sixth son of the second and one of four brothers who each became partners in the firm, was out of the country when the inaugural meeting was held at Winchester House, but his letter was among the pile of correspondence that George Seymour had on the table in front of him approving the resolution that he was about to propose.

Edgar began his studies at the Royal School of Mines in 1878, but before completing his course he joined the family firm and was promptly despatched to Spain and Portugal to learn something of the practicalities of a mining engineer. Soon after he graduated he left for Canada, where the firm had a variety of interests, and over the following few years he worked in France, Italy, Costa Rica and made extensive tours in South Africa, Australia and South America before joining other members of the family in India. Perhaps his main contribution there was to obtain a concession from the Mysore Government that resulted in the construction of the Cauvery Falls hydroelectric scheme, which was to prove of enormous benefit both to the Kolar gold fields and the surrounding countryside.

When his brother Sir Robert retired in 1920 Edgar became senior partner of the firm. In the IMM he had two terms as President, each of more than the usual twelve months' duration, in 1909–11 and in the difficult war years from 1916 to 1918. He followed Arthur Claudet as honorary treasurer in 1913 and continued to handle the Institution's financial affairs for more than 25 years—a record that has not since been equalled. Most of the 'mining Taylors' were on the IMM register at some time or other, but it was not until 1948 that the family produced another President in Sydney Enfield Taylor. A great-grandson of the founder, he treated those attending the Institution's annual dinner to a brief but sparkling history of the firm, of which he had become senior partner on the death of his cousin Kenneth.

Sydney Taylor's education, begun at Rugby School, was interrupted by the First World War, in which he served in the airship section of the Royal Naval Air Service and the RAF. He never lost his interest in airships and was advising a group restudying them only a couple of years before his death at the age of 80 in 1978.

Of all the Taylors, Sydney had the longest association with the Kolar gold fields, grappling with the problems of deep mining, rockbursts, pneumoconiosis, ventilation and the environmental effects of working in high temperatures. He had a special interest in hoisting ropes which led him to propose and take a leading part in the IMM's first conference, 'Wire ropes in mines', in 1950.

Besides technical problems, the Kolar mines had to face political difficulties and Sydney was involved in long negotiations with government on taxation methods and later the transfer of the mines from British to Indian control and moving management from London to Mysore. When the mining companies were nationalized in 1956 the transition was handled smoothly and efficiently, largely due to the firm's policy of employing and training increasing numbers of Indian staff over the previous 25 years.

Elsewhere, Sydney Taylor was much concerned in the revival of mineral exploration in the United Kingdom after the Second World War and many old mining areas were investigated on behalf of the British Metal Corporation. This activity gave rise to the IMM's symposium in 1958, 'The future of non-ferrous mining in Great Britain and Ireland', and again Sydney took a prominent part in its organization and deliberations.

Sydney Taylor was a quiet, unassuming man, always interested to hear what others had to say. For this reason some may have underestimated his abilities and achievements, but once he had decided on a course of action, he carried it through by persistent and courteous persuasion. His contribution to the IMM was considerable: most of the proposals he made when he took over the Presidency in 1948 were later implemented, including raising the standards of entry, improving services for overseas members and, above all, increasing the number and maintaining the high standard of papers published in the *Transactions*.

The third and last member of this remarkable family to become President of the IMM was John Tillard Meadows Taylor, who assumed the chair in May 1980. Apart from Edgar Pam, who died in office in 1945, he is the only President who failed to complete his term: he resigned after seven months as a result of views on policy incompatible with those of the Council that had unanimously elected him.

Like Sydney Taylor before him, his education was interrupted by war—in John's case World War II, in which he served as a RNVR radio operator in the North Atlantic. After the war he resumed studies at McGill University in Canada; he joined the family firm in 1948 and became a partner four years later. When the Kolar mines were nationalized in 1956 he was a managing director of John Taylor and Sons (India) Limited, which remained technical consultants to the state-owned enterprise for the next three years.

In 1962, when the partnership came to a close, John joined the London staff of Union Corporation, where he was closely concerned with mineral exploration, mining, mine project evaluation and, later in his career, oil and gas exploration in many parts of the world.

His association with the IMM was close and continual from his days as a student to his resignation from the Presidency at the end of 1980. He published several papers in the *Transactions* and other journals, and in 1964 was awarded the Consolidated Gold Fields gold medal for his paper on research into ground control and rockbursts on the Kolar gold fields, with which the name of his company, whose mining interests spanned the world for more than 150 years, will for ever be associated.

*   *   *

Thomas Pryor came from a family famed in the annals of Cornish mining. His father, his grandfather and his great-grandfather were all well-known mining men since the closing years of the eighteenth century when John Taylor took charge of the Wheal Friendship mine on what Cornishmen regard as the 'wrong side of the Tamar' on the edge of Dartmoor.

Though Cornish through and through, Tom spent more years of his life in the Kolar gold fields than any of the Taylors. He served the consultancy there and in other parts of the world for 40 years. He was, in fact, born in India—the first European child to begin life at a Kolar property, the mine to which he was to devote so much of his career.

Another 'first' of which he was always proud was that when he became President of the IMM in 1940 it was the first time that a student of the old Redruth school, forerunner of Camborne School of Mines, had been so honoured. What is more, George Laycock, who proposed the vote of thanks to him for his Presidential address, had been a class-mate of his at Redruth and was thus able to testify to his achievements there. 'He captured', said George, 'almost every medal and prize there was to be won, including several of the highest awards, in examinations open to the whole of Great Britain. . . . It was obvious even in those early days, that he was bound to rise to the top of his profession, and the Institution could feel flattered that it had such a worthy representative of the mining engineering profession to preside over it during the coming session.'

Members were suitably impressed by this eulogy. They would probably also have been surprised to know that it was only the second time in 48 years that anyone who graduated from any Cornish mining school had become President of the Institution, though Council would, of course, have been quick to deny any 'upstairs, downstairs' attitude in its choice of leaders. Both Tom Pryor and H.M. Morgans, who seconded the vote of thanks, were then governors of Camborne, which had yet to capture the same universal prestige as the RSM.

As if to redress the balance, Thomas's son Robert was not only a graduate of the RSM but, after 20 years of practical mining, he was in 1968 appointed Professor of Mining at the school, later becoming Head of the Department of Mineral Resources Engineering at Imperial College.

Born in 1921, Bob saw war service with the Chindits in India and Burma before he entered the RSM, from which he emerged with first-class honours. In 1948 he joined the Rio Tinto company, working first in Spain and then as consultant in the RTZ London office. Returning to Spain in 1966, he was general manager of the Rio Tinto Patiño project in Huelva, taking up his RSM chair two years later.

Maurice Cahalan, a close friend, says that Bob, though doubtless inspired by his father's example, never sought patronage because of it. 'He showed firmness and resolution in all he undertook, coupled with compassion and encouragement for those less endowed with industry or the blessings of nature. I soon came to appreciate these attributes after first meeting him at Rio Tinto in 1952.

'He left an indelible mark on the Rio Tinto mines and indeed on operations in the pyrites belt of Andalusia. For some 20 years he was the ultimate authority on the problems of underground mining there and his involvement in open-pit operations was unique—from operations in Corta Atalaya. with steam shovels once used in the construction of the Panama Canal, to the design of the new pit at Aznalcóllar.

'His second period of residence at Rio Tinto was especially productive. In the immediate post-war period low profitability and limited foreign exchange greatly restricted capital investment and hampered innovation. He supervised the Cerro Colorado project and derived particular satisfaction from the later success of the gossans gold plant as an early generator of revenue.

'Robert had something of the great Victorian engineers in his approach. He was conservative in that he never offered speculative solutions to well-defined, immediate problems—he was progressive in seeking means of testing new ideas and developing new techniques. And, like the Victorians, he had the broad vision of the civil engineer, having early in his career obtained additional professional qualification through the Institution of Civil Engineers.

'Part of the great success he achieved at Imperial College can be put down to the unqualified respect he enjoyed. No one doubted that his students would get a proper introduction to the nature and problems of the industry they were being prepared to enter. And his students could have been in no doubt about the authority underlying his teaching.

'In the IMM his main concern over many years was the Council of Engineering Institutions, and he was the Institution's representative on the Executive Committee of that body. He was deeply concerned about closer links with other organizations covering earth resources science and engineering, particularly the Institution of Mining Engineers, of which he was a Fellow.'

The full range of Bob Pryor's technical, intellectual and organizational abilities became evident to a wider audience during his term as President of the IMM. His Presidential address in 1978 raised questions on national mineral policy in clear, objective, compelling terms and thus aroused interest in all quarters, in professions, government and industry. His death, following an open-heart operation only a few weeks after completing his term of office, came as a shock to his friends and deprived the industry of his further participation in the great debate that he had stimulated.

Brought up in Rio Tinto, it was natural for Bob's son Bernard to follow the family tradition when the time came for him to choose a career. Not only could his father trace ancestry to the early days of Cornish mining but his mother also came from a mining family, her father being a graduate of the Otago School of

Mines in New Zealand.

Bernard studied metallurgical engineering at the RSM and during holidays worked at Mount Isa in Queensland, Australia. After graduating he had a year or two with Randfontein Estates in South Africa and, following a short spell with a London-based company, returned to Australia, eventually becoming commercial manager of an engineering and project management consultancy with some 600 employees worldwide.

As well as keeping in touch with IMM affairs, Bernard is a member of both the Australasian and South African IMM. As President of the IMM, Bob Pryor signed his son's membership certificate in 1978—just as his father had signed his when he occupied the chair nearly 40 years earlier.

*   *   *

There is no record in the archives of a father and son both having been founder members of the IMM, though the McDermotts came very near to achieving such a distinction.

When Walter McDermott, who had been at the inaugural meeting at Winchester House, was serving as the Institution's sixth President in 1899, his son Edward Duffield McDermott was admitted to student membership. Forty-one years later Edward followed his father into the chair—to be succeeded, incidentally, by Thomas Pryor—by which time his son, Edward Keith, an RSM graduate, was making a mining career in southern Africa. Between the three of them, the McDermotts' membership of the IMM has so far totalled more than 170 years.

Walter McDermott, son of a London journalist, was one of the leading figures in metallurgical engineering for a period of 70 years spanning two centuries. Born in 1851, the year of the Great Exhibition in Paxton's Crystal Palace, he was barely 20 when he got himself his first job as an analytical chemist at the Glaisdale Iron Works in Yorkshire. He obviously learned a lot in a very short time for in the following year he sailed for North America to join the romantically named Silver Islet mine on Lake Superior, there to take charge of the concentrating plant as well as doing some surveying and prospecting in his spare time.

While at Silver Islet he was associated with a 'Captain'

(obviously in the mining sense, for he was a Cornishman) Frue in the invention and development of what became known as the Frue Vanner machine for gravity separation of finely ground ore—a process that quickly gained worldwide reputation. (According to his grandson, Walter's special contribution to the invention was 'the sideways shake that ensured that the wash water did not cause channels in the pulp on the endless belt'.)

He returned to Europe after about five years to make a grand tour of concentration methods in Cornwall, Germany, Austria and Italy, and took his accumulated knowledge back to America, incorporating it in the design of numerous plants that he built for companies throughout the United States. He also reported on many gold, silver and copper projects in the mining States, in Mexico and Newfoundland.

By 1890, his reputation firmly established internationally, McDermott felt it time to return home and set up a consultancy but, before he left, the partners of a firm called Fraser and Chalmers, which had been making mining and other machinery since the middle of the century, approached him with a proposition to establish their company in England. McDermott opened offices at Bucklersbury and laid down works at Erith, near deposits of fine moulding sand for which the district was famous. As managing director, he was the leading spirit in the firm's activities and expansion until 1912 when it was bought by the General Electric Company.

Meanwhile, Walter collected some important directorships, including the chairmanship of Consolidated Mines Selection, which contributed valuable gold rights on South Africa's East Rand to the Anglo American Corporation when it was formed by Ernest Oppenheimer. His consultancy flourished, his advice on both metallurgical and mining problems being highly valued because of his long experience in many parts of the world.

Apart from his early Presidency of the IMM, he represented the Institution for many years on the Board of Governors of Imperial College, in the establishment of which he played a prominent part. He was also much concerned in the equipping of the Bessemer Laboratory at the RSM, and it was on his recommendation in conjunction with Professors Gowland and Cox that the freehold of the Tywarnhale mine in Cornwall was bought to facilitate training in mine surveying.

For his services in these and many other matters, Walter was awarded the Gold Medal of the Institution in 1911 and, just before his death at the age of 88, and during the Presidency of his son, he was made an honorary member. As one of the few, probably the only Englishman, to have been a member of the American Institute of Mining Engineers as early as 1874, he also joined those enrolled in its Legion of Honor.

Outside of mining he found time to pursue a variety of interests, not the least in the political implications of the growth of the Trade Union movement. At his own expense he produced pamphlets running into hundreds of thousands of copies, showing how political 'labour' was weakening the progress of the nation despite the loyalty of the vast number of working men. His work in this connection brought him into contact with the Duke of Northumberland, with whom in 1922 he founded *The Patriot*, a punchy crusading journal, applying to it the inherited flair of his father, and was honorary editor until his death.

To follow such a father was not easy, particularly as the paths that each of them trod were closely related. Edward, or Duffield as he was more generally known in the family, took an early opportunity after graduating at the RSM to gain experience in North America. In 1907 he returned to Europe to become manager of the Estrella copper mine in Spain and three years later he was in Russia, working for Russo–Asiatic. Then with the coming of peace he was out in India managing the Rakha copper mines.

There followed a hectic trail that took in South America, Rhodesia, Burma, Siam and Australia until 1928 when he came to comparative rest in London. There he joined The Mining Trust as consulting engineer and remained with it until his 80th birthday in 1961, his clients including, among others, Mount Isa Mines, New Guinea Goldfields, the Saudi Arabian Mining Syndicate, Gebeit Gold Mines in the Sudan, and the Britannia Lead Company. He also engineered the takeover by The Mining Trust of the non-Russian interests of Russo–Asiatic, for which he had worked before and during World War I.

Early in the 1930s Duffield joined his father on the board of Consolidated Mines Selection and was still a director in 1965 when it merged with The British South Africa Company and Central Mining to form Charter Consolidated, where a seat had been reserved for him.

Like his father, Duffield represented the IMM for many years on the governing body of Imperial College, of which he became an Honorary Fellow, and in the dark and difficult days of World War II he did much to keep the RSM Association together. Like his father, too, he was not only awarded the Institution's Gold Medal (in 1959) but later became an honorary member of both the IMM and the AIME.

In his Presidential address on the eve of the outbreak of the Second World War, Duffield looked back on half a century of mining and 40 years of IMM membership since his father was President and he was a student. Of the many changes that had taken place since then was the growth in importance, scope and numbers of the big mining groups.

'This growth', he told his audience, 'has been regarded with a certain amount of distrust and dislike by some of our members, and has had disadvantages such as curtailing the opportunities of work for independent consulting engineers. These dis-advantages, however, have been more than counter-balanced by the services rendered by them to the industry, not only in the development and equipment of properties which could not have been made profitable without a very large preliminary expen-diture, but also by the assistance given to research work for the improvement of technique and of the health and safety of their employees.

'Their influence on our profession may be summed up by the statement of the difference in the advice usually given to the graduate from a school of mines. Forty years ago that advice would probably have been to avoid staying too long at any one mine during the first six or seven years, and to try during that period to get as wide an experience as possible of different mines and countries. Nowadays, the best advice for most men is to try to get a job with one of the big companies and to make himself sufficiently useful to be kept on for the rest of his career.

'This may sound dull and uninteresting compared with the former advice, but it is not necessarily so. No mine lasts for ever and a company to keep alive must be always looking for new properties to replace those which it is working out or which changing conditions may make unprofitable.'

His advice is as valid today as when he spoke these words 50 years ago.

Duffield's son Ted was at Charterhouse School at the same time as Harry Oppenheimer and when Harry went on to Oxford to study philosophy and economics, Ted went to the RSM to learn about mining. While there he became secretary of the management committee of the Imperial College Union, of which his grandfather (governor) and his father (old student) were both members. On one momentous occasion they all turned up for a meeting—grandpa in his 80s, father in his 60s, and Ted in his early 20s. It was the first and only time so far that three generations had been represented at a meeting of the Union.

Ted's first two jobs provided a big contrast between conditions on a modern base-metal mine in Newfoundland and the revival of an ancient gold mine—one of the fabulous mines of King Solomon—in Saudi Arabia. Ted's wife went out as a bride to Saudi Arabia and, as her husband remarked in 1989, 'it says much for her adaptability that we celebrated our golden wedding last year'. Later, while working in the Copperbelt of Northern Rhodesia, Ted lost a leg in an underground accident. The mine medical officer refused him permission to work underground again, but that did not prevent him from doing so when he went to South Africa as consulting engineer for the Rooiberg tin mine, Apex Colliery and the South West Africa Company's lead, zinc and vanadium mine at Berg Augas.

On his retirement from active mining, Ted joined first one and then another Johannesburg stockbroking firm as mining adviser and at the time of writing was still employed in this work.

*   *   *

During its 6000 years of almost continuous operations the Rio Tinto complex in the Huelva province of southwestern Spain has produced many generations of distinguished mining men, from Bronze Age Tartessians, adventurous Phoenicians from Tyre and Sidon, colonizing Carthaginians from North Africa, Romans between the reign of Nerva in the first century AD to the collapse of the empire nearly 400 years later, Moors, native Spaniards—and Englishmen.

Of the Englishmen, it would be difficult to find a family who have contributed more to the mine's development over the past 100 years than the Hills, whose members also have an unbroken line of association with the IMM since 1902. In that year

Alexander Hill joined the Institution and was a member of Council when he died 10 years later. By then his son Laurence Carr Hill was already a student member, becoming President in 1950, the year in which his son, Laurence Alexander, popularly known as 'Sandy', graduated in mining engineering at the RSM. Today, Sandy's son Jeremy, born in the same house as his father at Rio Tinto, is a mining engineer who has been working with African Explosives and Chemicals Industries (AECI) in Johannesburg since 1983.

To make a proper study of the Hills' genealogical tree one would need to go back to the Battle of Flodden in 1513 when English troops commanded by the Earl of Surrey, though greatly outnumbered, caught the invading Scots in the rear and killed 10 000 of them, including their King James IV, who fell within a spear's length of his adversary. James Hill was a Scottish survivor of this battle and for the next 250 years or so his descendants flourished, eventually becoming closely identified with the Industrial Revolution in their native land. An eighteenth century Laurence Hill was a lifelong friend of Telford and was said to have been the first to propose linking Edinburgh and Glasgow by railway line in a scheme for which George Stephenson was consulting engineer; unfortunately, they were a little ahead of their time and the project had to be postponed through lack of capital.

Alexander's father—another Laurence—was the inventor of many wondrous things, having acquired the knack at a very early age. As a boy, he made a boat 20 inches long, powered by 'three fat mice'. The mice slept in the stern and food was put in the bow. In the middle was a drum with a treadmill that turned paddles on each side of the boat. As the designer explained, 'Two fat mice propel the boat easily; three take it quickly across the pond'. He also harnessed the wind to draw a carriage with a 10 ft kite, which 'in a good breeze will pull my mother's donkey chaise with me in it up a considerable incline'.

Later in life when he had moved on to inventing more practical things, such as climbing machines and various aids to marine architecture, Laurence became a close friend of the banker Hugh Matheson, who in 1873 headed a group of international businessmen that bought the Rio Tinto mine from the Spanish Government, harassed by armed insurrectionists, for £3.5 million, and became chairman of the company which the syndicate registered in London to run it. A word from Laurence in Matheson's ear secured an appointment for his son as technical assistant to the head of the project's mining and extraction department.

Young Alexander, who had early experience in Scottish coal mines and at the Tharsis Sulphur and Copper Company in Glasgow, sailed to Spain from Falmouth aboard the *Fun-Shun*, one of Matheson's boats, together with the chairman himself and other senior officials. Arriving at the port of Huelva, the party stayed overnight at the home of the mine's general manager Mark Carr and his wife—a visit of some significance in that it was the first of many that Alexander was to make during which he fell in love with the Carrs' daughter Polly. They married and had three sons, the eldest of whom, inevitably named Laurence, married Nan Ross,* daughter of the celebrated head of the company's medical service, Dr Russell Ross.

Alexander's adventures in Rio Tinto's early years under British ownership—as wild as any in America's West—are preserved in his own account in the family archives. After leaving Spain he worked in Mexico and California and subsequently took a partnership in a London consultancy.

His son Laurence lost no time in heading for Rio Tinto after graduating at the RSM and had been there for only a few months when he was involved in what general manager Walter Browning described as the 'most appalling catastrophe that has ever happened in these mines'. During a bitterly violent strike malcontents set fire to the Alicia Shaft workings and many miners and would-be rescuers died in the inferno. Laurence was one of 35—23 British and 12 Spaniards—who took part in the rescue operations and are still remembered today as 'the heroes of Alicia'. The burning galleries had to be closed off from the rest of the workings by concrete walls, behind which the fire continued to smoulder for more than 60 years.

Commissioned in the Royal Engineers in 1914, Laurence served the whole of the Great War with the Tunnelling Companies, meeting up with Ralph Stokes under unusual circumstances in a trench in France (Chapter Six). Back at Rio Tinto, he worked his way to chief mining engineer and technical deputy manager before 1936, when the Spanish Civil War

*She died in October 1990 in her 95th year.

plunged the mines into chaos. Rival unions fought each other to the death and a British destroyer steamed into Huelva to evacuate women and children of Rio Tinto employees to Gibraltar. Almost simultaneously, Huelva fell to the nationalists, but another month went by before a direct assault was made on the mines.

By that time Laurence Hill was the only member of the British staff remaining. On 25 August three columns of nationalist troops, numbering 10 000 well-armed men, moved in to put down the miners, whose leaders at first offered stiff resistance. But the outcome was inevitable. After suffering severe casualties they asked Hill to negotiate their surrender, but few of the terms were kept and Rio Tinto became the centre of some terrible atrocities. As conditions began to improve Laurence was able to join his wife and two sons in England, his arrival being preceded by a telegram from Colonel Richard Preston on behalf of the company directors: 'I want to congratulate you doubly; first, because your husband is safe and on his way to rejoin you; and secondly on his brave and generous action in staying on at the mines in order to try and save the lives of the Spanish staff. You must be a proud woman today.'

Normality did not last very long for the Hills. Four short years and the outbreak of World War II saw him back in uniform with the Tunnellers, this time as Chief Engineer in Malta. Then, when his commission ran out with his advancing years, he continued the war as a deck-hand in the Admiralty Runner Service, laconically explaining to his friends that he had 'always been fond of small boats'.

It was typical of a man for whom danger and excitement had been the chief ingredients of his career that for his Presidential address to the IMM in 1950 he should modestly choose to talk on 'The cupriferous pyrites industry'. But then Colonel Laurence Carr Hill, DSO, MC, three times mentioned in dispatches, knew a lot about that subject also.

While his father was in Malta, Sandy Hill was serving with the Royal Engineers in Madagascar and Burma, and it was not until the war was over that he was able to get to the Royal School of Mines, where he graduated in 1950.

It was, of course, inconceivable that he should start his career anywhere other than at Rio Tinto, where he stayed until 1956, after which he held appointments with Cyprus Mines, at Kilembe

Top left, Laurence Carr Hill. He, his father and his son were all engineers at Rio Tinto. Top right, two members of the Harbord family became Presidents of the IMM—Frank (pictured here) for 1921–22 and Vernon for 1952–53. Both were metallurgists, as was Vernon's son John who carried on the family consultancy. Bottom, four generations of the McDermotts pictured in 1938—Walter, Ted with son Keith, and Duffield in Uganda, Orissa in India, and with the Anglo American Corporation and Charter Consolidated—in the Copperbelt with the former and in London and Beralt in Portugal with the latter.

He retired in 1985, since when he and his wife Dorothy have lived in Grantham, Lincolnshire, not far from the famous grocer's shop where Margaret Thatcher first learned her economics. Their son Jeremy, born in 1952, was a pupil of Bob Pryor at the RSM and worked on the Zambian mines before joining AECI in Johannesburg.

*   *   *

Three generations of the Harbord family have made substantial contributions to the development of both ferrous and non-ferrous metallurgy and provided the IMM with two Presidents. All three were graduates of the Royal School of Mines and two were winners of the coveted Bessemer Medal.

First of the line, Frank Harbord joined the Institution in 1903 after working ten years with iron and steel manufacturers in the Midlands. Two years later he joined Edward Riley to form the metallurgical consulting firm of Riley, Harbord and Law, for which both his son Vernon and his grandson John also later worked.

Frank was IMM President in 1921–22 and when Vernon was elected to the chair 30 years later it was only the second time that the office had gone to the son of a Past-President: the first was when Duffield McDermott was so appointed in 1939, and it was a happy coincidence that on the day that Vernon began his Presidency Duffield received honorary membership.

Meanwhile John, after gaining practical experience in British steel works, spent a year in Europe on a Mond Nickel Travelling Fellowship, taking 'continuous casting' as his main theme in both its ferrous and non-ferrous application. Returning home, he joined the family consultancy and remained with it until it was merged with British Inspecting Engineering in 1972.

*   *   *

The lives of Frederick George Hatch and his son Gilbert, better known to his friends as Peter, spanned one hundred years of mining and reflected two widely different faces of the Institution of Mining and Metallurgy during that period.

A scholar of distinction, Frederick Hatch was just the sort of man that the Institution needed as its President when it obtained its Charter in the First World War. Geologist, petrologist, chemist, mining engineer and surveyor, he was a prolific writer on these and other disciplines: several of his books had already by then become standard works; he was a master of a fine literary style, all his writing being couched in clear graceful language.

His scientific education began at University College London in 1879 and was continued after four years at the University of Bonn, where he studied geology and mineralogy under Professor von Lasaulx, geology, crystallography and mineralogy under Professors von Rath and Hintze, geography under Professor Rein, and chemistry under Professors von Kekulé, Wallach and Anschütz.

When he returned home he joined the Geological Survey, serving as Petrographer for England and Wales for the next six years and, as has been seen, John Hays Hammond, who always knew a good man when he saw one, snapped him up on his way through London to take charge of Barney Barnato's mining interests on the developing Witwatersrand. There Hatch walked with the great—Cecil Rhodes, Wernher, Beit and many others, playing a major part in the elucidation of the geology of the Rand and the development of its mineral resources.

The political and economic upheavals of the late nineties broke the thread of his work in the Transvaal, but he was back again after the Boer War and contributed much to the opening up of the great mines of the East and West Rand. In due course he was elected President of the Geological Society of South Africa.

Hatch remained in South Africa until 1906—two years after Peter was born—before returning to London to practise as a consulting mining geologist. His work in World War II was of great value to the Ministry of Munitions and after 1918 he served on a government commission to examine iron and steel works in occupied Germany, in France and in Belgium.

Frederick Hatch was an indefatigable worker for whom the project in which he was engaged at any one time was a matter of supreme importance. His son Peter took a much more relaxed and philosophical view of life. True, he inherited some of his father's gift of reducing the most highly technical problems to understandable proportions and was a regular contributor to the *Transactions* of the IMM, which he joined as a student in 1927 and later became a Fellow. But he was never such a prolific writer as his father. Nor did he achieve international eminence in any of those disciplines to which Frederick had brought such lustre.

The most generous thing one can say about Peter's professional career is that he was an instinctive engineer of high competence. In any situation he seemed to know the right answer and his opinion on the most abstruse subjects was widely sought and respected. Friends put this down not only to his innate ability but to a first-class basic training in engineering at Oundle School and to a spell in a foundry, which he seemed to find stimulating.

He spent most of his early years helping to develop the great lead–zinc mine at Trepca and was honoured by the Yugoslavs with the Order of St Sava. In the war he worked in the Middle East to further their cause on the sort of missions that have not been documented, and probably never will be. He returned to South Africa, which he always regarded as his home, to work for Selection Trust and was largely responsible for developing the Bikita mine, just over the border in Rhodesia, famous for its rare minerals, some of them unique. Later he was transferred to London, where he worked at Selection Trust's head office as a mining analyst.

Some men will be remembered in the IMM for their leadership, or for their consistent work for its interests over many years; some for the number of committees on which they served; some for their handling of delicate situations, or as liaison between the Institution and Government and other professional and learned bodies. But the hard core of the IMM membership is made up of people like Peter Hatch, men who never strove to achieve greatness and did not have it thrust upon them, men who contributed what they could, when they could, serving perhaps for a short spell on one committee or another, at best the proposers of votes of thanks at annual general meetings, but seldom the recipients.

Peter Hatch was one such man. Perhaps his greatest merit lay in his efforts to keep together a small group of friends from his days in Yugoslavia and South Africa. As Jim Rogers wrote when Peter died in 1988: 'The Friday lunches that we all attended for many years, first in South Africa at the Phoenix Hotel (it had the

best beer in Johannesburg) and later at the Mining Club in
London, were largely his doing, although he was by nature
unassuming, even diffident, and I never heard him make a
speech. His presence was the unifying force. The word and
custom were spread throughout the world that, if you happened
to be in these places on a Friday, you could be sure of meeting
kindred spirits and that, more often than not, Peter would be
there . . .

'He never drank anything except beer. I only hope that the beer
is good in heaven: it should be. I also know that if I get there
sometime on a Friday, Peter will be there, quietly waiting for us
all with his pint tankard in his hand, his red hair and his
beaming face.'

Who could wish for a better eulogy? And who can say who was
the better man—father or son? Together they were the essence of
the IMM and of the industry that they served.

CHAPTER SEVENTEEN

Closing Ranks

The year 1965 produced some notable happenings nationally and internationally. In January the world bid a sad farewell to the old warhorse Winston Churchill, the 'greatest Englishman for more than a hundred years'; President Lyndon Johnson, successor to the assassinated John F. Kennedy, sent US troops to fight in the rapidly escalating war in Vietnam; Edward Heath became leader of the British Conservative Party; Liverpool won the FA Cup for the first time; and in Rhodesia Prime Minister Ian Smith declared UDI and put the country on a war footing.

In the engineering world it was a year in which the Institution of Mining and Metallurgy joined with a dozen other professional bodies of like interests to form the Council of Engineering Institutions (CEI). Represented among its members were bodies concerned with a wide range of engineering disciplines, including civil, mining, mechanical, marine, gas, electrical, radio and electronics.

CEI was very much the brainchild of the Duke of Edinburgh, who saw the need to bring the various branches of the profession together. Hitherto, contacts between them had been tenuous and in some cases non-existent. The flood flow of change that had been taking place in higher education in the early 1960s required bold decisions in the qualifying process for professional engineers. The profession was badly in need of a better public image and the individual engineer, tired of being thought of as someone who mended bicycles and changed washers on taps, was demanding greater status in the community. Prince Philip believed that such objectives could not be attained unilaterally. The IMM, which had already gone a long way towards improving the qualifications and prestige of its members, agreed that unity was strength and backed the project enthusiastically.

While Lord Hailsham, then Minister for Science, undertook to support a petition for a Royal Charter, he laid down some specific conditions: CEI was to proceed with all reasonable speed to raise the academic standard for entry to the profession to that of a degree of a British university, and it was bidden to maintain bridges and ladders so that it was still possible to achieve the same status 'the hard way'.

The charter was granted and CEI got down to work. Its first and most important action was to create an Engineers' Register in three sections for Chartered Engineers, Technical Engineers and Engineering Technicians. Qualifications were related to passing the CEI or equivalent nationally recognized examinations, together with a period of training and experience under the eye of a member institution.

As far as the IMM was concerned, corporate members were automatically accepted on existing qualifications, and a minimum amount of paper work was required before they could use, rather self-consciously at first, the title Chartered Engineer with the cordal appendage 'C.Eng.', which quickly became recognized by other professionals and more gradually by the community at large. Those entering the profession 'the hard way' had to satisfy the old academic standard by the end of 1970 and complete training and experience requirements within three years.

The provision of this rapid transition to a fully graduate standard of entry to chartered status was perhaps CEI's greatest achievement. There was less dramatic success in attempts to introduce properly monitored training, and some 15 or more years were to pass before this matter was given the serious attention that it deserved.

Conscious of the fact that the public standing of scientists had been greatly enhanced over 300 years by the activities of the Royal Society, CEI decided in 1976 to set up a comparable body for engineers who, in the view of their peers, justified membership of an elite cadre of engineering excellence, carrying with it the appendage 'F. Eng.' It was hoped that the Fellowship would become a centre of authoritative opinion that Government and other bodies might consult on engineering issues, thus complementing for the profession the role played by the Royal Society in respect of science. Inhibited in its early development by its constitutional position as a 'subsidiary' of CEI, lack of funds and, by no means least, the predominance among its members of engineers nearing the end of their careers, the Fellowship had to wait a few more years and changed circumstances before it attained its 'independence' and began to become a force in the promotion of engineering at national level.

Like many other bodies that have ventured into the communications field inadequately prepared and unprofessionally represented, CEI never made much headway in public affairs and had to be content with a modest claim that it was consulted on many matters by Government and that its advice was generally well received. Undoubtedly it was listened to on various subjects of public interest, such as health, safety at work and trade union affairs, but lack of funds limited its activities and its successes depended largely on voluntary effort.

It was therefore not altogether surprising when in July 1977 the Secretary of State for Industry announced the setting up of a committee to review 'for manufacturing industry and in the light of national economic needs' the whole structure of British engineering, including the role of the institutions in the education and qualification of engineers at professional and technician level, and to make recommendations.

Sir Monty Finniston, a former chairman of the British Steel Corporation, was appointed to preside over the inquiry, which in the next couple of years received more than 700 written submissions of evidence and heard the views of scores of individual engineers at meetings organized on its behalf by CEI and attended by more than 600 people up and down the country. Its conclusions, published in a 250-page report in 1980, did not make happy reading. To help correct what he called 'the historic neglect by Britain of the engineering dimension', Finniston proposed the establishment of a statutory engineering authority on similar lines to CEI, but in much greater proportions. The new body would take charge of registration procedure and introduce and monitor new degrees leading to higher standards of educational proficiency. Naturally, CEI, which for 15 years had struggled towards the same ends virtually unaided, offered stiff resistance to some of the proposals. After months of cogitation

Government came up with a draft charter for an Engineering Council that was eventually composed of more than 50 professional bodies, compared with a CEI corporate membership of 16, with a dozen or so affiliates.

From the start the Engineering Council made it clear that it expected to take over most of the activities in which CEI was involved, including its register. The situation was accepted with restraint by CEI, whose chairman at this critical time was Gerald Mortimer, a Past-President of the IMM and deputy chairman and chief executive of Consolidated Gold Fields.

Whilst CEI cooperated to the full in arrangements for its own funeral—including putting the issue to the vote of its entire membership, comprising 200 000 chartered engineers—this did not prevent Mortimer from giving the new authority some stringent warnings. 'Engineers are not likely to be convinced that the country, industry and the profession will benefit from merely replacing one registration system by another, even if it is improved in detail', he told the new Council. 'They will wish to be assured that there will soon be a real improvement in the way in which the capabilities of the profession are used and recognized by employers for the benefit of the nation as a whole.' And again: 'Engineers will want to know what the relationship will be between the Engineering Council and the institutions, both chartered and non-chartered. They will want to know how effectively the views of their separate institutions will be sought and heard on major matters of policy at Council level in areas such as those relating to their employment and the standards required for qualification. Equally, they will want to know how their institutions will be able to represent and argue for them individually in any matter of personal dispute.'

It is not clear to what extent these questions were answered before the Engineering Council eventually took over the functions of CEI in the second half of 1983 and issued a policy statement, most of which appeared to have a familiar ring. The IMM expressed and published its views on a number of aspects of the proposals, making it clear that it considered any diminution in the role of the professional institutions to be undesirable and damaging. In the event, there have been few really significant changes in the qualifying pattern and things have continued very much as before.

*   *   *

An interesting and, for the IMM, somewhat amusing consequence arose from the Engineering Council's inheritance of the Fellowship of Engineering from the CEI. Although in terms of the IMM's charter 'minerals' had always been taken to include oil, the number of petroleum engineers who actually became members of the Institution was never very great. However, the discovery of vast oil resources in the North Sea in the 1970s and the importance that the petroleum engineer suddenly assumed in local society prompted the IMM to attempt to step up recruitment in this field.

Moreover, the two engineering branches had recently been brought into closer contact as a result of an increasing interest by the oil companies in the metal business. Warnings that the world's oil reserves could become seriously depleted by the twenty-first century had much to do with this trend as many of the big petroleum producers sought to diversify into other extractive industries. Among those which followed this trail were Atlantic Richfield (in Anaconda), Exxon (in the Disputada mine in Chile), Shell (through its subsidiary Billiton), Gulf, Texaco, Mobil and Conoco. In fact, when Standard Oil—subsequently absorbed by BP—bought Kennecott Corporation, then the largest domestic copper producer in America, oil companies found themselves owning half the total US copper capacity.

By the time of the BP takeover of Selection Trust in 1980 the only American copper producers not in oil company hands, partially or completely, were Phelps Dodge, Asarco and Newmont. Moreover, Standard Oil (California) held 20 per cent of AMAX and tried hard, but unsuccessfully, to take over the whole of this natural resources group.

To some extent the increasing interest of the oil companies in base metals was not a bad thing for the industry. In the case of copper, for example, diminishing ore grades and a variety of other factors had begun to weaken the financial muscle of the mining companies to develop them. By the mid-1970s the capital cost of starting new mines had escalated so much that the oil conglomerates were just about the only source—certainly in the private sector—capable of putting together enough finance for exploration and development and to provide the necessary infrastructure.

Unfortunately, disillusionment for the oil corporations was not far off. BP's excursion into the metal-mining field was singularly badly timed. Within a week or two of its acquisition of Selection Trust—at £412 million the most expensive takeover to date in the City of London—copper and other base-metal prices fell to levels at which few mines were able to continue to produce at a profit and the oil moguls started to wonder if oil and metal really did mix. In the next eight years the big oil companies of the world—including BP, which parted with most of its newly acquired mineral assets to RTZ—sold, spun off or closed down all the copper properties that they had so eagerly bought, at losses running into many billions of dollars. Ironically, since the oil corporations have withdrawn, most base-metal mines have been doing quite nicely as world demand for metal once more improved.

But to return to the 1970s, the British offshore oil boom was such a dramatic stimulant to the national economy that the Fellowship of Engineering began to feel some embarrassment that its membership included none of those who were making such a major contribution to the developments in the North Sea. Instructions were given—instigated, it has been said, by the Duke of Edinburgh—that this omission should be rectified immediately.

Before this could be done, however, there was a small matter of protocol to be overcome. To become a member of the Fellowship one had to be a 'chartered engineer'—and very few petroleum engineers at that time could put C. Eng. after their name. The quickest and most convenient route to such status was through the relevant CEI constituent body, in this case the IMM.

Apart from organizing an annual lecture and an occasional meeting and facility visit, the IMM had tended to soft-pedal its oil-related activities, partly because of the small number of members concerned but, more importantly, because it did not wish to be seen as competing with such learned societies as the Institute of Petroleum and the United Kingdom branches of the US Society of Petroleum Engineers. What it could provide, however, was an entrée to C. Eng. status, and here was an opportunity to demonstrate its effectiveness.

IMM acted quickly. In November 1978, on the proposition of President Bob Pryor, Council agreed to set up a Petroleum Committee 'to consider ways and means in which the Institution can, in line with its objects, best meet the professional and learned society requirements of engineers engaged in the science and practice of the discovery and extraction of petroleum minerals from the earth's crust; and to advise the Council on all such matters'.

Very shortly thereafter two distinguished personalities of the British oil industry, Peter (soon to become Sir Peter) Baxendell and Dr Jack Birks, became IMM Fellows, chartered engineers and members of the Fellowship of Engineering in rapid succession.

To ensure there would no misunderstanding in future about the eligibility of oil men as members of the IMM—or of the Fellowship of Engineering—the Institution revised its Charter to spell out the position in more precise terms. Today more than 200 petroleum engineers belong to the IMM, representing some four per cent of total membership.

Since its inception the IMM has always been a multi-disciplinary organization, ranging from mining engineering and geology to metallurgy and mineral processing, its members' activities embracing all minerals except, as stipulated in the Royal Charter, the mining of coal and the metallurgy of iron. The Institution's title does not, however, immediately suggest an involvement in the quarrying of roadstone or the extraction of sand and gravel—indeed, in its early years little attention was paid to these or any other so-called industrial minerals. But at about the time when metalliferous mining in Britain began to decline in the second part of the last century the importance of industrial minerals increased and today the country is a world-class producer of various clays, fluorspar, barytes and potash, and the limestone, gypsum, aggregates, sand and gravel industries are busy meeting ever-increasing national demands. Equally, in other parts of the mining world served by the IMM, industrial minerals have become of high importance and their extraction and processing have developed from haphazard beginnings to highly professional and sophisticated operations.

The post World War II period was a particularly busy time for industrial mineral producers and, in 1964, in pace with this development, the IMM for the first time devoted two sessions on the subject to its symposium on opencast mining, quarrying and alluvial mining. In the 1980s some 130 papers published in the *Transactions* dealt with various aspects of the matter, and at the 1990 CMMI congress in Edinburgh no fewer than seven papers were devoted to industrial minerals, and tours were arranged to production and processing operations both in the United Kingdom and Ireland. In addition, the biennial conference on extractive industry geology, held jointly by the IMM with the Institution of Geologists and the Geological Society, is today essentially concerned with industrial minerals.

Whilst no IMM President has come directly from the industrial minerals industry, at least one, Gerald Mortimer (1977–78), played a major part in its development in Britain: in 1966 he took over the building up of Consolidated Gold Fields' position in this business, becoming chairman of Amalgamated Roadstone. Other Presidents, especially consultants, have been closely associated with various facets of the industry, which, as the Institution approaches its centenary, is strongly represented on Council and its various committees.

In the sort of 'classless society' envisaged by Britain's Prime Minister John Major, there should be no room for distinction between those who serve the same cause. Inevitably, however, some degree of 'one-upmanship' will continue in most institutions and professions. It has been said that in the IMM gold and diamonds are Upper Class; base metals Middle Class; and minor metals and industrial minerals Lower Class. No one has yet suggested where coal might fall if ever it should become a concern of the Institution.

*   *   *

With the western world firmly in the grip of economic depression, the early 1980s offered little encouragement for the mining industry. The root cause of its problems lay in a 150 per cent increase in international oil prices, which made life extremely difficult for all companies and especially for marginal-cost producers of base metals. It was, in fact, a repeat of the oil price explosion of 1973–74, similar in magnitude and in effect. Incidentally, it is not widely appreciated that the IMM had a very important 'oil man' among its members in the 1980s—none other than the Chairman of OPEC. Dr Rilwanu Lukman KBE has served as the Overseas Member of Council for Nigeria since 1979 and was made an Honorary Fellow in 1989. He joined the Nigerian Government as Minister of Mines, Power and Steel in 1984, becoming Minister of Petroleum Resources and Chairman of OPEC two years later.

Other international happenings against a background of

increasing tension between East and West made their mark: 1980 was the year in which the Russians invaded Afghanistan, the year of the rise of Solidarity in Poland, the election of Ronald Reagan as President of the United States, and a final settlement of the Rhodesian problem. Individually, each of these events had an importance for the minerals industry. Collectively, their main significance was the new attitude that they created to the whole question of strategic materials supplies, and if there was any consolation to be found in this situation it was the awareness that it brought to consumers that metals have to be *mined*, often in far-distant and inhospitable parts of the world, and do not just 'materialize' in local warehouses.

The problems of the mining industry were further aggravated by a lack of discipline among many state-owned metal producers in developing and mono-economy countries in failing to adjust their production to a falling market—not, as some commentators seemed to suggest, that this was a new phenomenon, but it was certainly seen in sharper focus in the early 1980s than ever before. The greater the fall in metal prices, the more the governments of these countries increased their production, ignoring the consequences of further market depression in their desperation to keep foreign exchange flowing and to insure themselves against internal political repercussions that would inevitably follow any substantial reduction in the workforce.

The unhappy result of such a policy was that depression in the metal markets tended to last longer than in other sectors of the economy whose members exercised restraint at times of low prices. Several metal producers fell by the wayside: Anaconda, once one of the most powerful American mining corporations, went out of business; others survived only with massive losses; Phelps Dodge lost more than $400 million in the early 1980s and came close to bankruptcy. The shock of such events transformed the culture of many western world producers, driving them to operate at the lowest cost possible and, in consequence, throwing thousands of skilled workers out of jobs.

Repercussions on the IMM took various forms. For many years membership had increased steadily, but at the end of the 1970s the number of corporate members levelled off at about 3600, and those in the student and graduate categories dropped by around 500 to fewer than 1000. Ten years later there was still no improvement—in fact, in 1990 the overall total of 4800 was 150 down on the 1979 figure, though the number of corporate members was roughly the same. Inevitably, subscriptions and charges for the *Transactions* and other publications were increased and a new category of 'companion'—a sort of up-market affiliate—was introduced. But it was a vicious circle and prospective members shied away from the escalating subscriptions. It was quite beyond the capacity of the IMM to tackle the root cause of the problem: depressed market prices for most metals and a low level of activity throughout the minerals industry forced employers to reduce staff, resulting not only in redundancies but a sharp fall in the numbers of those studying minerals engineering at the universities.

It was a particularly frustrating time for those concerned with an organization that had been the outcome of the Ninth Commonwealth Mining and Metallurgical Congress in London in 1969. For many years industry's middle- and long-term requirements for most professional staff had been almost impossible to estimate, with the result that there was invariably a mad scramble for recruits in times of high production and good metal prices, and severe retrenchment in periods of recession. The coming together of leading figures in the international minerals industry for the CMMI congress provided an opportunity to attempt to put forecasting on a more scientific basis and, supported in the main by a number of London-based mining houses, the Mineral Industry Manpower and Careers Unit (MIMCU) was set up and housed in a little suite of offices tucked away in a corner of the Royal School of Mines. Its job, basically, was to make science and careers masters at some 300 schools up and down the country more aware of the needs of metalliferous mining and the functions and responsibilities of its decision-makers.

In Britain where, despite the efforts of the IMM and other professional bodies, mining was still predominantly associated in the public mind with coal, strikes and redundancies, such a task was a pretty thankless one. But within the limits of its frugal finances the unit, led by Geoffrey Cox, a mining man of infinite ingenuity, made some progress. Unfortunately, it was quickly discovered that forecasting the minerals industry's requirements could never be an exact science; the imponderables were legion and there must have been occasions when Cox was tempted to buy himself a crystal ball. After several years of uncertainties industry at last appeared to be unanimous in its belief that it was about to face a serious shortage of trained technologists, and MIMCU stepped up its pressure on the schools to give more attention to training for the minerals industry. Then came the recession and almost overnight mining groups across the world began drastically to reduce their employment of new graduates; geologists were especially adversely affected as expenditure on exploration was cut to the bone.

Professor Marston Fleming, who had been a member of the organizing committee of the Ninth CMMI congress, out of which MIMCU was born, and became President of the IMM a couple of years later, was prominent among eminent academics who believed strongly that the minerals industry should demonstrate confidence in its own future by investing more in its professional manpower. One of his colleagues went so far as to propose a scheme under which the big employers might devote a proportion of their profits in good times to a fund for the education of selected students, with a guarantee of employment at the end of training. He emphasized that such a process need not be too costly, pointing out that professional engineers, though vital to the industry, were never required in very big numbers; in Canada, for example, 'professionals' accounted for no more than 2.5 per cent of the manpower on the mines and in Africa the proportion was even lower. 'Such men', he asserted, 'are an essential part of the diverse and complex organism of mining; their influence and authority permeate its entire structure, and the industry has come to expect an uninterrupted top-quality supply. But even to maintain present standards, the education given in the world's mining schools and universities must be matched by the training offered within the industry itself. In a graduate's early years he must be given real opportunities to bite into the challenging problems which will give him experience and maturity—and provide a substantial return for the company that has invested in him. In any enterprise, people are always the most important factor, too often their development is haphazard, unplanned and almost casual.'

Professor Fleming fully endorsed these sentiments. 'The professional minerals engineer deserves better than this', he declared. 'If the young engineer is to recognize his responsibilities he must see them in the example of his seniors; and if he is to accept those responsibilities he is justified in expecting a satisfying career with commensurate rewards and, above all, respect for his competence, achievement and independence.'

By and large, the mining companies—certainly most of those in the western world—were not unsympathetic to these views, but the problem demanded unanimity and a commitment that few boards of directors were prepared to give. Things were therefore allowed to drift along in the same old way, each crisis being dealt with as it arose, the biggest loser invariably being the man at the bottom of the ladder, the graduate just beginning his career, or the student forced to change direction in the middle of his university course.

*   *   *

For those who managed IMM's finances, the year 1980–81 was the most difficult in living memory. At the 1980 annual general meeting, treasurer Robert MacWilliam painted a gloomy picture of relentlessly rising costs and falling revenue, but he was hopeful that measures planned by Council would alleviate the position. In the event, results turned out even worse than MacWilliam expected. After the financial successes of many of the earlier conferences, the symposium 'National and international management of mineral resources' in London in May 1980 did not attract the support expected, particularly from overseas, and a loss of £20 000 resulted, whereas a profit of near similar size had been expected. The overall deficit for the year was more than £45 000; moreover, at the year-end there were liabilities of £140 000, reduced by no more than £35 000 after taking into account 'sundry debtors, payments in advance and cash in the bank'. MacWilliam believed it essential for the Institution to balance its budget annually and to try to build up its capital position. Its biggest asset was its head office building, then valued at around £1 million. There was talk of raising a mortgage, or arranging a sale and lease back; there was even a suggestion to move out of London to less expensive premises, but it was generally accepted that in the long run implementation of any of these possibilities would only be a palliative and did not touch the root of the problem.

Inevitably, the main burden of the economies fell on the staff at Portland Place. Several redundancies were declared and the duties of other employees were changed considerably. Shouldering the chief strain was the secretary and his staff, to whom MacWilliam paid special tribute: 'I have been glad to see that Michael Jones has still managed to keep a smile on his face, but at times I have wondered how he has been able to carry on. If ever our thanks were due to him, they were never more deserved than they are now.' The annual dinner for 1981 was cancelled and the Institution's auditors were brought in to assist in working out a new system of budgetary control and cash forecasting, and to advise on more accurate costing of each activity.

In such circumstances of anxiety and strain it was not surprising that differences of opinion should arise about the extent to which the economy measures should be pursued. As a result, John Taylor, the current President, found himself so much out of line with most Council members that he felt unable to carry on and resigned with five months of his term of office still to run. In accordance with the by-laws, the senior vice-President, Dennis Day, moved in to chair Council and other meetings for the remainder of the session, at the end of which Professor Rex Davis was elected to the office.

As the 1980s progressed, the IMM's financial position gradually improved. For this it had largely to thank some better returns from its conferences and publications, though, like the copper price, profits from these sources varied widely from year to year. In the light of the 1982 accounts, the staff cuts made two years earlier had obviously been overdone. The result was that as activity picked up so it became necessary to recruit more staff; to ensure getting the right candidates was often a long process and extra burdens were thrown on those who had survived the trauma of 1980 and had carried on, with little guarantee of job security.

Even in 1987, treasurer Barry Smale-Adams still found it necessary to warn members at the annual general meeting that it remained a matter of urgency that revenue generated by learned society activities should increase, not only to support the cost of those activities but to generate surpluses to help general funds. Another aspect affecting revenue was a decline in covenants and donations, more particularly from the big mining houses, which for many years had traditionally made substantial contributions to general funds but now confined their support to specific projects.

The situation was summed up in a trite if not original simile by S.D. Brooks when proposing a vote of thanks to retiring President Alan Robinson: he likened the Institution to a 'swan in rough water, moving serenely and confidently to the onlooker, but paddling very hard under the surface to move forward through changing conditions'.

As Brooks suggested, outwardly things did not appear to have changed very much for the IMM. Certainly, the basic pattern of events remained the same. Annual general meetings and certain other functions were still held, as they had been virtually since the beginning of the century, in the Geological Society's rooms at Burlington House, Piccadilly, by courtesy of the Council of that august body. Proceedings at these meetings continued to be conducted very much as they always had been with all the conventions and niceties strictly observed: outgoing Presidents spoke modestly about what had been achieved in their term of office; new incumbents professed their unworthiness to follow the steps of such distinguished predecessors but promised to do their best; treasurers reported optimistically or gloomily on the Institution's finances—depending on the prevailing climate; and, of course, there were fulsome tributes to the 'tireless work' and 'loyalty' of the staff. For proposers of votes of thanks the AGM was always a field day, an opportunity for eulogy, verbosity and a free use of the metaphor, even if it sometimes became a bit mixed. Although none was able to outdo Harry Denny's praise of Charles McDermid when in 1915 he compared the reigning secretary to the 'sturdy Eddystone . . . a familiar and trusted symbol of integrity and a tower of strength' (Chapter Seven), there were some who came very near.

A dozen or more standing committees, ranging from General Purposes to Professional Affairs (formerly EAT—Education, Accreditation and Training), from Membership and Qualifications to what was euphemistically termed 'Activities', usually had about 50 sessions between them in the course of a year; in addition there were regular meetings of conference organizing committees, editorial boards and a variety of *ad hoc* working groups.

In 1988, to improve management and forward planning, Council introduced an Executive Committee and a Management Committee. As well as taking over the functions of the former

Finance Committee, the Executive Committee was to ensure close liaison between standing committees and the staff, while the object of the Management Committee was to improve working relations between the various head office departments. A Planning Group was also formed to address itself to the future development of the Institution.

Internal communications have always been a problem for the IMM. With such a large proportion of its members overseas this has to some extent been inevitable, but in recent years the gap between Council and the general run of membership would appear to have widened almost to a 'them and us' situation. Some members, more especially younger ones, often complained of a lack of understanding, even of interest in their problems, by those who ran the Institution's affairs while, for its part, Council consistently urged a greater participation by members of all ages in Institutional matters, but without giving much advice as to how this might be achieved.

Bill Yuill summed up the position in 1986 when, as President, he published an open letter in *IMM Bulletin* in which he asked: 'Do we do enough for younger members?' He felt that the answer had to be 'no'. 'But', he continued, 'do the young members know what they want from the Institution and, if so, have they told us? . . . Before being elected to Council some 11 years ago, I felt that Council was not really concerned with what individual members felt. I can assure you that this has never been the case, but from talking to members I know that many still feel as I did, yet very few do anything about it except to make their points over a pint of beer, which is really not sufficient.

'For some years *IMM Bulletin* has published correspondence and this is an obvious place to put forward your views and possibly to stimulate some discussion. In addition, of course, issues raised in *IMM Bulletin* are also considered by the Institution's various committees and the Council.

'One matter that comes up quite often in informal discussions is the idea that somehow the Council is self-perpetuating. This raises two points. The first is the small number of members who actually vote in the annual election and the second is the lack of candidates proposed by the membership . . . To a large extent you get the Council that you deserve . . . [This] sounds very much like a criticism of the membership—and to a certain extent it is. This is your Institution and it has an enviable reputation worldwide . . .

It is up to you to help in its development.'

Fighting words from a blunt Scotsman! At the end of 1986 a Younger Members Committee was formed and began a programme of meetings, visits and discussions which it was hoped would help bridge the gap between them and 'more mature' members. A couple of years later the Committee sent a questionnaire to 1800 members aged 35 and under in an attempt to clarify their requirements and assess their use of the Institution's services and functions. There were only 103 replies.

'This disappointing response may be the most significant statistic to emerge from the survey', commented the *Bulletin*, adding somewhat ingenuously, 'alternatively, it could be interpreted to mean that 94.3 per cent of younger members are completely satisfied with their Institution and felt no need to respond!'

Some small consolation was gained from an indication that respondents taking part in events organized by the Committee felt them to have been worthwhile. But it could not be overlooked that nearly half of the 5.7 per cent who did reply to the questionnaire knew nothing of such events despite the fact that they were advertised in advance in the *Bulletin* and by 'mail shots' to universities and large employers. The obvious conclusion was that if the survey did anything at all, it turned the spotlight on the inadequacy of the Institution's internal communications.

In an attempt to remedy this situation a re-dressed bi-monthly publication with the rather presumptuous title *Minerals Industry International* was introduced in 1989 to take the place of the monthly *Bulletin*, which since 1976 had appeared in airmail format to speed distribution to overseas members. An editorial in the first issue explained that the journal owed its origin to two criticisms: dissatisfaction with the channelling of papers of general interest to only one-third of the membership as a result of the division of *Transactions* into the three main disciplines covered by the Institution; and 'hints', from younger members in particular, that the *Bulletin* was excessively 'dry'. The new publication had to be a compromise: for financial reasons content could not be expanded without a reduction in frequency of issue. It was accepted that some members would see the change as being for the worse because they would have to wait twice as long for their news; as against that, it was pointed out that the *Bulletin* was virtually unsaleable to non-members, whereas, with luck, increased revenue from a hoped-for wider readership could lead to an increase in the frequency of the new paper.

Whether the decision was the right one against a background of falling membership and revenue remains to be seen. It certainly defied the contention of most professional communicators that the essence of any publication that sets out to provide a link between those who 'manage' and those who are 'managed' is that it shall be published as often as possible, however thin its contents, and convey its message in clear and concise terms with none of the literary trimmings beloved of amateur editors. Exponents of this 'direct' method of communication do not hesitate to point to the fact that the greatest message of all time was chiselled in rock on Mount Sinai and delivered personally to the people!

Like many other publications of similar purpose, the IMM journal has a production staff, but relies largely on its readers for editorial contributions. Success therefore depends largely on the extent to which the reader/reporters respond. Anyone who has edited such periodicals knows that his readers have to be coaxed, cajoled and flattered into becoming contributors and educated to accept that what they write is going to be edited, often quite severely. Some editors have the knack and patience to establish a happy and fruitful relationship with their correspondents, but unqualified success is rare indeed.

Technical content of the new journal is undoubtedly of high standard and in the best traditions of the *Transactions*. The most serious deficiency—as with its predecessor—is the quality of the 'straight' reportage—accounts of traditional events such as annual general meetings, election of Presidents and Fellows, and the bestowal of honours and awards. Here the reports suggest either that there is little appreciation of the fact that journalistic styles have changed radically since the last century, or a conviction that what was good enough for the Victorians should be good enough for the present generation. Unfortunately, this is not so: one cannot address the youth of today in the terminology of the past; nor will glossy paper and pictures compensate for a reportage in which the hard news is often hidden among verbiage and excessive eulogy.

For its external relations the Institution has relied mainly on the performance of its senior members at national and international gatherings and on its sponsorship of, and participation in symposia of world importance. The list of bodies on which it has been represented used to occupy nearly two columns of the old *Bulletin* and ranged from the British Standards Institution to the Society of Chemical Industry, from the World Mining Congress Organizing Committee to the British Tunnelling Society, from the Watt Committee on Energy to the Royal Society. From earliest days members of the Institution have occupied seats on the governing boards of the Royal School of Mines, Camborne and many other educational bodies.

Public promotion of an IMM 'image' has seldom, if ever, been seriously attempted. The Institution has always accepted that its prime concerns are the advancement of the science and practices with which it is concerned, the spread of knowledge relating to its professions, and the education and competence of those engaged in the industry. To step outside these limits would be to enter a jungle that is impenetrable without a special kind of expertise and very large sums of money .

When, in the last decade of the twentieth century a 'quality' British newspaper can still headline a trade union meeting 'Engineers in conference', it suggests that there is yet a long way to go before the public concept of 'mining' and 'engineering' may change. In the meantime, members of the IMM will have to accept that they may still sometimes find themselves in a similarly embarrassing situation to Herbert Hoover when he had to confess to a fair travelling companion that he was an engineer. And all the time she had thought him a gentleman!

CHAPTER EIGHTEEN

The Way Ahead

The honours and awards that the IMM has bestowed on those who have made outstanding contributions to the minerals industry, both technical and non-technical, not only reflect the achievements of the recipients but have helped to bring to public attention the high status that the Institution itself occupies in international society.

In May 1990 Sir Alistair Frame, chairman of Rio Tinto Zinc Corporation, became the Institution's 78th Gold Medallist for his services to education and to the industry generally. The award was timely, not only because it marked a distinguished career but because it was made in a year when RTZ, which had begun life more than a hundred years earlier as a modest producer of pyrites and copper in southern Spain, had become the world's biggest mining company with profits of more than £1 billion.

Since its formation in 1892 the IMM has enjoyed a close association with RTZ, or Rio Tinto as it then was, as indeed it has with most of the larger groups whose engineers and metallurgists have always represented a substantial proportion of the Institution's membership. In fact, there must be relatively few members, other than academics and consultants, who have not at one time or another worked for such conglomerates as the Anglo American Corporation of South Africa and its various subsidiaries, RTZ, Consolidated Gold Fields, Union Corporation, Central Mining, Selection Trust and RST, to name but a few. This association has been of mutual benefit to the mining companies and the Institution: for the companies it has ensured a flow of recruits bearing the badge of professional competence, and for members of the Institution it has offered employment under some of the best conditions available throughout the world.

As well as the Institution's Gold Medal, there have been more than 150 winners of gold and silver medals, sponsored by Consolidated Gold Fields of South Africa, and awarded each year by the IMM Council for contributions of highest merit to the *Transactions* or for researches into the occurrence, treatment and mining of minerals. The winners have included half a dozen or so women—a very small proportion, it is true, but enough perhaps to demonstrate that the Institution is not entirely the male preserve that it has sometimes been thought to be. Time was when ladies were excluded from certain IMM functions on the pretence that their presence would inhibit speakers indulging in reminiscences of an intimate nature, or recounting stories that could fall harshly on delicate ears. Today the Institution has just over 60 women members, many of them geologists, who enjoy the same status and facilities as their male colleagues in similar classes of membership—and could doubtless tell stories as good as the men's.

Male members who speak to their wives have been consistently urged since the early 1980s to tell them about MINA, an association catering for the ladies' interests and which meets periodically in the Council chamber of Imperial College to hear talks by guests who to date have included the Princess Royal, David Battie of Sotheby's and Television's *Antiques Road Show*, Court jeweller Richard Ogden, and Santina Levy and other lecturers from the Victoria and Albert Museum. Visits have been made to some of London's famous establishments, among them Goldsmiths' Hall, the Bank of England, Mansion House, Lambeth Palace and the diamond sorting rooms at De Beers, and dinner and supper parties and other social functions have been arranged with such success as to enable donations to be made to the IMM Benevolent Fund and the Imperial College day nursery.

Among trust funds and bequests administered by the IMM are some that commemorate the names of several of the Institution's pioneers. Students still compete annually for the 'Arthur Claudet' and 'William Frecheville' prizes, awarded for technical papers of high merit. Both Claudet, a member of a family firm of metallurgists in London's Coleman Street, and Frecheville, a

Freiberg graduate who took his expertise to many countries, were among those who attended the inaugural meeting of the Institution at Winchester House in 1892. Percy Bosworth Smith, who spent most of his career in India, was also a founder member and his trust fund provides assistance for postgraduate research. George Vernon Hobson, a veteran of two world wars, whose work spanned four continents, provided a legacy for the advancement and teaching of geology. The Edgar Pam Fellowship provides for postgraduate study in a variety of disciplines ranging from exploration geology to extractive metallurgy. Pam, a World War I Tunneller, died while serving a second consecutive term as IMM President in 1945.

For many years some mystery surrounded the Stanley Elmore Fellowships, awarded for researches into extractive metallurgy and mineral processing. Although the IMM selected the beneficiaries, the fund was managed by solicitors and it was not until the mid-1970s when they asked the Institution to take over the whole of the administration that the size of the bequest and more precise details of the benefactor came to be known.

Some time in the latter part of the last century the technique of froth flotation began to emerge as an integral part of the process of concentration—the liberation of minerals from rock recovered by mining. In simple terms, the operation consists of adding water and chemicals to the material after it has been finely crushed; the mixture is then agitated to produce bubbles, to which particles of minerals cling as they rise to the surface, where they are skimmed off for further treatment.

The origins of this technique are part of the folklore of extractive metallurgy: for years the discovery was generally credited to a lead miner's wife who, when washing her husband's overalls, noticed that tiny pieces of galena stuck to the soap bubbles. But the story was claimed by too many countries and involved too many different minerals to be given scientific credence. The facts are that between about 1885 and 1916 the process developed with both separate and linked contributions from England, Australia and the USA.

Inevitably, there were many 'inventors' and much bitterness arose between them over patents. In the forefront were the brothers Stanley and Frank Elmore, both members of the IMM. Frank filed a patent in 1898 after visiting his father's copper mine, the Glasdir, where he noticed that chalcopyrite was selectively retained in oil drips falling from a shaft bearing. His process was immediately applied at Glasdir and in 1902 he installed a similar plant at a gold mine in Australia.

From then onwards many other contestants entered the field, notably G. A. Chapman, who was granted a patent in 1906 and consolidated the hold that the London firm, Minerals Separation, eventually obtained on the process internationally. But the battle went on: in 1911 both the Elmore brothers resigned from the IMM when Henry Livingstone Sulman, one of their leading antagonists, became President of the Institution, and it must have been particularly galling for them eight years later when the IMM awarded Sulman its Gold Medal for contributions to metallurgical science, 'with special reference to his work in the development of flotation and its application to the recovery of minerals'.

The unpleasant and hurtful contest was never properly resolved, either locally or globally. However, in 1916, T.A. Rickard, back in his editorial chair of *Mining and Scientific Press* in San Francisco after five years in London, declared that the profession at large should recognize the great service to the industry by the Elmore brothers in their early development of flotation and their later invention of the vacuum method.

Fortunately, whatever the Elmores thought of Henry Sulman and their other opponents it did not prevent them from bequeathing a large sum of money to help the researches of new generations into the science of metallurgy.

*   *   *

Ever since man first began to meditate, his mind has been directed to two of nature's deepest mysteries: time and change. Nearly two thousand years ago, the Roman emperor and philosopher Marcus Aurelius concluded that 'everything is the result of change . . . time is a sort of river of passing events, and strong is its current; no sooner is a thing brought to sight than it is swept by and another takes its place, and this too will be swept away'. In more recent times, Disraeli was of the opinion that 'change is inevitable . . . change is constant', and although Samuel Johnson had doubtless been of like mind when he published his *Dictionary* a hundred years earlier, he warned in his Preface that 'change is not made without inconvenience, even from worse to better'.

The IMM has seen many changes since its foundation in 1892, and the tempo has accelerated as time has gone by. Changes in overseas countries, in which the majority of the Institution's members, directly or indirectly, still find their employment, have been more dramatic than at home, but in Britain too they have been sharply felt, particularly over the past twenty years or so. Here, even the language has changed, as one mining engineer discovered when he returned home from a year or two abroad to find that the street in which he lived had been 're-accessed', 'pedestrianized' and 'bollardized', according to a notice on his doormat from the Highways Committee of the local Council.

In his Presidential address in 1989 Dr Peter Hackett, principal of Camborne School of Mines, observed that the United Kingdom was currently going through something of a cultural revolution. The 'swinging sixties', he said, were now only a memory and the enthusiastic expansionism of that period, which extended into the early 1970s, was stopped in its tracks by the petroleum crisis and the ensuing raging inflation.

'These two latter events', continued Dr Hackett, 'have led to a vigorous reappraisal of the commercial fabric of our industrially based society and it is not surprising that a harsh reaction—perhaps overreaction—has resulted in a demand for efficiency, for cost-effectiveness or just good old-fashioned value for money on an unprecedented scale. Since the mid-1970s we have all experienced a substantial recession in trade, with the consequential changes in employment patterns, job losses, liquidations and restructuring of industry.

'The minerals industry has been affected and none of it looks quite the same as it did two decades ago. Many organizations that were once not shy to be known as mining companies are now finance houses with mining interests. Others once proud to be British now wish to be seen in the European dimension or as intercontinental companies. There are hardly any workers left anywhere—they're all managers, executives, directors or consultants. With sophisticated data acquisition, data processing and control developing at a very high rate, there is a much lower need for human involvement in many of the irksome tasks of yesteryear, and there are even greater revolutions to come.'

Having been professionally involved in educational matters for some 30 years, it was appropriate for Dr Hackett to go on to discuss one of the minerals industry's most serious problems—that of fuelling future expansion in face of an inevitable decrease in the supply of graduates and diplomates. He called for the IMM to take a positive part in recruitment to the profession, pointing out that, in any case, this was a matter of self-interest: as the numbers of graduates fell, so ultimately would the Institution's membership, and its very lifeblood could drain away. He suggested that the task might be undertaken in concert with other institutions and interested parties—the Institution of Mining Engineers, the Institute of Quarrying and the Minerals Engineering Society, to name but three.

Whether by accident or design, Dr Hackett's call was timely in that the Council over which he was soon to preside was currently seriously debating the possibilities of closer association between the Institution and other professional bodies, more particularly with that with which it cohabited for more than thirty years—the coal industry-related Institution of Mining Engineers.

In fact, there had seldom been a time in IMM history when relationship with the IME was not a topic of discussion. Even before the IMM was officially inaugurated in 1892 a number of prospective members had argued for amalgamation with the IME, founded only 18 months earlier. But, as has been seen, George Seymour, 'father' of the Institution, would have none of it, maintaining vigorously that metal men would be swamped by the numerically stronger organization of coal-mining engineers and their voice would never be heard.

In 1910 the IME, together with the Institution of Civil Engineers, successfully opposed the IMM's application to the Privy Council for a Royal Charter, the IME claiming that it always had in mind to seek similar recognition but deferred doing so 'in the hope of effecting an amalgamation with its sister society'. A year or two later both institutions applied for charters and, largely because the Privy Council saw no possibility of compromise, each was successful on the understanding that the IMM confined its interest to metals and the IME to coal and iron.

In the next five years, partly as a result of members of both institutions being thrown together in Norton-Griffiths's private army on the Western Front, relationship between them improved and when, in 1920, the IME made a further approach for closer association, it did not receive the same rebuff as before. In fact,

IMM President Frank Merricks publicly welcomed the coal miners' 'open-hearted, broad-minded action' and the two institutions set up house together in London under a joint secretariat; but they stopped short of amalgamation and each retained its own identity. The arrangement continued for 34 years; it is doubtful if it would have lasted so long had it not been for the disruptions of World War II and the problems of office accommodation in London in the immediate post-war period. That it did so was a tribute to the restraint and diplomacy shown by both sides, but at times relationship was far from easy and in 1954 they decided to go their separate ways.

However, there were still some who felt that amalgamation was in the best interests of the two institutions and the subject began to reappear on agendas, albeit in the lower half, in the 1970s. On 13 March 1975 the IMM Council rejected a proposal for merger with the IME by an overwhelming vote, but did not slam the door on the possibility of some sort of federation or facility-sharing arrangement with bodies of like nature. A few years later, by the early 1980s, there were tripartite talks between the IMM, the IME and the Institution of Metallurgists, a qualifying body with a membership of around the 10 000 mark. Discussions collapsed when the metallurgists withdrew and merged with the Metals Society, an organization that had come into being a few years earlier as a result of amalgamation between the original Institute of Metals and the Iron and Steel Institute.

By then Britain and much of the rest of the industrialized world had fallen into the grip of 'merger mania'; takeovers were commonplace; they were only headline news when the biggest and richest were involved; names that had been familiar for generations vanished overnight and, with consequential rationalization, more and more skilled workers and professional people found themselves unemployed. This new wind of change disturbed even the most traditional society, obliging all sorts of organizations with complementary interests to seek shelter together, often at the sacrifice of treasured independence.

Against this background the IMM Council decided to take yet another look at the possibilities of closer association with the IME, whose troubles were no less than its own: the British coal industry presented a gloomy picture of closing pits and job losses; current IME membership was substantially smaller than IMM's and the possibilities of much improvement in the foreseeable future appeared even more remote.

However, in the belief that in unity there is strength, the two institutions agreed that an independent consultant should examine the feasibility of bringing them into closer association, preferably in shared accommodation. In 1989 the consultant reported that an outright merger would give significant benefits in costs and other savings, together with advantages such as a larger membership base, a stronger voice in Engineering Council affairs, and improved services to members.

It is doubtful if the report told the IMM Council any more than it knew already, but it helped to persuade a substantial number of Councillors that a merger might be desirable and a Working Party was appointed to study how best it could be effected. Somewhere along the line the Institution of Mining Electrical and Mining Mechanical Engineers (IMEMME), whose membership stood at around 2750, joined the discussions. With IMM strength at 4820 and the IME at just over 3300, any merger of the three institutions would result in a total membership not far short of 11 000.

Seven months after its appointment the Working Party presented its 'final' report and Council voted on whether or not to continue these deliberations. The result, by a 28–18 majority, was surprisingly 'yes'—surprisingly as there were already rumblings of dissent among many members (including the most recent Gold Medallist, Sir Alistair Frame) who were loath to see the Institution sacrifice its independence for reasons of questionable viability—not that Council ever made much attempt to take members into its confidence about its day-to-day thinking on the matter.

It was generally known that the chief reason that Council had agreed to a new round of merger talks in 1988 was its concern with the Institution's annual deficits in the financial years 1986 and 1987—shortfalls that could only be met by selling off appreciating investments. However, by the time the Working Party produced its 'final' report, the argument had been overturned by the introduction of some staff economies and contracting out certain activities, with the result that, as stated in the documentation sent to members, 'the viability of the Institution is not dependent upon merger with IME and IMEMME'.

Even those who had inclined towards merger in principle included many who felt that more suitable bedfellows than those proposed should be sought. They pointed out that the interests of both the IME and IMEMME were largely confined to the United Kingdom and to one mineral, coal, whereas the IMM was concerned with metalliferous mining in all its aspects and half its members were overseas. Furthermore, it was argued that the IMM was a multi-disciplinary organization whose members' interests ranged from geology and mining engineering to mineral processing and metallurgy. And, whilst strictly speaking a UK body, the IMM was acknowledged to be multinational, its large overseas groupings having direct representation on its Council. It was widely feared that merger with the suggested partners would put these and other unique characteristics of the IMM at risk and diminish its international standing and influence.

No. 44 Portland Place had been the focal point of IMM organization and activity ever since it settled its headquarters there in the mid-1950s after 35 years of sharing accommodation and services with the IME. Its location in one of the most prestigious parts of London reflected the importance of the profession that it served and its status as a truly international body. Under the proposed merger all assets of the three institutions would be pooled. This meant that the IMM building, currently valued at £2–3 million and by far the greatest capital asset of any of the prospective partners, would be sold and a new joint head office established outside London, possibly at Doncaster, home of the IME, or Nottingham. The prospects of 'provincialization' together with a new branch structure and election procedures were viewed with dismay by many, particularly those overseas members for whom a visit to Portland Place was traditional when home on leave. There is no doubt that a move out of London would result in a sharp decline of that personal contact between the Institution and those working abroad—a contact vital to the continued development of the ideals for which the IMM had stood for nearly one hundred years.

*   *   *

It was left to Past-President Ken Heath, a doughty fighter for IMM causes for more than 40 years, to enter debate on the issue among rank and file members in the Institution's journal *Minerals*

Industry International. Tragically, it was his last battle for he died soon after his letter was published.

Heath voiced the feelings of many when he said that he believed that merger with the IME would result in the loss of much of the overseas membership. 'The merged institution', he wrote, 'would be a United Kingdom-based institution with overseas members, and not, as at present, an international institution based in the United Kingdom. I believe that it is largely the international aspect of our Institution that has led to so many joining it or retaining their membership when they have local bodies that can qualify them as professional engineers in the countries in which they work.'

He continued: 'It has been suggested that a merged institution would have a louder voice in the Engineering Council. I see no reason to believe that this is true. Even if it were, any benefit would accrue mostly to members working in the United Kingdom and possibly the EEC. I see little or no benefit to our members working in other countries worldwide. Any benefit would mean more to members of the IME than those of the IMM.'

Maurice Cahalan, another Past-President and member of Council (from which he was soon to resign), acknowledged Heath's emphasis on the importance of overseas members but pointed to evidence that 'the proportion of United Kingdom mining school graduates taking up permanent employment in this country is increasing, which implies that our traditional expatriate membership is declining. This evidence is taken by some of us to support the need to direct more effort to understanding and catering for changed aspirations and different careers for those entering the profession.'

M.T. Anthony, a member of the Working Party, declared that 'the conditions that will result from the Working Party will be strongly to the advantage of *all* members'—a contention sharply challenged by Past-President Bill Yuill, who maintained that compromise was an essential feature of any merger; he knew of none that was ever to the benefit of *all.*

Critics of the proposal continued to claim most space in the Institution's journal. From Swakopmund, Namibia, Colin Lindsay wrote to express concern at the 'seemingly indecent haste with which this whole proposal is being pushed through. I do not believe that this is a matter that can be debated in Council and put to the members as a resolution; it is imperative that, before any firm proposals are put forward, sufficient time is allowed for all points of view to be considered by the whole membership before the matter is put to a vote.'

From the Mining University at Leoben in Austria, Professor E.F. Stumpfl declared his opposition forcefully: 'The IMM has, for almost one century, successfully linked exploration, mining and processing of metalliferous ores and industrial minerals on a global scale. In the process, it has established a closely knit, international and truly interdisciplinary fraternity of Fellows and Members. This has been of immense benefit to the minerals industry. The proposed merger would swiftly destroy these achievements and leave many in the IMM membership to wonder whether the new, amorphous mega-institution is worth the annual dues.'

D.J.W. Jones, of RTZ Mining and Exploration, maintained that the crucial point missed by those who looked at nothing more than balance sheets and assets was that the Institution *was* its members, not a bank balance or a building. 'This', he said, 'is why we are all members in the first place. If the membership is subsumed into a merged conglomerate, then the world loses for ever its premier and most prestigious metalliferous mining professional body. That, the membership must never condone.'

On the proposed sale of 44 Portland Place, Derek Green wrote from Devon to declare: 'It seems patently ridiculous to contemplate disposing of a valuable real estate property to achieve reduced standing in the world, while at the same time achieving what could be no more than a temporary palliative in the financial context. We should hold on to our property and concentrate on good management to overcome present financial problems. Why throw away a major asset and dilute our own effectiveness just to avoid raising subscriptions?'

And D.J. Barratt, Overseas Member of Council for Canada, wrote to say: 'Having read all the submissions and the [Working Party] report, I have come to the conclusion that this proposal has been driven more by an insular desire to solve the organizational and deficit problems of the participating bodies than a desire to maintain what is for the IMM a growing complement of corporate members overseas.'

*   *   *

Despite such opposition, Council evidently believed that a point of no return had been reached and the matter should now be put squarely to the membership: did they, or did they not, accept the proposals for merger as outlined by the Working Party? If they did, discussions would continue; if they did not, then they would be terminated forthwith. It was to be as simple as that.

Accordingly, in October 1990, in an atmosphere of increasing tension at 44 Portland Place, voting papers, together with copies of the Working Party's so-called 'final report', accompanied by a summary of 'points arising' collated by President Barry Scott, were despatched to 3650 corporate members scattered throughout the world. The decision to restrict voting to corporate members produced some mild protest, but this was in line with traditional procedure; Affiliates, Associates and the like had long accepted a second-class status with little voice in Institutional affairs.

The result was an overwhelming victory for those who opposed the merger. Of 1840 valid voting papers received, only 542 were in favour of merger, and 1298 were against. Merger—for the foreseeable future, at any rate—was dead. It had cost many thousands of pounds to kill it off and it had left behind a trail of stringent argument that, alas, had on occasions resulted in considerable bitterness.

*   *   *

The trauma of the merger controversy will not easily be forgotten, but the IMM's centenary year could well provide a more favourable atmosphere in which to debate and plan the future.

Financial viability, initially the key issue of the merger argument, is now no longer a major problem, the events of 1990 having demonstrated that this can be more successfully tackled by tighter management and budgetary control than by seeking alliance with other institutions whose financial difficulties are no less, and in some cases potentially greater than those of the IMM. This is not to suggest that all that needs to be done is to continue to rationalize staff and jack up the membership fees, for the time will come—if it has not already arrived—when such a course would be counterproductive and the overall rate of fall in membership over the past few years would accelerate.

One of Council's main tasks must therefore be to make the Institution more attractive to its members—not merely to those who qualify for corporate status, but affiliates, associates, students and graduates, who represent about a quarter of the total. With the possible exception of students, members in these categories do not get a great deal for their money, other than the privilege of being associated with such an august body; they are second-class citizens in a world in which apartheid is steadily being abolished. It should be remembered, too, that many of them are, or have been part of the industry that corporate members serve, and their familiarity with its wider aspects is something that the Institution cannot afford to ignore. Time was when the IMM had very close association with the big mining companies, several of which contributed substantially and regularly to its funds. More recently, largely on the initiative of the Institution itself, such support has been restricted to special projects, such as the launch of IMMAGE in 1984. Admittedly, there has been a big change in the pattern of mine ownership across the world during the past 30 years; even so, there is room for improvement in the relationship between those who now control exploration, development and production and those who provide the specialized skills to ensure that such operations are performed efficiently and economically.

In the collection and dissemination of technical information the IMM continues to maintain the high standard it set in its early years, the value of which has been incalculable both to its members and the minerals industry generally. Unfortunately, the Institution has not been as successful in its internal communications. The result of the 1990 merger ballot showed how out of touch some Council members can be with those who elect them to office. All too often in recent years Council has been slow to take the membership into its confidence on major matters, partly because it has on occasions preferred to keep the cards close to its chest, and partly because it has felt it has not the means to get its message across, despite the fact that 15 of Council's 53 seats are currently held by overseas representatives, and 'official correspondents' are dotted around in 20 or more countries.

Regrettably, many of these so-called links with members are little more than 'paper chains', and the glossy bi-monthly

Minerals Industry International, which should provide the main vehicle of communication between headquarters and the worldwide membership, is little more than an expensive supplement of *Transactions*, chronicle of the technical papers.

As mentioned in an earlier chapter, the style of reportage of Institutional meetings and other happenings is rich in the verbiage of the nineteenth century: the rule seems to be never use one word when two or more can confuse the issue; to younger members, brought up to express themselves concisely, the style is not only out of date but out of character with an institution that should be forward in its thinking. For much less than the cost of production and distribution of the present glossy, a simple newsletter, covering matters of importance to the Institution and written in the modern idiom, could be in the hands of members every two or three weeks, wherever they might be.

When the debate on the proposed merger between the IMM, IME and IMEMME was at its liveliest, a classically minded leader-writer in the London-based *Mining Magazine* quoted Terence, the slave from Carthage who became one of the greatest Roman writers: *Quot homines, tot sententiae*—'for as many men, so many opinions'.

Throughout history thousands have fought and died for the right to express their views. There will be no lack of opinion in plotting the IMM's path as it enters its second century, and it is important that the ideas of the widest possible spread of membership should be sought and carefully listened to. What is certain is that nothing that may be said or done will diminish the Institution's record of 100 years' service to its members, its struggle for their professional status, and its enormous contribution to the development of the minerals industry internationally.

Four hundred years ago Francis Bacon held 'every man a debtor to his profession'. Every member of the IMM is a debtor to his Institution. Rarely in history have so many been so well served by so few.

Presidents

George Seymour	..	..	..	1892–1894
Arthur Kirby Huntington	..	..	1894–1895
Joseph Henry Collins ..	..	..	1895–1896
Joseph Garland	..	..	..	1896–1897
James Mactear	..	..	..	1897–1898
Walter McDermott	..	..	..	1898–1899
Samuel Herbert Cox ..	..	..	1899–1900
Charles Algernon Moreing	..	..	1900–1902
Arthur G. Charleton ..	..	..	1902–1903
Hennen Jennings	..	..	..	1903–1905
William Frecheville ..	..	..	1905–1906
Arthur Crozier Claudet	..	..	1906–1907
William Gowland	..	..	..	1907–1908
Alfred James	..	..	..	1908–1909
Edgar Taylor	..	..	1909–1911; 1916–1918
Henry Livergstone Sulman	..	..	1911–1912
Edward Hooper	..	..	..	1912–1913
Bedford McNeill	..	..	..	1913–1914
Frederick H. Hatch ..	..	..	1914–1915
Sir Thomas Kirke Rose	..	..	1915–1916
Sir Richard A.S. Redmayne	..	..	1916
Hugh F. Marriott	..	..	..	1918–1919
Hugh F.K. Picard	..	..	..	1919–1920
Frank Merricks	..	..	..	1920–1921
Frank William Harbord	..	..	1921–1922

Savannah Johnson Speak	.. ..	1922–1923
R. Gilman Brown ..	.. ..	1923–1924
Humphrey M. Morgans	.. ..	1924–1925
Sir Thomas Henry Holland	.. ..	1925–1927
Robert Edward Palmer	.. ..	1927–1928
Samuel John Truscott	.. ..	1928–1929
William Cullen ..	.. ..	1929–1930
James Gunson Lawn ..	.. ..	1930–1931
W. Pellew-Harvey ..	.. ..	1931–1932
Sydney William Smith..	.. ..	1932–1933
George Wynter Gray ..	.. ..	1933–1934
Sir Henry Cort Harold Carpenter ..	..	1934–1935
Carl Raymond Davis ..	.. ..	1935–1936
Robert Annan ..	.. ..	1936–1937
Charles Gilbert Cullis ..	.. ..	1937–1938
Charles Burrard Kingston	.. ..	1938–1939
Edward Duffield McDermott	.. ..	1939–1940
Thomas Pryor ..	.. ..	1940–1941
Edward Herbert Clifford	.. ..	1941–1942
John Allen Howe ..	.. ..	1942–1944
Edgar Pam ..	.. ..	1944–1945 and May–December 1945
George Francis Laycock		December 1945–May 1946 and 1946–1947
William Richard Jones..	.. ..	1947–1948
Sydney Enfield Taylor..	.. ..	1948–1949
William Alfred Cyril Newman	.. ..	1949–1950
Laurence Carr Hill ..	.. ..	1950–1951
Sir Lewis Leigh Fermor	.. ..	1951–1952
Vernon Harbord ..	.. ..	1952–1953
John Anthony Sidney Ritson	.. ..	1953–1954
Ralph Shelton Griffin Stokes	.. ..	1954–1955
Stanley Robson ..	.. ..	1955–1956
Cecil William Dannatt..	.. ..	1956–1957
George Keith Allen ..	.. ..	1957–1958
John Beck Dennison ..	.. ..	1958–1959
Joseph Herbert Watson	.. ..	1959–1960
David Williams ..	.. ..	1960–1961
Arthur Robert Owen Williams	.. ..	1961–1962
John Bell Simpson ..	.. ..	1962–1963
Kingsley Charles Dunham	.. ..	1963–1964

Douglas Sidney Burwood	..	1964–1965
Robert Frederick St. George Lethbridge	..	1965–1966
Robert Herman MacWilliam	..	1966–1967
John Edward Denyer ..	..	1967–1968
Sydney Herbert Shaw ..	..	1968–1969
Douglas John Rogers ..	..	1969–1970
Maurice James Cahalan	..	1970–1971
Marston Greig Fleming	..	1971–1972
Thomas Hope Brendan Lawther ..	..	1972–1973
John Stuart Webb ..	..	1973–1974
Kenneth Christopher Griffith Heath	..	1974–1975
Frederick Denys Richardson	..	1975–1976
Stanley Hay Umphray Bowie	..	1976–1977
Gerald James Mortimer	..	1977–1978
Robert Nelson Pryor ..	..	1978–1979
Derek Anthony Temple	..	1979–1980
John Tillard Meadows Taylor	..	(resigned December 1980)
Sidney Dennis Day (appointed Acting President January 1981)		
Grosvenor Rex Davis ..	..	1981–1982
Michael John West ..	..	1982–1983
Kenneth Barry Smale-Adams	..	1983–1984
Philip Malcolm James Gray	..	1984–1985
William Godson Yuill ..	..	1985–1986
Alan Jeffery Robinson..	..	1986–1987
Alan Gavin Moncrieff ..	..	1987–1988
Herbert Roy Bichan ..	..	1988–1989
Peter Hackett ..	..	1989–1990
Barry Scott ..	..	1990–1991
Hugh Edward Keith Allen	..	1991–1992

Gold Medallists

John Stewart MacArthur	..	..	1902
Hennen Jennings	..	..	1903
Hilary Bauerman	..	..	1906
Sir Archibald Geike	..	..	1907
James Douglas	..	..	1908
William Gowland	..	..	1909
Rossiter Worthington Raymond	..	..	1910
Sir Julius Wernher	..	..	1910
Edward Payson Mathewson	..	..	1911
Walter McDermott	..	..	1911
Willet G. Miller	..	..	1915
Henry Livingstone Sulman	..	..	1919
Sir Thomas Kirke Rose	..	..	1920
Edward T. McCarthy	..	..	1921
Sir Alfred Keogh	..	..	1922
Edgar Taylor	..	..	1922
Herbert William Gepp	..	..	1923
Gilbert Rigg	..	..	1923
Richard Pearce	..	..	1924
Sir Robert N. Kotze	..	..	1925
William Frecheville	..	..	1926
The Rt. Hon. Sir Alfred Mond	..	..	1927
Hon. William Lawrence Baillieu	..	..	1928
William Sydney Robinson	..	..	1928
Sir Thomas H. Holland	..	..	1929

Charles Camsell	..	..	1930
Sir Henry Cort Harold Carpenter	..	..	1931
Thomas Arthur Rickard	..	..	1931
Sir John Cadman	..	..	1932
John Alexander Agnew	..	..	1933
Alfred Chester Beatty	..	..	1934
Sir Lionel Phillips	..	..	1935
James G. Lawn	..	..	1935
Samuel John Truscott	..	..	1937
Selwyn Gwillym Blaylock	..	..	1939
Carl Raymond Davis	..	..	1945
Guy Carleton Jones	..	..	1947
Robert Annan	..	..	1949
George Kenneth Williams	..	..	1951
Sir Ernest Oppenheimer	..	..	1952
Essington Lewis	..	..	1953
William Richard Jones	..	..	1954
Joseph Austen Bancroft	..	..	1955
Randolphe William Diamond	..	..	1956
John Fairfield Thompson	..	..	1957
Alexander Jeremiah Orenstein	..	..	1958
Edward Duffield McDermott	..	..	1959
Julius Kruttschnitt	..	..	1959
The Rt. Hon. Lord Baillieu	..	..	1960
Frank Arthur Forward	..	..	1961
Francis George Hill	..	..	1962
Sir Maurice Edgar Mawby	..	..	1963
George Read Fisher	..	..	1963
Stephen William Kenneth Morgan	..	..	1964
Bennett Gregory Perry	..	..	1964
Harry Frederick Oppenheimer	..	..	1965
Kingsley Charles Dunham	..	..	1967
Sir Ronald L. Prain	..	..	1968
Sir George Stephen Harvie-Watt	..	..	1969
William Justin Kroll	..	..	1970
Sir Val Duncan	..	..	1971
Frderick Denys Richardson	..	..	1972
Plato Malozemoff	..	..	1973
John Lumsden	..	..	1974
Duncan Ramsey Derry	..	..	1975
Vladmir Nicolaus Mackiw	..	..	1976

Robert Herman MacWilliam	..	..	1977
Adrian Louw	..	..	1978
Paul E. Queneau	..	..	1979
Marston Greig Fleming	..	..	1980
Willem Johannes de Villiers	..	..	1981
Paul-Emile Corbiau	..	..	1982
Sir Arvi Parbo	..	..	1983
Evert Hoek	..	..	1984
Kenneth Christopher Griffith Heath		..	1985
Sir James William Foots	..	..	1986
Jean Louis Leroy	..	..	1987
Zimbabwe Local Section	..	..	1988
Sir Alistair Frame	..	..	1989
Sir Robert Haslam	..	..	1990

Bibliography

Agricola, Georgius, *De Re Metallica* (1556). Transl, Hoover, H.C. and Hoover L.W., Mining Magazine Ltd., London, 1912

Avery, David, *Not on Queen Victoria's Birthday*, Collins, London, 1974

Barrie, Alexander, *War Underground*, Frederick Muller Ltd., London, 1962

Bradley, Kenneth, *Copper Venture*, privately by Mufulira Copper Mines Ltd. and Roan Antelope Copper Mines Ltd., London, 1952

Burt, Roger, *John Taylor, Mining Entrepreneur & Engineer*, Moorland Publishing Company, Buxton, 1977

Cartright, A.P., *The Gold Miners*, Purnell & Sons, 1962; *The Corner House*, Purnell & Sons, 1965; *Golden Age*, Purnell & Sons, Cape Town and Johannesburg, 1968

Churchill, Winston S., *The Second World War*, Cassell & Co. Ltd., London, 1951

Fraser, Maryna (edited), *Some Reminiscences of Lionel Phillips*, A. D. Donker, South Africa, 1986

Grieve, W. Grant, and Newman, Bernard, *The Story of the Tunnellers in the World War*, Herbert Jenkins, London, 1936

Gregory, Theodore, *Ernest Oppenheimer and the Economic Development of Southern Africa*, Oxford University Press, Cape Town, 1962

Hammond, John Hays, *Autobiography of John Hays Hammond*, Ferrar and Reinhart Inc., New York, 1935; *Professional Ethics for the Mining Engineer*, American Institute of Mining and

Metallurgical Engineers, New York, 1908

Hodder, Edwin, *The Life of a Century, 1800–1900*, George Newnes Ltd., London, 1901

Hoover, Herbert C., *The Memoirs of Herbert Hoover, 1874–1920*, Macmillan, New York, 1951

Manchester, William, *The Last Lion: Winston Spencer Churchill*, Sphere Books Ltd., London and Sydney

Middlemass, Keith, *The Master Builders*, Hutchinson, London, 1963

Nash, George H., *The Life of Herbert Hoover, Engineer, 1874–1914*, W.W. Norton & Co., New York and London, 1983

Parsons, A.B., *The Porphyry Coppers*, American Institute of Mining and Metallurgical Engineers, New York, 1933

Prain, Sir Ronald L., *Copper, the Anatomy of an Industry*, Mining Journal Books Ltd., London, 1975; *Reflections on an Era*, Metal Bulletin Books Ltd., London, 1981; *Selected Papers* (four volumes: 1958, 1961, 1964, 1968), privately by RST Library, Salisbury, Lusaka and London

Rayner, R.M., *Nineteenth Century England*, Longmans, Green and Co., London, 1927

Rickard, T.A., *Retrospect*, McGraw-Hill, New York,1937; *Technical Writing*, John Wiley & Sons Inc., New York, 1920

Rogers, Jim, *Tunnelling into Colditz*, Robert Hale, London, 1986

Rothwell, R.P., *The Mineral Industry, its Statistics, Technology and Trade*, New York (*1892 –1942*)

Strong, George R., *A History of the Institution of Mining Engineers 1889–1989*, IME, Doncaster, 1988

Wilson, A.J., *The Pick and the Pen*, Mining Journal Books Ltd., 1979; *The Life and Times of Sir Alfred Chester Beatty*, Cadogan Publications Ltd., London, 1985

The Work of the Royal Engineers in the European War 1914–19, W. & J. Mackay & Co. Ltd., Chatham, 1922

Index